THERMODYNAMIC
PROPERTIES
IN SI

THERMODYNAMIC PROPERTIES IN SI

Graphs, Tables, and
Computational Equations
for forty substances

William C. Reynolds
Department of Mechanical Engineering
Stanford University

Published by the Department of Mechanical Engineering
Stanford University, Stanford CA 94305

THERMODYNAMIC PROPERTIES IN SI

This book was set in Times Roman by Textype, Palo Alto, California. All graphs and computer-printed tables were prepared by the author. Printing and binding were by George Banta Co., Inc.

Library of Congress cataloging in Publication Data

Reynolds, William Craig,
Thermodynamic properties in SI; graphs, tables, and computational equations for forty substances

1. Thermodynamics — Tables, calculations, etc.   I. Title

Includes bibliographical references

QC311.3.R38   79-84863
ISBN 0-917606-05-1

Preface

This book is intended to provide the engineer, and engineering student, with a basic resource on the thermodynamic properties of a wide variety of working fluids. It grew out of the need for certain properties for thermodynamic cycle analysis being conducted at Stanford as part of our energy conversion research programs and out of my desire to construct a set of self-consistent, easily readable, student-oriented graphs and tables of the properties of several substances, in SI (the International System of Units), for inclusion in my books *Thermodynamics* and *Engineering Thermodynamics* (with H. C. Perkins), published by the McGraw-Hill Book Company. A selection from this compilation will appear in the next editions of these books.

For each substance, I have included a saturation table, a property graph, and a skeleton superheat table that can be used to check a user's programming of the equations given herein. For air, ammonia, Refrigerant-12, Refrigerant-22, and water, the most common working substances, more extensive superheat tables are given. For water I have provided four graphs, u-v, T-s, P-h, and h-s, which instructors may find useful. An h-s diagram for ammonia has been included which is useful in low-temperature ammonia vapor power system analysis. A psychrometric chart is also included.

As I began to search the rather obscure literature for suitable equations, it quickly became clear that a very useful contribution could be made by including the equations used to prepare the graphs and tables. Therefore, my process was first to find the best P-v-T equation that I could for each substance, convert the constants in the equation to values appropriate for SI units, and then to verify my conversion and program by spot calculation of values of $v(P, T)$ given by the original worker. In an incredible number of instances the values did not check because of typographical errors in the original publications. These were ferreted out by conversations with the authors where possible. I also resorted to such tricks as assuming that one constant was wrong and calculating what its correct value must be from the original tables, trying each constant in turn until all test points gave the same value for the trial incorrect constant. The error usually was due to single digits incorrectly typeset, or to pairs of digits transposed, or to sign errors. In one case I was frustrated for some time by an error of 1000 in an unfamiliar conversion factor repeated several times in an otherwise flawless NBS publication. The equations and constants reported here are now (hopefully) error free.

I had begun by naively thinking it would be an easy task for me to fit all substances to a single equation; I rapidly gained considerable appreciation for the difficulty of least-squares fitting of P-v-T surfaces, and great respect for the workers who have done this most carefully and thoroughly, particularly those at the NBS in Washington and Boulder. I decided that, as a basic policy, I would not develop any P-v-T fits of my own. However, for completeness I was forced to develop fits for mercury and lithium, using Russian tables as a base.

In addition to P-v-T equations, one needs equations for the ideal gas specific heat (see Section 2), and where I had confidence in the fit of the original worker it was adapted to SI. However, in many instances I found that the range of this fit was smaller than one might like, and so I developed my own fits using least-squares processes and data from reliable sources.

Although the P-v-T and c_v^0 equations are really all that is needed to define all of the thermodynamic properties, including the saturation conditions, it became evident in our cycle studies that equations for the saturation pressure as a function of saturation temperature, and for the saturated liquid density, would be extremely useful in engineering analysis. Many workers also give these equations, usually because they used them to obtain "smooth" data for the P-v-T fitting. Where these were judged reliable, they were adapted to SI, and where they were not I used the P-v-T surface to calculate the saturation conditions and then did the least-squares fittings required to obtain equations for the saturation pressure and saturated liquid density. In either case, the Clapeyron equation was used to calculate the enthalpy of vaporization; consequently, the tabulated property values are all exactly consistent with the pertinent thermodynamic relationships.

I decided to set new datum states for each substance, with the only consistent aspect being that the enthalpy and entropy of the saturated liquid were chosen to be zero at some convenient low temperature (the triple point, if the equation of state was valid at that temperature). Therefore, values of h, u, and s reported here will be shifted from values converted directly from the original tables.

The thought of hiring a draftsperson to draw all of the charts, and then of my having to check them carefully, was so hideous that I decided to teach our IBM 360 computer and its accessory CALCOMP plotter how to draw the diagrams. Once the program had been perfected, it took only milliseconds to calculate a graph and only a few minutes to draw it, and so I was able to repeat the process several times, if necessary, to get a drawing that was acceptable. Type was purchased, and I chose to do all the paste-up myself, in the hope that this would keep the graphs error-free.

After my experience with typographical errors in the work of others, and with those that slipped through my fingers in our *Thermodynamics* books, I decided that the best bet would be to carry the numbers directly from the computer into camera-ready copy; as a result, the numbers given herein are exactly as used by or given by my computer programs.

As the work was nearing completion, it occurred to me that I was in a good position to develop a new generalized equation of state, since I had the capability to generate huge numbers of ''data'' points for a great many substances over wide ranges. To do so I had to depart again from my basic policy of letting more reliable persons do the *P-v-T* fitting; the result is the new generalized equations of state and generalized charts, given in Section 4, which probably are as good as the Principle of Corresponding States to pressures as high as 300 critical pressures.

Having done virtually all of the work on this project myself, I must bear the sole responsibility for any errors that may have crept over the barriers that I set against them. I do hope that the good detectives among the users will let me know about these, so that they can be corrected in subsequent editions.

My role was one of conversion, systematization, and checking, and the efforts of many fine workers lie behind the source references. Without their efforts this compilation would not have been possible.

But what made this publication possible, more than anything else, was the marvelous tolerance of my wife and family to the extended commitment to long, late hours that this project demanded. Their support is, as always, very much appreciated.

W. C. Reynolds
Stanford University
January 1979

Table of Contents

Preface v

Ordered List of the Substances ix

SECTION 1. TABLES AND GRAPHS 1
    Psychrometric Chart 3
    Air 4
    Ammonia 12
    Argon 20
    Butane 22
    Carbon Dioxide 24
    Cesium 26
    Ethane 28
    Ethylene 30
    Helium 32
    Heptane 36
    Hexane 38
    Hydrogen (para) 40
    Isobutane 42
    Isopentane 44
    Lithium 46
    Mercury 48
    Methane 50
    Neon 52
    Nitrogen 54
    Octane 56
    Oxygen 58
    Pentane 60
    Potassium 62
    Propane 64
    Propyl Alcohol 66
    Propylene 68
    Refrigerant 11 70
    Refrigerant 12 72
    Refrigerant 13 78
    Refrigerant 14 80
    Refrigerant 22 82
    Refrigerant 23 88
    Refrigerant 114 90
    Refrigerant C-318 92
    Refrigerant 500 94
    Refrigerant 502 96
    Refrigerant 503 98
    Rubidium 100
    Sodium 102
    Water 104

SECTION 2. COMPUTATIONAL EQUATIONS AND METHODS 115
    A. General Approach 117
    B. Fitting the Data 118

C. Saturation Data 119
D. Summary: The Four Basic Equations 119
E. Basic Computer Programs 119
F. Special Treatment in the Liquid Region 120
G. Datum States 120
H. Graph and Table Preparation 121
I. Air Properties 121
J. Psychrometric Chart 121
Table 2.1 *P-v-T* Equations 122
Table 2.2 c_v^0 Equations 124
Table 2.3 Saturation Pressure Equations 125
Table 2.4 Saturated Liquid Density Equations 126
Table 2.5 Useful Integrals 127
Table 2.6 Sources and References 128

SECTION 3. CONSTANTS IN THE COMPUTATIONAL EQUATIONS 131

SECTION 4. GENERALIZED EQUATIONS OF STATE 155
Table 4.1 Generalized Equations 158
Constants in the Generalized Equations 159
Generalized Compressibility Charts 160
Generalized Enthalpy and Entropy Charts 164

ANNOTATED BIBLIOGRAPHY OF IMPORTANT THERMODYNAMIC
PROPERTY TABULATIONS 167

APPENDIX. GENERAL PURPOSE COMPUTER PROGRAMS 169
PROP(T,P,V,U,H,S,NOP,PXXX) 170
SAT(T,P,DPDT,NOP,SXXX) 173

Substances Ordered by Saturation Temperature at 1 Atmosphere

Values as given by the computational equations in Section 3; these may differ slightly from the true values.

Substance	Chemical Formula	Molal Mass, kg/kmol	Critical Temperature, K	Critical Pressure, MPa	Saturation Temperature at 1 atm., K
Helium-4	He^4	4.0026	5.20	0.2275	4.22
Hydrogen (para)	$H_2(p)$	2.0159	32.94	1.28	20.3
Neon	Ne	20.18	44.4	2.65	27.1
Nitrogen	N_2	28.01	126.2	3.4	77.4
Air	—	28.96	132.5	3.77	78.8
Argon	A	39.95	150.7	4.86	87.3
Oxygen	O_2	32.00	154.6	5.04	90.2
Methane	CH_4	16.04	190.6	4.60	111.6
Refrigerant 14	CF_4	88.01	227.5	3.75	145.2
Ethylene	C_2H_4	28.05	282.7	5.08	169.4
Ethane	C_2H_6	30.07	305.9	5.01	184.3
Refrigerant 503	(1)	87.5	292.6	4.33	184.4
Refrigerant 23	CHF_3	70.02	299.1	4.84	191.1
Refrigerant 13	$CClF_3$	104.5	302.0	3.87	191.7
Carbon Dioxide	CO_2	44.01	304.2	7.38	194.6*
Propylene	C_3H_6	42.08	364.9	4.61	225.4
Refrigerant 502	(2)	111.64	355.3	4.07	227.7
Propane	C_3H_8	44.09	369.8	4.24	231.3
Refrigerant 22	$CHClF_2$	86.48	369.2	4.98	232.4
Refrigerant 500	(3)	99.31	378.7	4.43	239.6
Ammonia	NH_3	17.03	406.8	11.6	239.8
Refrigerant 12	CCl_2F_2	120.9	385.2	4.12	243.4
Isobutane	C_4H_{10}	58.12	409.1	3.68	261.3
Refrigerant C-318	C_4F_8	200.04	388.5	2.78	267.3
Butane	C_4H_{10}	58.12	424.0	3.72	272.7
Refrigerant 114	$C_2Cl_2F_4$	170.94	418.9	3.27	276.9
Refrigerant 11	CCl_3F	137.4	471.2	4.41	297.0
Isopentane	C_5H_{12}	72.15	461.0	3.41	301.1
Pentane	C_5H_{12}	72.15	467.0	3.24	309.0
Hexane	C_6H_{14}	86.18	506.1	2.93	342.4
Propyl Alcohol	C_3H_7OH	60.09	536.9	5.08	370.6
Heptane	C_7H_{16}	100.20	537.7	2.62	371.6
Water	H_2O	18.016	647.3	22.1	373.1
Octane	C_8H_{18}	114.22	567.5	2.40	398.4
Mercury†	Hg	200.6	1763	153	629.9
Cesium†	Cs	132.9	2048	11.7	942
Rubidium†	Rb	85.48	2106	13.4	965
Potassium†	K	39.10	2173	16.7	1030
Sodium†	Na	22.99	2573	34.1	1155
Lithium†	Li	6.940	3800	97	1614

(1) Azeotrope 40.1% (by mass) CHF_3 and 59.9% $CClF_3$.
(2) Azeotrope 48.8% (by mass) $CHClF_2$ and 51.2% C_2ClF_5.
(3) Azeotrope 73.8% (by mass) CCl_2F_2 and 26.2% $C_2H_4F_2$.
* Solid-gas.
† Critical values from sources referenced in Table 2.6.

Section 1
Graphs and Tables

The substances are listed in alphabetical order. For each a saturation table and a skeleton superheat table are given, and a graph. For air a low-density table and several graphs are included. For Refrigerant 11, Refrigerant 22, ammonia, and water, the superheat tables are more extensive. *P-h*, *T-s*, *h-s*, and *u-v* diagrams are given for water. The datum state for each substance is indicated by the saturation table.

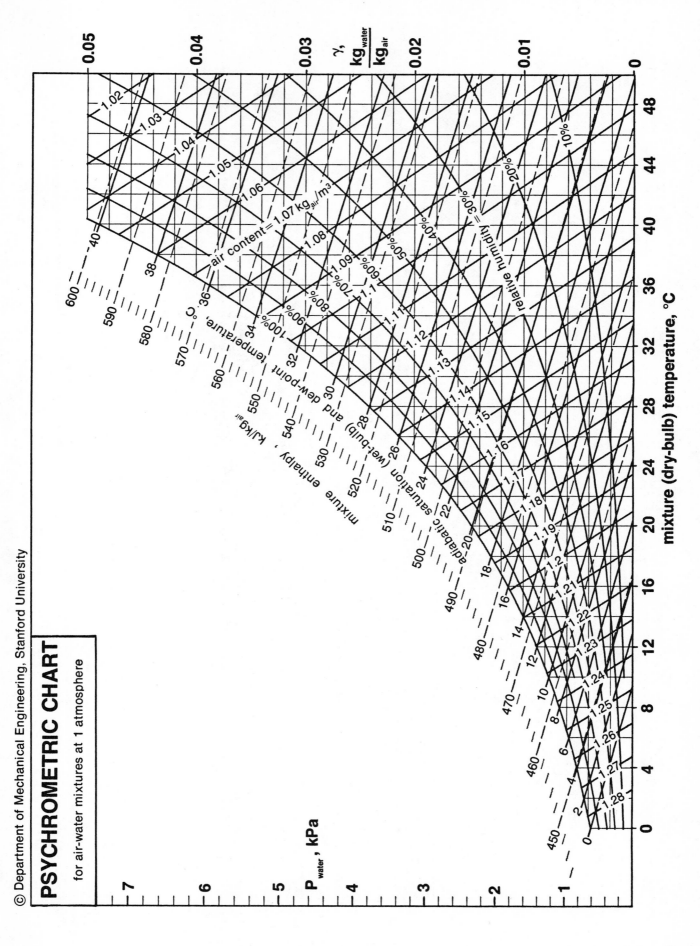

PSYCHROMETRIC CHART

for air-water mixtures at 1 atmosphere

© Department of Mechanical Engineering, Stanford University

mixture (dry-bulb) temperature, °C

P_{water}, kPa

γ, $\dfrac{kg_{water}}{kg_{air}}$

mixture enthalpy, kJ/kg

dew-point (wet-bulb) and saturation temperature, °C

adiabatic

relative humidity = 30%

air content = 1.07 kg_{air}/m^3

3

LOW DENSITY PROPERTIES OF AIR

T K	h kJ/kg	u kJ/kg	ψ	ϕ kJ/(kg·K)	P_r	V_r	c_p	c_v kJ/(kg·K)	k
200	359.8	302.4	4.2910	7.4367	17.81	3224.	1.002	0.715	1.402
205	364.8	306.0	4.3086	7.4614	19.41	3032.	1.002	0.715	1.402
210	369.8	309.5	4.3258	7.4855	21.11	2855.	1.002	0.715	1.402
215	374.8	313.1	4.3427	7.5091	22.92	2693.	1.002	0.715	1.401
220	379.8	316.7	4.3591	7.5322	24.84	2543.	1.002	0.715	1.401
225	384.9	320.3	4.3752	7.5547	26.86	2404.	1.002	0.715	1.401
230	389.9	323.8	4.3909	7.5767	29.01	2276.	1.002	0.715	1.401
235	394.9	327.4	4.4063	7.5983	31.27	2157.	1.002	0.715	1.401
240	399.9	331.0	4.4213	7.6194	33.65	2047.	1.002	0.715	1.401
245	404.9	334.6	4.4361	7.6400	36.17	1945.	1.002	0.715	1.401
250	409.9	338.1	4.4505	7.6603	38.81	1849.	1.003	0.715	1.401
255	414.9	341.7	4.4647	7.6801	41.59	1760.	1.003	0.716	1.401
260	419.9	345.3	4.4786	7.6996	44.51	1677.	1.003	0.716	1.401
265	425.0	348.9	4.4922	7.7187	47.57	1599.	1.003	0.716	1.401
270	430.0	352.5	4.5056	7.7375	50.78	1526.	1.003	0.716	1.401
275	435.0	356.0	4.5187	7.7559	54.14	1458.	1.003	0.716	1.401
280	440.0	359.6	4.5317	7.7740	57.66	1394.	1.003	0.716	1.401
285	445.0	363.2	4.5443	7.7917	61.34	1334.	1.004	0.716	1.401
290	450.0	366.8	4.5568	7.8092	65.19	1277.	1.004	0.717	1.401
295	455.1	370.4	4.5690	7.8263	69.20	1224.	1.004	0.717	1.400
300	460.1	374.0	4.5811	7.8432	73.39	1173.	1.004	0.717	1.400
305	465.1	377.5	4.5930	7.8598	77.76	1126.	1.004	0.717	1.400
310	470.1	381.1	4.6046	7.8761	82.32	1081.	1.005	0.718	1.400
315	475.1	384.7	4.6161	7.8922	87.06	1039.	1.005	0.718	1.400
320	480.2	388.3	4.6274	7.9080	91.99	998.6	1.005	0.718	1.400
325	485.2	391.9	4.6385	7.9236	97.13	960.6	1.006	0.718	1.400
330	490.2	395.5	4.6495	7.9390	102.5	924.6	1.006	0.719	1.399
335	495.3	399.1	4.6603	7.9541	108.0	890.4	1.006	0.719	1.399
340	500.3	402.7	4.6710	7.9690	113.8	857.9	1.007	0.720	1.399
345	505.3	406.3	4.6815	7.9837	119.7	827.1	1.007	0.720	1.399
350	510.4	409.9	4.6919	7.9982	125.9	797.8	1.007	0.720	1.399
355	515.4	413.5	4.7021	8.0125	132.4	769.9	1.008	0.721	1.398
360	520.4	417.1	4.7122	8.0266	139.0	743.3	1.008	0.721	1.398
365	525.5	420.7	4.7221	8.0405	145.9	718.0	1.009	0.722	1.398
370	530.5	424.3	4.7319	8.0542	153.1	693.8	1.009	0.722	1.398
375	535.6	427.9	4.7416	8.0678	160.5	670.8	1.010	0.723	1.397
380	540.6	431.5	4.7512	8.0812	168.1	648.8	1.010	0.723	1.397
385	545.7	435.2	4.7607	8.0944	176.1	627.8	1.011	0.724	1.397
390	550.7	438.8	4.7700	8.1074	184.2	607.7	1.011	0.724	1.396
395	555.8	442.4	4.7792	8.1203	192.7	588.4	1.012	0.725	1.396
400	560.8	446.0	4.7884	8.1330	201.4	570.0	1.013	0.725	1.396
405	565.9	449.6	4.7974	8.1456	210.5	552.4	1.013	0.726	1.395
410	571.0	453.3	4.8063	8.1581	219.8	535.5	1.014	0.727	1.395
415	576.0	456.9	4.8151	8.1704	229.4	519.3	1.014	0.727	1.395
420	581.1	460.6	4.8238	8.1825	239.3	503.8	1.015	0.728	1.394
425	586.2	464.2	4.8324	8.1945	249.6	488.9	1.016	0.729	1.394
430	591.3	467.8	4.8410	8.2064	260.1	474.6	1.017	0.729	1.394
435	596.4	471.5	4.8494	8.2182	271.0	460.8	1.017	0.730	1.393
440	601.5	475.1	4.8577	8.2298	282.2	447.6	1.018	0.731	1.393
445	606.5	478.8	4.8660	8.2413	293.7	434.9	1.019	0.732	1.392
450	611.6	482.5	4.8742	8.2527	305.6	422.7	1.020	0.733	1.392
455	616.7	486.1	4.8823	8.2640	317.8	410.9	1.020	0.733	1.391
460	621.8	489.8	4.8903	8.2751	330.4	399.6	1.021	0.734	1.391
465	627.0	493.5	4.8982	8.2862	343.4	388.7	1.022	0.735	1.391
470	632.1	497.1	4.9061	8.2971	356.7	378.2	1.023	0.736	1.390
475	637.2	500.8	4.9139	8.3079	370.4	368.1	1.024	0.737	1.390
480	642.3	504.5	4.9216	8.3187	384.6	358.3	1.025	0.738	1.389
485	647.4	508.2	4.9293	8.3293	399.0	348.9	1.026	0.739	1.389
490	652.6	511.9	4.9369	8.3398	414.0	339.8	1.027	0.739	1.388
495	657.7	515.6	4.9444	8.3502	429.3	331.0	1.027	0.740	1.388

LOW DENSITY PROPERTIES OF AIR

T K	h kJ/kg	u kJ/kg	ψ	ϕ	P_r	V_r	c_p	c_v	k
			kJ/(kg·K)				kJ/(kg·K)		
500	662.8	519.3	4.9518	8.3606	445.0	322.6	1.028	0.741	1.387
505	668.0	523.0	4.9592	8.3708	461.1	314.4	1.029	0.742	1.387
510	673.1	526.7	4.9665	8.3809	477.7	306.5	1.030	0.743	1.386
515	678.3	530.4	4.9738	8.3910	494.8	298.8	1.031	0.744	1.386
520	683.4	534.2	4.9810	8.4010	512.3	291.4	1.032	0.745	1.385
525	688.6	537.9	4.9881	8.4109	530.2	284.3	1.033	0.746	1.385
530	693.8	541.6	4.9952	8.4207	548.6	277.3	1.034	0.747	1.384
535	699.0	545.4	5.0022	8.4304	567.5	270.6	1.035	0.748	1.384
540	704.1	549.1	5.0092	8.4400	586.9	264.1	1.036	0.749	1.383
545	709.3	552.9	5.0161	8.4496	606.7	257.9	1.038	0.750	1.383
550	714.5	556.6	5.0229	8.4590	627.1	251.8	1.039	0.752	1.382
555	719.7	560.4	5.0297	8.4685	648.0	245.9	1.040	0.753	1.381
560	724.9	564.1	5.0365	8.4778	669.4	240.2	1.041	0.754	1.381
565	730.1	567.9	5.0432	8.4870	691.3	234.6	1.042	0.755	1.380
570	735.3	571.7	5.0499	8.4962	713.8	229.2	1.043	0.756	1.380
575	740.5	575.5	5.0565	8.5053	736.8	224.0	1.044	0.757	1.379
580	745.8	579.3	5.0630	8.5144	760.4	219.0	1.045	0.758	1.379
585	751.0	583.1	5.0695	8.5234	784.6	214.0	1.046	0.759	1.378
590	756.2	586.9	5.0760	8.5323	809.3	209.3	1.047	0.760	1.378
595	761.5	590.7	5.0824	8.5411	834.6	204.6	1.049	0.762	1.377
600	766.7	594.5	5.0888	8.5499	860.6	200.1	1.050	0.763	1.376
605	772.0	598.3	5.0951	8.5586	887.1	195.8	1.051	0.764	1.376
610	777.2	602.1	5.1014	8.5673	914.2	191.5	1.052	0.765	1.375
615	782.5	605.9	5.1077	8.5759	942.0	187.4	1.053	0.766	1.375
620	787.8	609.8	5.1139	8.5844	970.4	183.4	1.054	0.767	1.374
625	793.0	613.6	5.1201	8.5929	999.5	179.5	1.056	0.768	1.374
630	798.3	617.5	5.1262	8.6013	1029.	175.7	1.057	0.770	1.373
635	803.6	621.3	5.1323	8.6096	1060.	172.0	1.058	0.771	1.372
640	808.9	625.2	5.1383	8.6179	1091.	168.4	1.059	0.772	1.372
645	814.2	629.0	5.1443	8.6262	1123.	164.9	1.060	0.773	1.371
650	819.5	632.9	5.1503	8.6344	1155.	161.5	1.061	0.774	1.371
655	824.8	636.8	5.1563	8.6425	1188.	158.2	1.063	0.776	1.370
660	830.1	640.7	5.1622	8.6506	1222.	155.0	1.064	0.777	1.370
665	835.4	644.5	5.1680	8.6586	1257.	151.9	1.065	0.778	1.369
670	840.8	648.4	5.1739	8.6666	1292.	148.8	1.066	0.779	1.368
675	846.1	652.3	5.1796	8.6745	1329.	145.9	1.067	0.780	1.368
680	851.4	656.2	5.1854	8.6824	1366.	143.0	1.069	0.782	1.367
685	856.8	660.1	5.1911	8.6903	1403.	140.1	1.070	0.783	1.367
690	862.1	664.1	5.1968	8.6980	1442.	137.4	1.071	0.784	1.366
695	867.5	668.0	5.2025	8.7058	1481.	134.7	1.072	0.785	1.366
700	872.9	671.9	5.2081	8.7135	1521.	132.1	1.073	0.786	1.365
705	878.2	675.9	5.2137	8.7211	1563.	129.5	1.075	0.788	1.365
710	883.6	679.8	5.2193	8.7287	1604.	127.0	1.076	0.789	1.364
715	889.0	683.7	5.2248	8.7363	1647.	124.6	1.077	0.790	1.363
720	894.4	687.7	5.2304	8.7438	1691.	122.2	1.078	0.791	1.363
725	899.8	691.7	5.2358	8.7512	1735.	119.9	1.079	0.792	1.362
730	905.2	695.6	5.2413	8.7587	1781.	117.7	1.081	0.794	1.362
735	910.6	699.6	5.2467	8.7660	1827.	115.5	1.082	0.795	1.361
740	916.0	703.6	5.2521	8.7734	1875.	113.3	1.083	0.796	1.361
745	921.4	707.5	5.2575	8.7807	1923.	111.2	1.084	0.797	1.360
750	926.8	711.5	5.2628	8.7879	1972.	109.2	1.085	0.798	1.360
755	932.3	715.5	5.2681	8.7952	2022.	107.2	1.087	0.799	1.359
760	937.7	719.5	5.2734	8.8023	2073.	105.2	1.088	0.801	1.359
765	943.1	723.5	5.2786	8.8095	2126.	103.3	1.089	0.802	1.358
770	948.6	727.5	5.2839	8.8166	2179.	101.4	1.090	0.803	1.358
775	954.0	731.6	5.2891	8.8236	2233.	99.63	1.091	0.804	1.357
780	959.5	735.6	5.2942	8.8306	2288.	97.85	1.092	0.805	1.356
785	965.0	739.6	5.2994	8.8376	2345.	96.11	1.094	0.806	1.356
790	970.4	743.7	5.3045	8.8446	2402.	94.41	1.095	0.808	1.355
795	975.9	747.7	5.3096	8.8515	2461.	92.75	1.096	0.809	1.355

LOW DENSITY PROPERTIES OF AIR

T K	h kJ/kg	u kJ/kg	ψ kJ/(kg·K)	ϕ	P_r	V_r	c_p kJ/(kg·K)	c_v	k
800	981.4	751.7	5.3147	8.8584	2520.	91.12	1.097	0.810	1.354
805	986.9	755.8	5.3197	8.8652	2581.	89.53	1.098	0.811	1.354
810	992.4	759.8	5.3248	8.8720	2643.	87.98	1.099	0.812	1.353
815	997.9	763.9	5.3298	8.8788	2706.	86.46	1.100	0.813	1.353
820	1003.4	768.0	5.3347	8.8855	2770.	84.97	1.102	0.814	1.352
825	1008.9	772.1	5.3397	8.8922	2836.	83.52	1.103	0.816	1.352
830	1014.4	776.1	5.3446	8.8989	2902.	82.10	1.104	0.817	1.351
835	1019.9	780.2	5.3495	8.9055	2970.	80.70	1.105	0.818	1.351
840	1025.5	784.3	5.3544	8.9121	3039.	79.34	1.106	0.819	1.351
845	1031.0	788.4	5.3593	8.9187	3110.	78.01	1.107	0.820	1.350
850	1036.5	792.5	5.3641	8.9252	3181.	76.71	1.108	0.821	1.350
855	1042.1	796.6	5.3689	8.9317	3254.	75.43	1.109	0.822	1.349
860	1047.6	800.7	5.3737	8.9382	3328.	74.18	1.110	0.823	1.349
865	1053.2	804.9	5.3785	8.9446	3404.	72.95	1.112	0.824	1.348
870	1058.7	809.0	5.3833	8.9510	3481.	71.76	1.113	0.826	1.348
875	1064.3	813.1	5.3880	8.9574	3559.	70.58	1.114	0.827	1.347
880	1069.9	817.3	5.3927	8.9638	3638.	69.43	1.115	0.828	1.347
885	1075.4	821.4	5.3974	8.9701	3719.	68.31	1.116	0.829	1.346
890	1081.0	825.5	5.4021	8.9764	3802.	67.20	1.117	0.830	1.346
895	1086.6	829.7	5.4067	8.9826	3886.	66.12	1.118	0.831	1.345
900	1092.2	833.8	5.4114	8.9889	3971.	65.07	1.119	0.832	1.345
905	1097.8	838.0	5.4160	8.9951	4058.	64.03	1.120	0.833	1.345
910	1103.4	842.2	5.4206	9.0012	4146.	63.01	1.121	0.834	1.344
915	1109.0	846.4	5.4252	9.0074	4235.	62.02	1.122	0.835	1.344
920	1114.6	850.5	5.4297	9.0135	4327.	61.04	1.123	0.836	1.343
925	1120.2	854.7	5.4342	9.0196	4419.	60.08	1.124	0.837	1.343
930	1125.9	858.9	5.4388	9.0257	4514.	59.15	1.125	0.838	1.342
935	1131.5	863.1	5.4433	9.0317	4610.	58.23	1.126	0.839	1.342
940	1137.1	867.3	5.4477	9.0377	4707.	57.33	1.127	0.840	1.342
945	1142.8	871.5	5.4522	9.0437	4806.	56.44	1.128	0.841	1.341
950	1148.4	875.7	5.4566	9.0496	4907.	55.58	1.129	0.842	1.341
955	1154.1	879.9	5.4611	9.0556	5010.	54.73	1.130	0.843	1.340
960	1159.7	884.1	5.4655	9.0615	5114.	53.89	1.131	0.844	1.340
965	1165.4	888.4	5.4698	9.0673	5219.	53.07	1.132	0.845	1.340
970	1171.0	892.6	5.4742	9.0732	5327.	52.27	1.133	0.846	1.339
975	1176.7	896.8	5.4786	9.0790	5436.	51.49	1.134	0.847	1.339
980	1182.4	901.1	5.4829	9.0848	5547.	50.71	1.135	0.848	1.338
985	1188.1	905.3	5.4872	9.0906	5660.	49.96	1.136	0.849	1.338
990	1193.7	909.5	5.4915	9.0964	5775.	49.21	1.137	0.850	1.338
995	1199.4	913.8	5.4958	9.1021	5891.	48.49	1.138	0.851	1.337
1000	1205.1	918.1	5.5001	9.1078	6009.	47.77	1.139	0.852	1.337
1005	1210.8	922.3	5.5043	9.1135	6130.	47.07	1.140	0.853	1.337
1010	1216.5	926.6	5.5086	9.1191	6252.	46.38	1.141	0.854	1.336
1015	1222.2	930.9	5.5128	9.1248	6376.	45.70	1.142	0.855	1.336
1020	1227.9	935.1	5.5170	9.1304	6501.	45.04	1.143	0.856	1.336
1025	1233.7	939.4	5.5212	9.1360	6629.	44.39	1.144	0.856	1.335
1030	1239.4	943.7	5.5253	9.1416	6759.	43.75	1.144	0.857	1.335
1035	1245.1	948.0	5.5295	9.1471	6891.	43.12	1.145	0.858	1.334
1040	1250.8	952.3	5.5336	9.1526	7025.	42.50	1.146	0.859	1.334
1045	1256.6	956.6	5.5378	9.1581	7161.	41.89	1.147	0.860	1.334
1050	1262.3	960.9	5.5419	9.1636	7299.	41.30	1.148	0.861	1.333
1055	1268.0	965.2	5.5460	9.1691	7439.	40.71	1.149	0.862	1.333
1060	1273.8	969.5	5.5500	9.1745	7581.	40.14	1.150	0.863	1.333
1065	1279.5	973.8	5.5541	9.1799	7725.	39.58	1.151	0.864	1.332
1070	1285.3	978.1	5.5581	9.1853	7872.	39.02	1.152	0.864	1.332
1075	1291.1	982.5	5.5622	9.1907	8020.	38.48	1.152	0.865	1.332
1080	1296.8	986.8	5.5662	9.1960	8171.	37.94	1.153	0.866	1.331
1085	1302.6	991.1	5.5702	9.2013	8324.	37.42	1.154	0.867	1.331
1090	1308.4	995.5	5.5742	9.2066	8479.	36.90	1.155	0.868	1.331
1095	1314.1	999.8	5.5782	9.2119	8637.	36.39	1.156	0.869	1.330

LOW DENSITY PROPERTIES OF AIR

T K	h kJ/kg	u kJ/kg	ψ kJ/(kg·K)	ϕ	P_r	V_r	c_p kJ/(kg·K)	c_v	k
1100	1319.9	1004.1	5.5821	9.2172	8797.	35.90	1.157	0.870	1.330
1105	1325.7	1008.5	5.5861	9.2225	8959.	35.41	1.157	0.870	1.330
1110	1331.5	1012.8	5.5900	9.2277	9124.	34.92	1.158	0.871	1.330
1115	1337.3	1017.2	5.5939	9.2329	9291.	34.45	1.159	0.872	1.329
1120	1343.1	1021.6	5.5978	9.2381	9460.	33.99	1.160	0.873	1.329
1125	1348.9	1025.9	5.6017	9.2432	9632.	33.53	1.161	0.874	1.329
1130	1354.7	1030.3	5.6056	9.2484	9807.	33.08	1.161	0.874	1.328
1135	1360.5	1034.7	5.6094	9.2535	9983.	32.64	1.162	0.875	1.328
1140	1366.3	1039.1	5.6133	9.2586	10163.	32.20	1.163	0.876	1.328
1145	1372.1	1043.4	5.6171	9.2637	10345.	31.77	1.164	0.877	1.327
1150	1378.0	1047.8	5.6209	9.2688	10529.	31.35	1.165	0.878	1.327
1155	1383.8	1052.2	5.6248	9.2738	10716.	30.94	1.165	0.878	1.327
1160	1389.6	1056.6	5.6286	9.2789	10906.	30.53	1.166	0.879	1.327
1165	1395.4	1061.0	5.6323	9.2839	11098.	30.14	1.167	0.880	1.326
1170	1401.3	1065.4	5.6361	9.2889	11293.	29.74	1.168	0.881	1.326
1175	1407.1	1069.8	5.6399	9.2939	11490.	29.36	1.168	0.881	1.326
1180	1413.0	1074.2	5.6436	9.2988	11691.	28.97	1.169	0.882	1.325
1185	1418.8	1078.6	5.6473	9.3038	11894.	28.60	1.170	0.883	1.325
1190	1424.7	1083.0	5.6511	9.3087	12100.	28.23	1.171	0.884	1.325
1195	1430.5	1087.5	5.6548	9.3136	12309.	27.87	1.171	0.884	1.325
1200	1436.4	1091.9	5.6585	9.3185	12520.	27.51	1.172	0.885	1.324
1205	1442.2	1096.3	5.6621	9.3234	12735.	27.16	1.173	0.886	1.324
1210	1448.1	1100.7	5.6658	9.3283	12952.	26.82	1.174	0.886	1.324
1215	1454.0	1105.2	5.6695	9.3331	13172.	26.48	1.174	0.887	1.324
1220	1459.8	1109.6	5.6731	9.3379	13395.	26.14	1.175	0.888	1.323
1225	1465.7	1114.1	5.6767	9.3427	13622.	25.82	1.176	0.889	1.323
1230	1471.6	1118.5	5.6804	9.3475	13851.	25.49	1.176	0.889	1.323
1235	1477.5	1123.0	5.6840	9.3523	14083.	25.17	1.177	0.890	1.323
1240	1483.4	1127.4	5.6876	9.3570	14318.	24.86	1.178	0.891	1.322
1245	1489.3	1131.9	5.6912	9.3618	14557.	24.55	1.178	0.891	1.322
1250	1495.2	1136.3	5.6947	9.3665	14798.	24.25	1.179	0.892	1.322
1255	1501.0	1140.8	5.6983	9.3712	15043.	23.95	1.180	0.893	1.322
1260	1507.0	1145.2	5.7018	9.3759	15291.	23.65	1.180	0.893	1.321
1265	1512.9	1149.7	5.7054	9.3806	15542.	23.36	1.181	0.894	1.321
1270	1518.8	1154.2	5.7089	9.3852	15797.	23.08	1.182	0.895	1.321
1275	1524.7	1158.7	5.7124	9.3899	16054.	22.80	1.182	0.895	1.321
1280	1530.6	1163.1	5.7159	9.3945	16315.	22.52	1.183	0.896	1.320
1285	1536.5	1167.6	5.7194	9.3991	16580.	22.25	1.184	0.897	1.320
1290	1542.4	1172.1	5.7229	9.4037	16847.	21.98	1.184	0.897	1.320
1300	1554.3	1181.1	5.7298	9.4129	17393.	21.46	1.186	0.899	1.319
1310	1566.1	1190.1	5.7367	9.4220	17953.	20.95	1.187	0.900	1.319
1320	1578.0	1199.1	5.7436	9.4310	18526.	20.45	1.188	0.901	1.319
1330	1589.9	1208.1	5.7504	9.4400	19114.	19.97	1.189	0.902	1.318
1340	1601.8	1217.1	5.7571	9.4489	19717.	19.51	1.191	0.904	1.318
1350	1613.7	1226.2	5.7639	9.4578	20335.	19.06	1.192	0.905	1.317
1360	1625.6	1235.2	5.7706	9.4666	20968.	18.62	1.193	0.906	1.317
1370	1637.6	1244.3	5.7772	9.4753	21617.	18.19	1.194	0.907	1.316
1380	1649.5	1253.4	5.7838	9.4840	22281.	17.78	1.195	0.908	1.316
1390	1661.5	1262.5	5.7904	9.4926	22961.	17.38	1.196	0.909	1.316
1400	1673.5	1271.6	5.7969	9.5012	23658.	16.99	1.198	0.911	1.315
1410	1685.4	1280.7	5.8034	9.5097	24372.	16.61	1.199	0.912	1.315
1420	1697.4	1289.8	5.8098	9.5182	25102.	16.24	1.200	0.913	1.315
1430	1709.4	1298.9	5.8162	9.5266	25849.	15.88	1.201	0.914	1.314
1440	1721.4	1308.1	5.8226	9.5350	26614.	15.53	1.202	0.915	1.314
1450	1733.5	1317.2	5.8289	9.5433	27397.	15.19	1.203	0.916	1.313
1460	1745.5	1326.4	5.8352	9.5516	28198.	14.86	1.204	0.917	1.313
1470	1757.6	1335.6	5.8415	9.5598	29017.	14.54	1.205	0.918	1.313
1480	1769.6	1344.7	5.8477	9.5680	29856.	14.23	1.206	0.919	1.312
1490	1781.7	1353.9	5.8539	9.5761	30713.	13.93	1.207	0.920	1.312
1500	1793.7	1363.1	5.8601	9.5842	31589.	13.63	1.208	0.921	1.312

PROPERTIES OF SATURATED AIR

P MPa	temperature, K T$_f$	T$_g$	volume, m³/kg v$_f$	v$_g$	enthalpy, kJ/kg h$_f$	h$_g$	entropy, kJ/(kg·K) s$_f$	s$_g$
0.0800	76.5	79.9	0.001126	0.2774	30.56	237.28	0.6143	3.2579
0.0900	77.6	80.8	0.001132	0.2489	31.86	238.03	0.6324	3.2345
0.1013	78.8	81.8	0.001138	0.2231	33.28	238.79	0.6517	3.2111
0.1200	80.4	83.3	0.001148	0.1908	35.51	239.89	0.6811	3.1778
0.1400	82.0	84.7	0.001158	0.1654	37.75	240.89	0.7097	3.1474
0.1600	83.3	86.0	0.001166	0.1461	39.87	241.75	0.7359	3.1212
0.1800	84.6	87.1	0.001175	0.1310	41.87	242.52	0.7601	3.0980
0.2000	85.7	88.1	0.001182	0.1188	43.76	243.19	0.7826	3.0773
0.2500	88.1	90.5	0.001200	0.09642	48.14	244.60	0.8330	3.0333
0.3000	90.2	92.4	0.001216	0.08125	52.08	245.71	0.8769	2.9971
0.3500	92.0	94.2	0.001230	0.07024	55.70	246.61	0.9159	2.9663
0.4000	93.6	95.8	0.001244	0.06188	59.04	247.35	0.9512	2.9394
0.4500	95.1	97.2	0.001257	0.05530	62.15	247.96	0.9834	2.9154
0.5000	96.5	98.5	0.001270	0.04997	65.08	248.47	1.0131	2.8937
0.6000	98.9	100.9	0.001294	0.04188	70.48	249.24	1.0665	2.8556
0.7000	101.0	103.0	0.001317	0.03600	75.39	249.75	1.1137	2.8226
0.8000	103.0	104.9	0.001339	0.03153	79.92	250.07	1.1561	2.7933
1.0000	106.3	108.2	0.001382	0.02515	88.09	250.26	1.2305	2.7423
1.2000	109.2	111.1	0.001424	0.02080	95.41	249.99	1.2948	2.6981
1.4000	111.8	113.6	0.001466	0.01762	102.10	249.34	1.3520	2.6584
1.6000	114.2	115.9	0.001510	0.01519	108.34	248.38	1.4040	2.6215
1.8000	116.4	117.9	0.001555	0.01327	114.25	247.13	1.4521	2.5865
2.0000	118.4	119.8	0.001603	0.01170	119.91	245.60	1.4973	2.5526
2.5000	122.9	124.0	0.001739	0.008746	133.53	240.44	1.6030	2.4689
3.0000	127.0	127.7	0.001919	0.006600	147.47	232.75	1.7077	2.3775

PROPERTIES OF GASEOUS AIR

P, MPa (T$_{sat}$,K)		200	300	400	500	600	700	800	900	1000
0.050	v,m³/kg	1.147	1.722	2.297	2.871	3.445	4.020	4.594	5.168	5.742
(76.24)	h,kJ/kg	359.56	459.96	560.79	662.81	766.71	872.87	981.41	1092.23	1205.16
	s,kJ/(kg·K)	4.3298	4.7368	5.0269	5.2544	5.4438	5.6074	5.7523	5.8828	6.0018
	u,kJ/kg	302.22	373.86	445.95	519.25	594.44	671.89	751.72	833.83	918.04
0.101325	v,m³/kg	0.5653	0.8497	1.133	1.417	1.701	1.984	2.267	2.551	2.834
(81.82)	h,kJ/kg	359.31	459.85	560.73	662.79	766.70	872.88	981.43	1092.26	1205.19
	s,kJ/(kg·K)	4.1261	4.5337	4.8239	5.0516	5.2410	5.4046	5.5495	5.6800	5.7990
	u,kJ/kg	302.03	373.75	445.88	519.20	594.40	671.86	751.69	833.81	918.03
0.14	v,m³/kg	0.4088	0.6149	0.8204	1.026	1.231	1.436	1.641	1.846	2.051
(84.70)	h,kJ/kg	359.12	459.76	560.69	662.77	766.70	872.89	981.44	1092.28	1205.21
	s,kJ/(kg·K)	4.0326	4.4407	4.7310	4.9587	5.1481	5.3118	5.4567	5.5872	5.7062
	u,kJ/kg	301.90	373.67	445.83	519.16	594.37	671.84	751.67	833.79	918.01
0.20	v,m³/kg	0.2857	0.4304	0.5744	0.7182	0.8619	1.006	1.149	1.293	1.436
(88.14)	h,kJ/kg	358.83	459.63	560.62	662.74	766.70	872.90	981.47	1092.31	1205.25
	s,kJ/(kg·K)	3.9291	4.3379	4.6284	4.8562	5.0457	5.2093	5.3543	5.4848	5.6038
	u,kJ/kg	301.68	373.55	445.75	519.11	594.32	671.80	751.65	833.77	918.00
0.30	v,m³/kg	0.1900	0.2868	0.3830	0.4789	0.5748	0.6706	0.7663	0.8621	0.9578
(92.45)	h,kJ/kg	358.34	459.40	560.51	662.69	766.69	872.92	981.50	1092.36	1205.31
	s,kJ/(kg·K)	3.8110	4.2208	4.5116	4.7396	4.9291	5.0928	5.2378	5.3684	5.4873
	u,kJ/kg	301.33	373.35	445.61	519.01	594.25	671.74	751.60	833.73	917.97
0.40	v,m³/kg	0.1422	0.2151	0.2873	0.3593	0.4313	0.5031	0.5750	0.6468	0.7186
(95.78)	h,kJ/kg	357.85	459.18	560.40	662.64	766.68	872.94	981.54	1092.41	1205.37
	s,kJ/(kg·K)	3.7266	4.1375	4.4287	4.6568	4.8464	5.0102	5.1552	5.2857	5.4047
	u,kJ/kg	300.97	373.15	445.48	518.91	594.17	671.68	751.55	833.70	917.94
0.70	v,m³/kg	0.08069	0.1228	0.1643	0.2056	0.2467	0.2878	0.3289	0.3700	0.4110
(103.0)	h,kJ/kg	356.37	458.50	560.07	662.50	766.65	872.99	981.65	1092.56	1205.55
	s,kJ/(kg·K)	3.5606	3.9749	4.2671	4.4956	4.6854	4.8493	4.9943	5.1250	5.2440
	u,kJ/kg	299.89	372.54	445.07	518.61	593.95	671.51	751.41	833.58	917.84

PROPERTIES OF GASEOUS AIR

P, MPa (T$_{sat}$,K)		200	300	400	500	600	700	800	900	1000
1.0 (108.2)	v,m³/kg	0.05609	0.08590	0.1151	0.1440	0.1729	0.2017	0.2305	0.2592	0.2880
	h,kJ/kg	354.89	457.83	559.74	662.36	766.63	873.04	981.76	1092.72	1205.74
	s,kJ/(kg·K)	3.4527	3.8705	4.1637	4.3926	4.5826	4.7466	4.8918	5.0224	5.1415
	u,kJ/kg	298.80	371.94	444.66	518.32	593.72	671.33	751.27	833.47	917.75
1.4 (113.6)	v,m³/kg	0.03969	0.06130	0.08227	0.1030	0.1237	0.1443	0.1649	0.1854	0.2060
	h,kJ/kg	352.89	456.95	559.31	662.17	766.60	873.12	981.91	1092.92	1205.99
	s,kJ/(kg·K)	3.3488	3.7712	4.0657	4.2952	4.4856	4.6497	4.7950	4.9257	5.0448
	u,kJ/kg	297.33	371.13	444.12	517.93	593.43	671.10	751.09	833.32	917.63
2.0 (119.8)	v,m³/kg	0.02739	0.04285	0.05767	0.07228	0.08679	0.1012	0.1157	0.1301	0.1445
	h,kJ/kg	349.87	455.63	558.67	661.90	766.56	873.23	982.14	1093.23	1206.36
	s,kJ/(kg·K)	3.2353	3.6649	3.9614	4.1917	4.3824	4.5468	4.6922	4.8230	4.9422
	u,kJ/kg	295.09	369.92	443.32	517.34	592.98	670.75	750.81	833.10	917.45
3.0 (127.7)	v,m³/kg	0.01784	0.02852	0.03855	0.04836	0.05808	0.06775	0.07739	0.08701	0.09661
	h,kJ/kg	344.78	453.46	557.62	661.46	766.50	873.43	982.52	1093.75	1206.98
	s,kJ/(kg·K)	3.0999	3.5419	3.8417	4.0734	4.2648	4.4296	4.5753	4.7062	4.8255
	u,kJ/kg	291.26	367.91	441.98	516.37	592.24	670.18	750.35	832.73	917.15
5.0	v,m³/kg	0.01022	0.01707	0.02326	0.02924	0.03513	0.04097	0.04677	0.05256	0.05834
	h,kJ/kg	334.39	449.26	555.63	660.66	766.43	873.86	983.31	1094.80	1208.24
	s,kJ/(kg·K)	2.9142	3.3824	3.6887	3.9230	4.1158	4.2814	4.4275	4.5588	4.6783
	u,kJ/kg	283.27	363.91	439.34	514.46	590.79	669.04	749.44	832.00	916.55
7.0	v,m³/kg	0.00701	0.01219	0.01672	0.02105	0.02529	0.02949	0.03365	0.03780	0.04194
	h,kJ/kg	323.93	445.27	553.77	659.93	766.41	874.33	984.12	1095.88	1209.51
	s,kJ/(kg·K)	2.7776	3.2734	3.5859	3.8228	4.0169	4.1832	4.3298	4.4614	4.5811
	u,kJ/kg	274.89	359.96	436.75	512.58	589.36	667.91	748.55	831.27	915.96
10.	v,m³/kg	0.00468	0.00855	0.01183	0.01492	0.01792	0.02088	0.02382	0.02673	0.02964
	h,kJ/kg	308.87	439.71	551.23	659.00	766.50	875.11	985.40	1097.53	1211.45
	s,kJ/(kg·K)	2.6169	3.1534	3.4747	3.7152	3.9112	4.0786	4.2258	4.3579	4.4779
	u,kJ/kg	262.09	354.16	432.96	509.82	587.26	666.26	747.22	830.20	915.09

P, MPa		200	300	400	500	600	700	800	900	1000
14.	v,m³/kg	0.00328	0.00617	0.00859	0.01084	0.01302	0.01515	0.01726	0.01936	0.02144
	h,kJ/kg	292.25	433.18	548.32	658.05	766.80	876.27	987.19	1099.80	1214.08
	s,kJ/(kg·K)	2.4561	3.0353	3.3672	3.6121	3.8104	3.9791	4.1272	4.2598	4.3802
	u,kJ/kg	246.28	346.76	428.10	506.28	584.54	664.12	745.50	828.81	913.95
20.	v,m³/kg	0.00244	0.00444	0.00618	0.00780	0.00935	0.01086	0.01235	0.01383	0.01529
	h,kJ/kg	277.13	425.39	544.95	657.23	767.64	878.29	990.07	1103.34	1218.14
	s,kJ/(kg·K)	2.2967	2.9053	3.2501	3.5008	3.7021	3.8727	4.0219	4.1553	4.2763
	u,kJ/kg	228.33	336.54	421.27	501.25	580.66	661.04	743.02	826.78	912.29
30.	v,m³/kg	0.00193	0.00318	0.00436	0.00546	0.00651	0.00753	0.00854	0.00953	0.01052
	h,kJ/kg	267.96	417.41	541.77	657.30	769.98	882.29	995.34	1109.58	1225.16
	s,kJ/(kg·K)	2.1437	2.7549	3.1136	3.3716	3.5771	3.7502	3.9012	4.0357	4.1575
	u,kJ/kg	209.97	322.16	411.12	493.61	574.68	656.26	739.13	823.59	909.66
50.	v,m³/kg	0.00159	0.00226	0.00295	0.00362	0.00426	0.00489	0.00550	0.00610	0.00670
	h,kJ/kg	269.73	414.72	542.54	661.80	777.54	892.28	1007.28	1123.10	1239.97
	s,kJ/(kg·K)	1.9797	2.5706	2.9392	3.2055	3.4166	3.5935	3.7470	3.8834	4.0065
	u,kJ/kg	190.47	301.91	395.05	480.91	564.45	647.89	732.23	817.86	904.89
70.	v,m³/kg	0.00143	0.00189	0.00237	0.00285	0.00331	0.00376	0.00420	0.00464	0.00507
	h,kJ/kg	279.48	421.23	549.50	670.41	787.92	904.27	1020.66	1137.67	1255.56
	s,kJ/(kg·K)	1.8784	2.4554	2.8252	3.0952	3.3095	3.4888	3.6442	3.7821	3.9062
	u,kJ/kg	179.21	288.78	383.32	471.01	556.16	640.94	726.38	812.93	900.73
100.	v,m³/kg	0.00131	0.00162	0.00195	0.00228	0.00260	0.00292	0.00323	0.00354	0.00384
	h,kJ/kg	298.89	438.15	566.11	687.97	806.89	924.73	1042.54	1160.85	1279.90
	s,kJ/(kg·K)	1.7710	2.3377	2.7064	2.9785	3.1953	3.3770	3.5343	3.6736	3.7991
	u,kJ/kg	168.38	275.91	370.94	459.94	546.51	632.61	719.21	806.78	895.47
200.	v,m³/kg	0.00112	0.00128	0.00145	0.00161	0.00177	0.00193	0.00209	0.00225	0.00240
	h,kJ/kg	374.30	512.21	639.81	762.39	882.84	1002.71	1122.77	1243.39	1364.71
	s,kJ/(kg·K)	1.5507	2.1118	2.4794	2.7530	2.9727	3.1575	3.3178	3.4598	3.5876
	u,kJ/kg	151.20	255.87	350.61	440.54	528.59	616.37	704.70	793.94	884.22

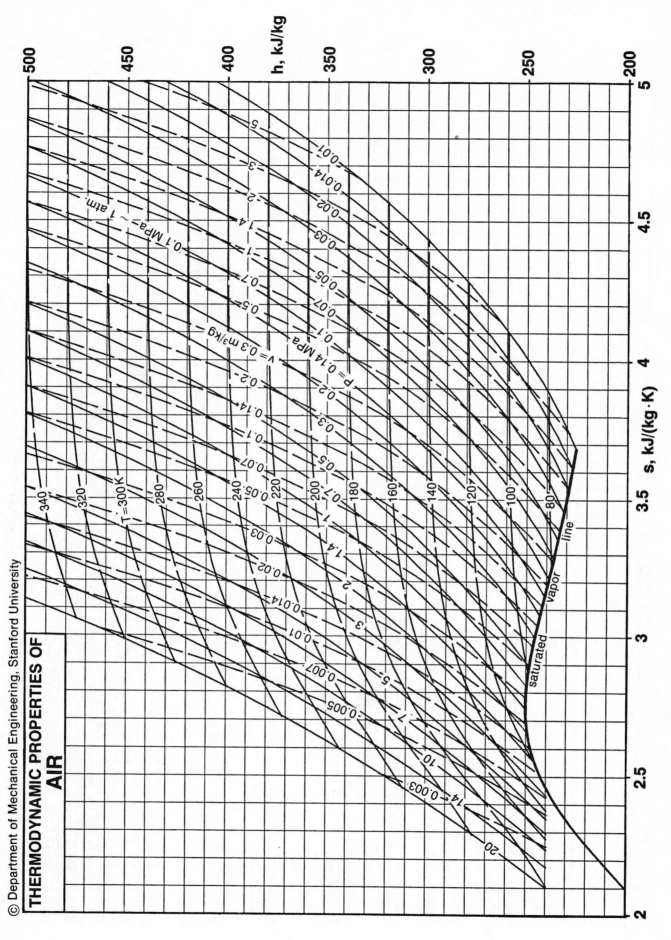

THERMODYNAMIC PROPERTIES OF AIR

© Department of Mechanical Engineering, Stanford University

h, kJ/kg

s, kJ/(kg·K)

P = 0.14 MPa

v = 0.3 m³/kg

T = 300 K

saturated vapor line

10

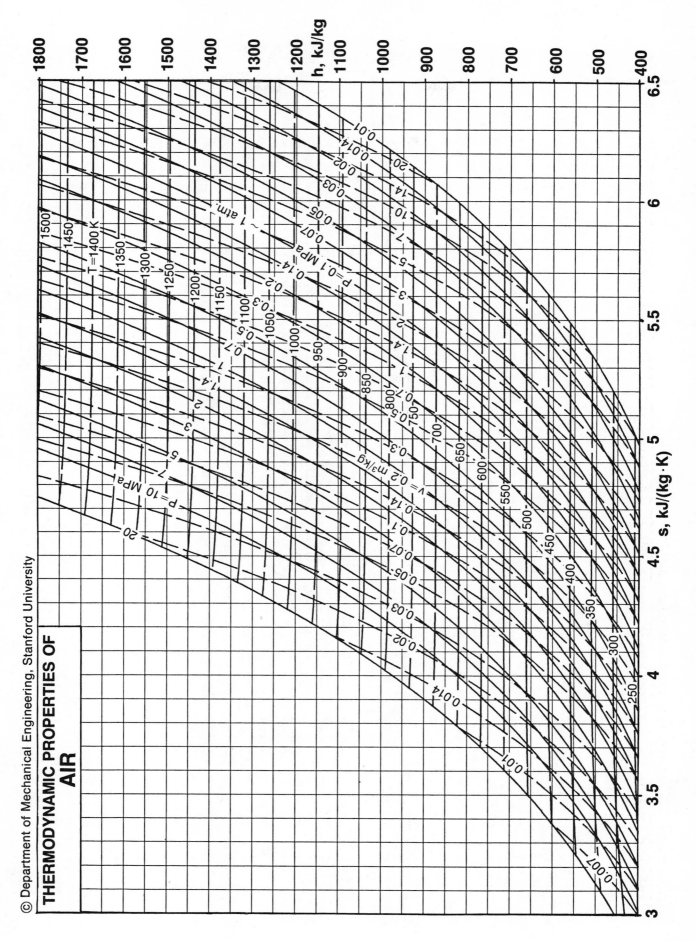

THERMODYNAMIC PROPERTIES OF
AIR

© Department of Mechanical Engineering, Stanford University

11

PROPERTIES OF SATURATED AMMONIA

T K	P MPa	volume, m³/kg v_f	volume, m³/kg v_g	enthalpy, kJ/kg h_f	enthalpy, kJ/kg h_{fg}	enthalpy, kJ/kg h_g	entropy, kJ/(kg·K) s_f	entropy, kJ/(kg·K) s_{fg}	entropy, kJ/(kg·K) s_g
200	0.008644	0.001372	11.24	0.0	1477.08	1477.08	0.0	7.3854	7.3854
204	0.01164	0.001381	8.506	17.63	1466.81	1484.44	0.0873	7.1902	7.2775
208	0.01546	0.001389	6.518	35.25	1456.44	1491.69	0.1728	7.0021	7.1749
212	0.02030	0.001398	5.053	52.86	1445.97	1498.83	0.2566	6.8206	7.0772
216	0.02633	0.001408	3.960	70.45	1435.40	1505.85	0.3388	6.6453	6.9841
220	0.03380	0.001417	3.136	88.02	1424.72	1512.74	0.4193	6.4760	6.8953
224	0.04295	0.001427	2.507	105.58	1413.90	1519.48	0.4983	6.3121	6.8104
228	0.05405	0.001436	2.022	123.13	1402.94	1526.07	0.5759	6.1533	6.7292
232	0.06741	0.001446	1.645	140.70	1391.80	1532.50	0.6522	5.9992	6.6514
236	0.08336	0.001457	1.349	158.30	1380.47	1538.77	0.7273	5.8495	6.5768
239.82	0.101325	0.001467	1.124	175.13	1369.46	1544.59	0.7980	5.7104	6.5084
240	0.1023	0.001467	1.115	175.92	1368.95	1544.87	0.8013	5.7039	6.5052
244	0.1245	0.001478	0.9272	193.65	1357.13	1550.78	0.8744	5.5620	6.4364
248	0.1505	0.001489	0.7764	211.42	1345.09	1556.51	0.9465	5.4237	6.3702
252	0.1806	0.001500	0.6542	229.30	1332.74	1562.04	1.0178	5.2887	6.3065
256	0.2154	0.001512	0.5545	247.29	1320.09	1567.38	1.0885	5.1565	6.2450
260	0.2554	0.001524	0.4725	265.40	1307.10	1572.50	1.1584	5.0273	6.1857
262	0.2775	0.001530	0.4371	274.51	1300.48	1574.99	1.1932	4.9636	6.1568
264	0.3010	0.001536	0.4048	283.64	1293.77	1577.41	1.2277	4.9007	6.1284
266	0.3261	0.001543	0.3753	292.80	1286.99	1579.79	1.2622	4.8383	6.1005
268	0.3528	0.001549	0.3484	301.99	1280.11	1582.10	1.2964	4.7766	6.0730
270	0.3812	0.001556	0.3238	311.21	1273.15	1584.36	1.3305	4.7154	6.0459
272	0.4114	0.001562	0.3013	320.46	1266.10	1586.56	1.3645	4.6548	6.0193
274	0.4433	0.001569	0.2807	329.75	1258.94	1588.69	1.3983	4.5947	5.9930
276	0.4772	0.001576	0.2617	339.06	1251.71	1590.77	1.4320	4.5352	5.9672
278	0.5131	0.001583	0.2442	348.41	1244.37	1592.78	1.4656	4.4761	5.9417
280	0.5510	0.001590	0.2282	357.78	1236.94	1594.72	1.4989	4.4177	5.9166
282	0.5911	0.001597	0.2134	367.19	1229.41	1596.60	1.5322	4.3596	5.8918
284	0.6334	0.001604	0.1997	376.62	1221.80	1598.42	1.5653	4.3021	5.8674
286	0.6780	0.001611	0.1871	386.08	1214.08	1600.16	1.5982	4.2450	5.8432
288	0.7250	0.001619	0.1755	395.57	1206.26	1601.83	1.6310	4.1884	5.8194
290	0.7744	0.001626	0.1647	405.09	1198.34	1603.43	1.6637	4.1322	5.7959
292	0.8264	0.001634	0.1547	414.63	1190.32	1604.95	1.6962	4.0764	5.7726
294	0.8810	0.001642	0.1454	424.18	1182.22	1606.40	1.7285	4.0211	5.7496
296	0.9383	0.001650	0.1367	433.77	1173.99	1607.76	1.7607	3.9662	5.7269
298	0.9984	0.001658	0.1287	443.40	1165.65	1609.05	1.7927	3.9116	5.7043
300	1.061	0.001666	0.1213	453.05	1157.20	1610.25	1.8247	3.8573	5.6820
304	1.197	0.001684	0.1078	472.43	1139.96	1612.39	1.8881	3.7499	5.6380
308	1.344	0.001701	0.09610	491.92	1122.25	1614.17	1.9510	3.6436	5.5946
312	1.506	0.001720	0.08586	511.54	1104.02	1615.56	2.0134	3.5385	5.5519
316	1.681	0.001739	0.07687	531.30	1085.24	1616.54	2.0753	3.4343	5.5096
320	1.872	0.001760	0.06896	551.21	1065.87	1617.08	2.1369	3.3308	5.4677
324	2.078	0.001781	0.06197	571.31	1045.84	1617.15	2.1982	3.2279	5.4261
328	2.301	0.001803	0.05578	591.61	1025.12	1616.73	2.2592	3.1254	5.3846
322	1.973	0.001770	0.06536	561.24	1055.94	1617.18	2.1676	3.2793	5.4469
336	2.800	0.001852	0.04538	632.96	981.30	1614.26	2.3810	2.9206	5.3016
340	3.079	0.001878	0.04100	654.08	958.06	1612.14	2.4420	2.8178	5.2598
345	3.455	0.001913	0.03615	680.98	927.57	1608.55	2.5184	2.6886	5.2070
350	3.864	0.001951	0.03191	708.50	895.34	1603.84	2.5953	2.5582	5.1535
355	4.309	0.001993	0.02818	736.73	861.13	1597.86	2.6729	2.4258	5.0987
360	4.791	0.002039	0.02488	765.75	824.73	1590.48	2.7514	2.2909	5.0423
365	5.313	0.002090	0.02196	795.67	785.80	1581.47	2.8310	2.1528	4.9838
370	5.876	0.002148	0.01935	826.62	743.95	1570.57	2.9119	2.0107	4.9226
375	6.483	0.002214	0.01700	858.78	698.62	1557.40	2.9947	1.8630	4.8577
380	7.136	0.002291	0.01488	892.46	648.94	1541.40	3.0800	1.7078	4.7878
385	7.840	0.002384	0.01294	928.19	593.51	1521.70	3.1691	1.5416	4.7107
390	8.598	0.002499	0.01113	966.96	529.87	1496.83	3.2644	1.3587	4.6231
395	9.416	0.002652	0.009405	1010.78	453.24	1464.02	3.3707	1.1474	4.5181
400	10.30	0.002879	0.007668	1064.30	352.44	1416.74	3.4992	0.8811	4.3803
406.80	11.627	0.004208	0.004208	1233.56	0.0	1233.56	3.9069	0.0	3.9069

PROPERTIES OF SATURATED AMMONIA

P MPa	T K	volume, m³/kg v_f	volume, m³/kg v_g	enthalpy, kJ/kg h_f	enthalpy, kJ/kg h_{fg}	enthalpy, kJ/kg h_g	entropy, kJ/(kg·K) s_f	entropy, kJ/(kg·K) s_{fg}	entropy, kJ/(kg·K) s_g
0.010	201.94	0.001376	9.805	8.53	1472.13	1480.66	0.0425	7.2900	7.3325
0.015	207.56	0.001388	6.706	33.34	1457.57	1490.91	0.1636	7.0222	7.1858
0.020	211.78	0.001398	5.123	51.90	1446.54	1498.44	0.2520	6.8305	7.0825
0.025	215.19	0.001406	4.158	66.88	1437.56	1504.44	0.3222	6.6805	7.0027
0.030	218.07	0.001412	3.506	79.53	1429.90	1509.43	0.3806	6.5571	6.9377
0.035	220.57	0.001418	3.036	90.52	1423.19	1513.71	0.4307	6.4522	6.8829
0.040	222.79	0.001424	2.680	100.28	1417.18	1517.46	0.4746	6.3610	6.8356
0.045	224.80	0.001428	2.400	109.07	1411.74	1520.81	0.5139	6.2800	6.7939
0.050	226.63	0.001433	2.175	117.09	1406.73	1523.82	0.5494	6.2073	6.7567
0.055	228.31	0.001437	1.990	124.48	1402.09	1526.57	0.5818	6.1412	6.7230
0.060	229.87	0.001441	1.835	131.33	1397.77	1529.10	0.6117	6.0807	6.6924
0.065	231.33	0.001445	1.702	137.74	1393.70	1531.44	0.6395	6.0247	6.6642
0.070	232.70	0.001448	1.588	143.75	1389.86	1533.61	0.6654	5.9728	6.6382
0.080	235.21	0.001455	1.402	154.82	1382.73	1537.55	0.7126	5.8787	6.5913
0.101325	239.82	0.001467	1.124	175.14	1369.45	1544.59	0.7980	5.7104	6.5084
0.12	243.24	0.001476	0.9596	190.28	1359.39	1549.67	0.8606	5.5887	6.4493
0.14	246.46	0.001485	0.8307	204.58	1349.75	1554.33	0.9189	5.4765	6.3954
0.16	249.33	0.001493	0.7330	217.36	1341.01	1558.37	0.9703	5.3785	6.3488
0.18	251.92	0.001500	0.6564	228.97	1332.97	1561.94	1.0165	5.2912	6.3077
0.20	254.29	0.001507	0.5946	239.62	1325.51	1565.13	1.0585	5.2125	6.2710
0.24	258.52	0.001520	0.5010	258.69	1311.94	1570.63	1.1326	5.0748	6.2074
0.28	262.22	0.001531	0.4334	275.50	1299.76	1575.26	1.1970	4.9567	6.1537
0.32	265.53	0.001541	0.3821	290.60	1288.63	1579.23	1.2540	4.8531	6.1071
0.36	268.52	0.001551	0.3419	304.36	1278.33	1582.69	1.3052	4.7607	6.0659
0.40	271.26	0.001560	0.3094	317.02	1268.73	1585.75	1.3519	4.6772	6.0291
0.44	273.80	0.001568	0.2827	328.81	1259.67	1588.48	1.3949	4.6008	5.9957
0.48	276.16	0.001576	0.2603	339.81	1251.12	1590.93	1.4347	4.5304	5.9651
0.52	278.37	0.001584	0.2412	350.15	1242.99	1593.14	1.4718	4.4652	5.9370
0.56	280.46	0.001591	0.2247	359.93	1235.23	1595.16	1.5066	4.4043	5.9109
0.60	282.43	0.001598	0.2104	369.21	1227.79	1597.00	1.5393	4.3472	5.8865
0.64	284.30	0.001605	0.1978	378.05	1220.64	1598.69	1.5703	4.2934	5.8637
0.68	286.09	0.001612	0.1866	386.50	1213.73	1600.23	1.5997	4.2425	5.8422
0.72	287.79	0.001618	0.1766	394.59	1207.07	1601.66	1.6276	4.1943	5.8219
0.76	289.43	0.001624	0.1677	402.36	1200.62	1602.98	1.6543	4.1483	5.8026
0.80	291.00	0.001630	0.1596	409.84	1194.36	1604.20	1.6799	4.1043	5.7842
0.84	292.51	0.001636	0.1522	417.06	1188.27	1605.33	1.7044	4.0623	5.7667
0.88	293.97	0.001642	0.1455	424.03	1182.34	1606.37	1.7279	4.0221	5.7500
0.92	295.37	0.001647	0.1394	430.77	1176.57	1607.34	1.7506	3.9834	5.7340
0.96	296.73	0.001653	0.1337	437.31	1170.93	1608.24	1.7725	3.9461	5.7186
1.0	298.05	0.001658	0.1285	443.65	1165.43	1609.08	1.7936	3.9101	5.7037
1.2	304.10	0.001684	0.1075	472.89	1139.55	1612.44	1.8896	3.7473	5.6369
1.4	309.42	0.001708	0.09231	498.86	1115.85	1614.71	1.9732	3.6062	5.5794
1.6	314.19	0.001731	0.08079	522.35	1093.80	1616.15	2.0474	3.4813	5.5287
1.8	318.53	0.001752	0.07174	543.90	1073.03	1616.93	2.1144	3.3686	5.4830
2.0	322.53	0.001773	0.06445	563.88	1053.30	1617.18	2.1756	3.2658	5.4414
2.4	329.68	0.001813	0.05339	600.23	1016.17	1616.40	2.2849	3.0822	5.3671
2.8	336.00	0.001852	0.04538	632.94	981.33	1614.27	2.3810	2.9206	5.3016
3.2	341.66	0.001889	0.03931	662.96	948.10	1611.06	2.4674	2.7749	5.2423
3.6	346.82	0.001927	0.03454	690.93	916.04	1606.97	2.5464	2.6412	5.1876
4.0	351.57	0.001964	0.03069	717.27	884.84	1602.11	2.6196	2.5168	5.1364
4.4	355.97	0.002002	0.02751	742.31	854.23	1596.54	2.6881	2.3997	5.0878
4.8	360.09	0.002040	0.02483	766.26	824.07	1590.33	2.7528	2.2885	5.0413
5.2	363.95	0.002079	0.02255	789.32	794.18	1583.50	2.8142	2.1821	4.9963
5.6	367.60	0.002119	0.02057	811.62	764.44	1576.06	2.8729	2.0795	4.9524
6.0	371.06	0.002161	0.01883	833.30	734.69	1567.99	2.9292	1.9801	4.9093
6.5	375.14	0.002216	0.01694	859.69	697.31	1557.00	2.9970	1.8588	4.8558
7.0	378.99	0.002274	0.01530	885.51	659.39	1544.90	3.0625	1.7399	4.8024
8.0	386.09	0.002406	0.01254	936.30	580.51	1516.81	3.1892	1.5035	4.6927
10.	398.35	0.002792	0.008253	1045.02	389.68	1434.70	3.4530	0.9782	4.4312
11.627	406.80	0.004208	0.004208	1233.56	0.0	1233.56	3.9069	0.0	3.9069

PROPERTIES OF GASEOUS AMMONIA

P,MPa (T_sat,K)		sat	220	230	240	250	260	270	280	290
0.020 (211.8)	v,m³/kg	5.123	5.329	5.579	5.828	6.076	6.324	6.570	6.817	7.063
	h,kJ/kg	1498.44	1515.27	1535.79	1556.37	1576.99	1597.68	1618.44	1639.28	1660.22
	s,kJ/(kg·K)	7.0825	7.1604	7.2517	7.3392	7.4234	7.5046	7.5829	7.6587	7.7322
0.030 (218.1)	v,m³/kg	3.506	3.539	3.708	3.875	4.042	4.208	4.373	4.538	4.703
	h,kJ/kg	1509.43	1513.44	1534.21	1555.00	1575.82	1596.67	1617.56	1638.52	1659.56
	s,kJ/(kg·K)	6.9377	6.9560	7.0484	7.1369	7.2218	7.3036	7.3825	7.4587	7.5325
0.040 (222.8)	v,m³/kg	2.679		2.772	2.899	3.025	3.150	3.275	3.399	3.523
	h,kJ/kg	1517.46		1532.61	1553.63	1574.64	1595.65	1616.69	1637.76	1658.89
	s,kJ/(kg·K)	6.8356		6.9025	6.9920	7.0777	7.1601	7.2395	7.3162	7.3903
0.050 (226.6)	v,m³/kg	2.175		2.210	2.313	2.414	2.515	2.616	2.716	2.815
	h,kJ/kg	1523.82		1531.00	1552.25	1573.46	1594.63	1615.80	1636.99	1658.22
	s,kJ/(kg·K)	6.7567		6.7881	6.8785	6.9651	7.0482	7.1281	7.2051	7.2796
0.070 (232.7)	v,m³/kg	1.588			1.643	1.717	1.790	1.862	1.935	2.006
	h,kJ/kg	1533.61			1549.46	1571.06	1592.58	1614.03	1635.45	1656.88
	s,kJ/(kg·K)	6.6382			6.7052	6.7934	6.8778	6.9588	7.0367	7.1118
0.101325 (239.8)	v,m³/kg	1.124			1.125	1.178	1.229	1.280	1.331	1.381
	h,kJ/kg	1544.59			1545.00	1567.26	1589.32	1611.23	1633.02	1654.75
	s,kJ/(kg·K)	6.5084			6.5101	6.6010	6.6875	6.7702	6.8495	6.9257
0.14 (246.5)	v,m³/kg	0.8307				0.8445	0.8829	0.9207	0.9579	0.9948
	h,kJ/kg	1554.33				1562.46	1585.23	1607.71	1629.98	1652.11
	s,kJ/(kg·K)	6.3954				6.4282	6.5175	6.6023	6.6833	6.7610
0.20 (254.3)	v,m³/kg	0.5946					0.6105	0.6380	0.6648	0.6913
	h,kJ/kg	1565.13					1578.71	1602.14	1625.18	1647.94
	s,kJ/(kg·K)	6.2710					6.3238	6.4122	6.4960	6.5759
0.30 (263.9)	v,m³/kg	0.4061						0.4178	0.4367	0.4551
	h,kJ/kg	1577.31						1592.51	1616.94	1640.81
	s,kJ/(kg·K)	6.1296						6.1865	6.2754	6.3591

P, MPa (T_sat,K)		300	310	320	330	340	350	360	370	380
0.020 (211.8)	v,m³/kg	7.308	7.554	7.799	8.044	8.289	8.534	8.779	9.024	9.268
	h,kJ/kg	1681.28	1702.45	1723.77	1745.22	1766.83	1788.59	1810.53	1832.63	1854.91
	s,kJ/(kg·K)	7.8036	7.8730	7.9407	8.0067	8.0712	8.1343	8.1961	8.2566	8.3160
0.030 (218.1)	v,m³/kg	4.867	5.032	5.195	5.359	5.523	5.686	5.850	6.013	6.176
	h,kJ/kg	1680.69	1701.93	1723.30	1744.80	1766.45	1788.25	1810.21	1832.33	1854.63
	s,kJ/(kg·K)	7.6041	7.6738	7.7416	7.8078	7.8724	7.9356	7.9975	8.0581	8.1176
0.040 (222.8)	v,m³/kg	3.647	3.770	3.894	4.017	4.139	4.262	4.385	4.508	4.630
	h,kJ/kg	1680.10	1701.41	1722.83	1744.38	1766.06	1787.90	1809.88	1832.03	1854.36
	s,kJ/(kg·K)	7.4622	7.5321	7.6001	7.6664	7.7311	7.7944	7.8564	7.9171	7.9766
0.050 (226.6)	v,m³/kg	2.915	3.014	3.112	3.211	3.310	3.408	3.506	3.605	3.703
	h,kJ/kg	1679.51	1700.89	1722.36	1743.96	1765.68	1787.54	1809.56	1831.74	1854.08
	s,kJ/(kg·K)	7.3518	7.4219	7.4901	7.5565	7.6214	7.6847	7.7468	7.8075	7.8671
0.070 (232.7)	v,m³/kg	2.078	2.149	2.220	2.290	2.361	2.432	2.502	2.572	2.643
	h,kJ/kg	1678.33	1699.84	1721.42	1743.11	1764.91	1786.84	1808.92	1831.14	1853.52
	s,kJ/(kg·K)	7.1846	7.2551	7.3236	7.3904	7.4554	7.5190	7.5812	7.6421	7.7018
0.101325 (239.8)	v,m³/kg	1.431	1.480	1.530	1.579	1.628	1.677	1.726	1.775	1.823
	h,kJ/kg	1676.46	1698.18	1719.95	1741.78	1763.71	1785.74	1807.90	1830.20	1852.65
	s,kJ/(kg·K)	6.9993	7.0706	7.1397	7.2068	7.2723	7.3362	7.3986	7.4597	7.5196
0.14 (246.5)	v,m³/kg	1.031	1.068	1.104	1.140	1.175	1.211	1.247	1.282	1.317
	h,kJ/kg	1674.14	1696.12	1718.11	1740.13	1762.21	1784.37	1806.65	1829.04	1851.58
	s,kJ/(kg·K)	6.8357	6.9077	6.9775	7.0453	7.1112	7.1755	7.2382	7.2996	7.3597
0.20 (254.3)	v,m³/kg	0.7173	0.7432	0.7688	0.7943	0.8196	0.8448	0.8699	0.8949	0.9199
	h,kJ/kg	1670.48	1692.90	1715.23	1737.54	1759.87	1782.24	1804.69	1827.23	1849.90
	s,kJ/(kg·K)	6.6523	6.7258	6.7967	6.8654	6.9320	6.9969	7.0601	7.1219	7.1823
0.30 (263.9)	v,m³/kg	0.4731	0.4908	0.5083	0.5257	0.5429	0.5599	0.5769	0.5938	0.6107
	h,kJ/kg	1664.26	1687.42	1710.37	1733.18	1755.93	1778.65	1801.40	1824.20	1847.08
	s,kJ/(kg·K)	6.4386	6.5146	6.5874	6.6576	6.7255	6.7914	6.8555	6.9180	6.9790

PROPERTIES OF GASEOUS AMMONIA

P, MPa (T$_{sat}$,K)		400	420	440	460	T,K 480	500	520	540	560
0.020 (211.8)	v,m³/kg	9.758	10.25	10.74	11.22	11.71	12.20	12.69	13.18	13.67
	h,kJ/kg	1900.02	1945.87	1992.50	2039.92	2088.12	2137.13	2186.92	2237.50	2288.87
	s,kJ/(kg·K)	8.4317	8.5436	8.6520	8.7574	8.8600	8.9600	9.0576	9.1531	9.2465
0.030 (218.1)	v,m³/kg	6.503	6.829	7.155	7.481	7.807	8.133	8.459	8.785	9.111
	h,kJ/kg	1899.78	1945.66	1992.31	2039.75	2087.97	2136.99	2186.80	2237.40	2288.78
	s,kJ/(kg·K)	8.2333	8.3453	8.4538	8.5592	8.6618	8.7618	8.8595	8.9550	9.0484
0.040 (222.8)	v,m³/kg	4.875	5.120	5.365	5.610	5.854	6.099	6.343	6.588	6.832
	h,kJ/kg	1899.53	1945.45	1992.12	2039.58	2087.82	2136.85	2186.68	2237.29	2288.68
	s,kJ/(kg·K)	8.0924	8.2044	8.3130	8.4185	8.5211	8.6212	8.7189	8.8144	8.9078
0.050 (226.6)	v,m³/kg	3.899	4.095	4.291	4.487	4.683	4.878	5.074	5.270	5.465
	h,kJ/kg	1899.29	1945.23	1991.93	2039.40	2087.66	2136.71	2186.55	2237.18	2288.59
	s,kJ/(kg·K)	7.9831	8.0951	8.2037	8.3092	8.4119	8.5120	8.6098	8.7053	8.7988
0.070 (232.7)	v,m³/kg	2.783	2.923	3.064	3.204	3.344	3.484	3.623	3.763	3.903
	h,kJ/kg	1898.81	1944.80	1991.55	2039.06	2087.36	2136.44	2186.31	2236.97	2288.40
	s,kJ/(kg·K)	7.8179	7.9301	8.0388	8.1444	8.2472	8.3474	8.4452	8.5407	8.6343
0.101325 (239.8)	v,m³/kg	1.921	2.018	2.115	2.212	2.309	2.405	2.502	2.599	2.696
	h,kJ/kg	1898.04	1944.13	1990.95	2038.52	2086.88	2136.01	2185.93	2236.63	2288.10
	s,kJ/(kg·K)	7.6360	7.7484	7.8573	7.9630	8.0659	8.1662	8.2641	8.3597	8.4533
0.14 (246.5)	v,m³/kg	1.388	1.459	1.529	1.600	1.670	1.740	1.810	1.880	1.950
	h,kJ/kg	1897.10	1943.30	1990.21	2037.86	2086.28	2135.48	2185.45	2236.21	2287.73
	s,kJ/(kg·K)	7.4764	7.5891	7.6982	7.8041	7.9072	8.0076	8.1056	8.2013	8.2950
0.20 (254.3)	v,m³/kg	0.9697	1.019	1.069	1.118	1.168	1.217	1.266	1.315	1.364
	h,kJ/kg	1895.64	1942.00	1989.05	2036.83	2085.36	2134.65	2184.72	2235.56	2287.16
	s,kJ/(kg·K)	7.2996	7.4127	7.5222	7.6283	7.7316	7.8322	7.9304	8.0263	8.1202
0.30 (263.9)	v,m³/kg	0.6442	0.6776	0.7108	0.7440	0.7770	0.8100	0.8429	0.8758	0.9086
	h,kJ/kg	1893.19	1939.84	1987.13	2035.11	2083.82	2133.28	2183.50	2234.47	2286.21
	s,kJ/(kg·K)	7.0972	7.2110	7.3210	7.4277	7.5313	7.6323	7.7307	7.8269	7.9210

P,MPa (T$_{sat}$,K)		sat	300	310	320	T,K 330	340	350	360	370
0.40 (271.3)	v,m³/kg	0.3094	0.3508	0.3646	0.3780	0.3913	0.4045	0.4175	0.4304	0.4433
	h,kJ/kg	1585.75	1657.87	1681.81	1705.40	1728.74	1751.93	1775.02	1798.07	1821.14
	s,kJ/(kg·K)	6.0291	6.2820	6.3605	6.4354	6.5072	6.5764	6.6433	6.7083	6.7715
0.50 (277.3)	v,m³/kg	0.2503	0.2774	0.2888	0.2998	0.3107	0.3214	0.3320	0.3425	0.3529
	h,kJ/kg	1592.06	1651.30	1676.07	1700.34	1724.23	1747.87	1771.34	1794.71	1818.05
	s,kJ/(kg·K)	5.9508	6.1563	6.2375	6.3145	6.3881	6.4586	6.5267	6.5925	6.6564
0.70 (287.0)	v,m³/kg	0.1815	0.1933	0.2020	0.2103	0.2185	0.2265	0.2343	0.2420	0.2497
	h,kJ/kg	1600.96	1637.54	1664.16	1689.88	1714.96	1739.57	1763.84	1787.88	1811.79
	s,kJ/(kg·K)	5.8319	5.9566	6.0439	6.1256	6.2027	6.2762	6.3466	6.4143	6.4798
1.0 (298.1)	v,m³/kg	0.1285	0.1299	0.1366	0.1430	0.1492	0.1551	0.1609	0.1666	0.1721
	h,kJ/kg	1609.08	1615.15	1645.04	1673.31	1700.40	1726.63	1752.22	1777.35	1802.16
	s,kJ/(kg·K)	5.7037	5.7240	5.8221	5.9118	5.9952	6.0735	6.1477	6.2185	6.2865
1.4 (309.4)	v,m³/kg	0.09231		0.09263	0.09785	0.1027	0.1074	0.1119	0.1162	0.1204
	h,kJ/kg	1614.71		1616.69	1649.24	1679.58	1708.34	1735.95	1762.72	1788.89
	s,kJ/(kg·K)	5.5794		5.5858	5.6892	5.7825	5.8684	5.9485	6.0239	6.0956
2.0 (322.5)	v,m³/kg	0.06445				0.06751	0.07132	0.07487	0.07825	0.08149
	h,kJ/kg	1617.18				1644.51	1678.22	1709.62	1739.35	1767.90
	s,kJ/(kg·K)	5.4414				5.5252	5.6259	5.7169	5.8007	5.8789
3.0 (338.9)	v,m³/kg	0.04215					0.04252	0.04561	0.04839	0.05096
	h,kJ/kg	1612.79					1617.68	1658.82	1695.57	1729.42
	s,kJ/(kg·K)	5.2713					5.2857	5.4050	5.5086	5.6013
4.0 (351.6)	v,m³/kg	0.03069							0.03299	0.03539
	h,kJ/kg	1602.10							1642.96	1685.05
	s,kJ/(kg·K)	5.1364							5.2513	5.3666
5.0 (362.0)	v,m³/kg	0.02365								0.02565
	h,kJ/kg	1587.00								1631.46
	s,kJ/(kg·K)	5.0186								5.1402

PROPERTIES OF GASEOUS AMMONIA

P, MPa (T$_{sat}$,K)		380	390	400	410	T,K 420	430	440	460	480
0.40 (271.3)	v,m³/kg	0.4561	0.4688	0.4815	0.4941	0.5067	0.5193	0.5318	0.5568	0.5817
	h,kJ/kg	1844.25	1867.44	1890.72	1914.13	1937.67	1961.35	1985.20	2033.38	2082.27
	s,kJ/(kg·K)	6.8331	6.8934	6.9523	7.0101	7.0668	7.1226	7.1774	7.2845	7.3885
0.50 (277.3)	v,m³/kg	0.3633	0.3736	0.3838	0.3940	0.4042	0.4143	0.4244	0.4445	0.4646
	h,kJ/kg	1841.39	1864.78	1888.24	1911.80	1935.48	1959.30	1983.26	2031.65	2080.73
	s,kJ/(kg·K)	6.7187	6.7795	6.8389	6.8970	6.9541	7.0101	7.0652	7.1728	7.2772
0.70 (287.0)	v,m³/kg	0.2572	0.2647	0.2722	0.2796	0.2870	0.2943	0.3016	0.3162	0.3306
	h,kJ/kg	1835.61	1859.42	1883.24	1907.12	1931.09	1955.16	1979.36	2028.18	2077.62
	s,kJ/(kg·K)	6.5433	6.6051	6.6655	6.7244	6.7822	6.8388	6.8945	7.0030	7.1082
1.0 (298.1)	v,m³/kg	0.1776	0.1831	0.1884	0.1938	0.1991	0.2043	0.2095	0.2199	0.2302
	h,kJ/kg	1826.76	1851.23	1875.63	1900.02	1924.43	1948.91	1973.47	2022.93	2072.93
	s,kJ/(kg·K)	6.3521	6.4156	6.4774	6.5376	6.5965	6.6541	6.7105	6.8204	6.9269
1.4 (309.4)	v,m³/kg	0.1245	0.1286	0.1326	0.1365	0.1404	0.1443	0.1481	0.1557	0.1632
	h,kJ/kg	1814.62	1840.04	1865.26	1890.36	1915.41	1940.45	1965.51	2015.86	2066.64
	s,kJ/(kg·K)	6.1642	6.2302	6.2941	6.3561	6.4164	6.4753	6.5330	6.6449	6.7529
2.0 (322.5)	v,m³/kg	0.08462	0.08766	0.09064	0.09356	0.09644	0.09927	0.1021	0.1076	0.1130
	h,kJ/kg	1795.57	1822.62	1849.21	1875.49	1901.56	1927.50	1953.38	2005.12	2057.08
	s,kJ/(kg·K)	5.9527	6.0229	6.0903	6.1552	6.2180	6.2790	6.3385	6.4535	6.5641
3.0 (338.9)	v,m³/kg	0.05338	0.05569	0.05791	0.06005	0.06214	0.06419	0.06619	0.07011	0.07391
	h,kJ/kg	1761.25	1791.62	1820.95	1849.53	1877.55	1905.18	1932.54	1986.80	2040.84
	s,kJ/(kg·K)	5.6862	5.7651	5.8394	5.9100	5.9775	6.0425	6.1054	6.2260	6.3410
4.0 (351.6)	v,m³/kg	0.03755	0.03954	0.04142	0.04321	0.04493	0.04659	0.04821	0.05134	0.05435
	h,kJ/kg	1722.78	1757.63	1790.46	1821.86	1852.22	1881.82	1910.88	1967.92	2024.21
	s,kJ/(kg·K)	5.4673	5.5578	5.6410	5.7185	5.7917	5.8613	5.9281	6.0549	6.1747
5.0 (362.0)	v,m³/kg	0.02780	0.02969	0.03141	0.03302	0.03453	0.03599	0.03738	0.04005	0.04260
	h,kJ/kg	1678.50	1719.69	1757.18	1792.15	1825.35	1857.28	1888.28	1948.44	2007.15
	s,kJ/(kg·K)	5.2657	5.3727	5.4676	5.5540	5.6340	5.7091	5.7804	5.9141	6.0391

P, MPa (T$_{sat}$,K)		500	520	540	560	T,K 580	600	620	640	660
0.40 (271.3)	v,m³/kg	0.6066	0.6314	0.6561	0.6808	0.7054	0.7300	0.7546	0.7791	0.8036
	h,kJ/kg	2131.90	2182.27	2233.39	2285.26	2337.87	2391.22	2445.30	2500.09	2555.59
	s,kJ/(kg·K)	7.4898	7.5885	7.6850	7.7793	7.8716	7.9621	8.0507	8.1377	8.2231
0.50 (277.3)	v,m³/kg	0.4845	0.5044	0.5243	0.5441	0.5638	0.5835	0.6032	0.6228	0.6425
	h,kJ/kg	2130.51	2181.04	2232.30	2284.30	2337.04	2390.51	2444.70	2499.60	2555.19
	s,kJ/(kg·K)	7.3788	7.4779	7.5746	7.6692	7.7617	7.8523	7.9412	8.0283	8.1138
0.70 (287.0)	v,m³/kg	0.3450	0.3594	0.3736	0.3879	0.4020	0.4162	0.4303	0.4443	0.4583
	h,kJ/kg	2127.74	2178.57	2230.11	2282.38	2335.37	2389.08	2443.49	2498.60	2554.39
	s,kJ/(kg·K)	7.2105	7.3101	7.4074	7.5024	7.5954	7.6864	7.7756	7.8631	7.9490
1.0 (298.1)	v,m³/kg	0.2404	0.2506	0.2606	0.2707	0.2807	0.2906	0.3005	0.3104	0.3203
	h,kJ/kg	2123.56	2174.84	2226.81	2279.48	2332.84	2386.90	2441.65	2497.07	2553.17
	s,kJ/(kg·K)	7.0302	7.1307	7.2288	7.3246	7.4182	7.5098	7.5996	7.6876	7.7739
1.4 (309.4)	v,m³/kg	0.1707	0.1780	0.1853	0.1926	0.1998	0.2069	0.2141	0.2212	0.2282
	h,kJ/kg	2117.94	2169.84	2222.38	2275.58	2329.44	2383.97	2439.16	2495.01	2551.50
	s,kJ/(kg·K)	6.8576	6.9594	7.0585	7.1553	7.2498	7.3422	7.4327	7.5213	7.6082
2.0 (322.5)	v,m³/kg	0.1183	0.1236	0.1288	0.1340	0.1391	0.1442	0.1492	0.1542	0.1592
	h,kJ/kg	2109.42	2162.26	2215.66	2269.66	2324.27	2379.50	2435.36	2491.83	2548.91
	s,kJ/(kg·K)	6.6709	6.7745	6.8753	6.9735	7.0693	7.1629	7.2545	7.3441	7.4319
3.0 (338.9)	v,m³/kg	0.07764	0.08130	0.08489	0.08844	0.09194	0.09540	0.09882	0.1022	0.1056
	h,kJ/kg	2094.98	2149.42	2204.27	2259.60	2315.46	2371.86	2428.82	2486.33	2544.40
	s,kJ/(kg·K)	6.4515	6.5583	6.6618	6.7624	6.8604	6.9560	7.0493	7.1406	7.2300
4.0 (351.6)	v,m³/kg	0.05728	0.06013	0.06292	0.06566	0.06836	0.07101	0.07362	0.07620	0.07875
	h,kJ/kg	2080.24	2136.32	2192.64	2249.32	2306.42	2363.99	2422.04	2480.59	2539.63
	s,kJ/(kg·K)	6.2890	6.3990	6.5053	6.6084	6.7086	6.8061	6.9013	6.9942	7.0851
5.0 (362.0)	v,m³/kg	0.04505	0.04743	0.04974	0.05200	0.05421	0.05639	0.05852	0.06062	0.06269
	h,kJ/kg	2065.18	2122.96	2180.79	2238.83	2297.18	2355.91	2415.05	2474.62	2534.63
	s,kJ/(kg·K)	6.1575	6.2708	6.3799	6.4855	6.5879	6.6874	6.7844	6.8789	6.9713

PROPERTIES OF GASEOUS AMMONIA

P,MPa (T_sat,K)		sat	370	380	390	400	420	440	460	480
5.0 (362.0)	v,m³/kg	0.02365	0.02565	0.02780	0.02969	0.03141	0.03453	0.03738	0.04005	0.04260
	h,kJ/kg	1586.99	1631.47	1678.50	1719.69	1757.18	1825.35	1888.28	1948.44	2007.15
	s,kJ/(kg·K)	5.0186	5.1402	5.2657	5.3727	5.4676	5.6340	5.7804	5.9141	6.0391
6.0 (371.1)	v,m³/kg	0.01883		0.02098	0.02292	0.02461	0.02754	0.03013	0.03251	0.03475
	h,kJ/kg	1567.99		1625.07	1676.23	1720.25	1796.64	1864.64	1928.32	1989.66
	s,kJ/(kg·K)	4.9092		5.0613	5.1943	5.3057	5.4922	5.6504	5.7920	5.9225
8.0 (386.1)	v,m³/kg	0.01254			0.01361	0.01566	0.01862	0.02097	0.02303	0.02492
	h,kJ/kg	1516.81			1556.02	1628.82	1731.96	1813.60	1885.85	1953.27
	s,kJ/(kg·K)	4.6927			4.7938	4.9783	5.2302	5.4202	5.5809	5.7244
10. (398.3)	v,m³/kg	0.00825				0.00897	0.01298	0.01536	0.01728	0.01898
	h,kJ/kg	1434.70				1469.65	1652.33	1756.08	1839.95	1914.82
	s,kJ/(kg·K)	4.4312				4.5188	4.9662	5.2078	5.3944	5.5537
12.	v,m³/kg						0.00877	0.01148	0.01340	0.01500
	h,kJ/kg						1542.38	1689.48	1789.89	1874.09
	s,kJ/(kg·K)						4.6530	4.9960	5.2193	5.3986
14.	v,m³/kg						0.00490	0.00858	0.01058	0.01214
	h,kJ/kg						1344.57	1609.71	1734.85	1830.91
	s,kJ/(kg·K)						4.1495	4.7693	5.0478	5.2524
16.	v,m³/kg						0.00319	0.00631	0.00843	0.00998
	h,kJ/kg						1186.09	1512.33	1674.22	1785.24
	s,kJ/(kg·K)						3.7542	4.5144	4.8749	5.1113
18.	v,m³/kg						0.00285	0.00464	0.00677	0.00831
	h,kJ/kg						1141.62	1405.51	1608.44	1737.32
	s,kJ/(kg·K)						3.6341	4.2470	4.6990	4.9736
20.	v,m³/kg						0.00268	0.00371	0.00551	0.00700
	h,kJ/kg						1117.74	1322.59	1540.67	1687.98
	s,kJ/(kg·K)						3.5641	4.0398	4.5251	4.8390

P, MPa (T_sat,K)		500	520	540	560	580	600	620	640	660
5.0 (362.0)	v,m³/kg	0.04505	0.04743	0.04974	0.05200	0.05421	0.05639	0.05852	0.06062	0.06269
	h,kJ/kg	2065.18	2122.96	2180.79	2238.83	2297.18	2355.91	2415.05	2474.62	2534.63
	s,kJ/(kg·K)	6.1575	6.2708	6.3799	6.4855	6.5879	6.6874	6.7844	6.8789	6.9713
6.0 (371.1)	v,m³/kg	0.03689	0.03895	0.04095	0.04289	0.04479	0.04664	0.04846	0.05024	0.05199
	h,kJ/kg	2049.80	2109.35	2168.72	2228.13	2287.74	2347.62	2407.85	2468.43	2529.41
	s,kJ/(kg·K)	6.0453	6.1621	6.2741	6.3821	6.4867	6.5882	6.6870	6.7831	6.8770
8.0 (386.1)	v,m³/kg	0.02668	0.02835	0.02996	0.03151	0.03301	0.03447	0.03589	0.03728	0.03864
	h,kJ/kg	2018.05	2081.38	2143.95	2206.17	2268.31	2330.51	2392.88	2455.48	2518.35
	s,kJ/(kg·K)	5.8566	5.9808	6.0989	6.2120	6.3210	6.4265	6.5287	6.6281	6.7248
10. (398.3)	v,m³/kg	0.02053	0.02199	0.02336	0.02468	0.02595	0.02718	0.02836	0.02952	0.03065
	h,kJ/kg	1984.94	2052.41	2118.38	2183.52	2248.22	2312.75	2377.25	2441.83	2506.56
	s,kJ/(kg·K)	5.6969	5.8292	5.9537	6.0721	6.1857	6.2950	6.4008	6.5033	6.6029
12.	v,m³/kg	0.01642	0.01773	0.01896	0.02013	0.02125	0.02232	0.02335	0.02436	0.02533
	h,kJ/kg	1950.44	2022.50	2092.10	2160.26	2227.58	2294.43	2361.06	2427.60	2494.16
	s,kJ/(kg·K)	5.5544	5.6958	5.8271	5.9511	6.0692	6.1825	6.2917	6.3974	6.4998
14.	v,m³/kg	0.01348	0.01470	0.01582	0.01688	0.01789	0.01885	0.01978	0.02067	0.02154
	h,kJ/kg	1914.54	1991.69	2065.17	2136.48	2206.47	2275.67	2344.41	2412.88	2481.22
	s,kJ/(kg·K)	5.4231	5.5745	5.7131	5.8428	5.9656	6.0829	6.1956	6.3043	6.4095
16.	v,m³/kg	0.01127	0.01242	0.01347	0.01445	0.01537	0.01626	0.01710	0.01791	0.01870
	h,kJ/kg	1877.32	1960.10	2037.72	2112.30	2185.01	2256.56	2327.39	2397.76	2467.86
	s,kJ/(kg·K)	5.2994	5.4618	5.6083	5.7439	5.8715	5.9928	6.1089	6.2206	6.3285
18.	v,m³/kg	0.00956	0.01065	0.01164	0.01256	0.01342	0.01424	0.01502	0.01577	0.01649
	h,kJ/kg	1838.99	1927.90	2009.89	2087.84	2163.30	2237.20	2310.10	2382.34	2454.16
	s,kJ/(kg·K)	5.1812	5.3556	5.5104	5.6521	5.7845	5.9098	6.0293	6.1440	6.2545
20.	v,m³/kg	0.00821	0.00925	0.01019	0.01106	0.01187	0.01263	0.01336	0.01406	0.01473
	h,kJ/kg	1799.94	1895.32	1981.85	2063.23	2141.47	2217.70	2292.64	2366.71	2440.20
	s,kJ/(kg·K)	5.0676	5.2548	5.4181	5.5661	5.7034	5.8326	5.9555	6.0731	6.1861

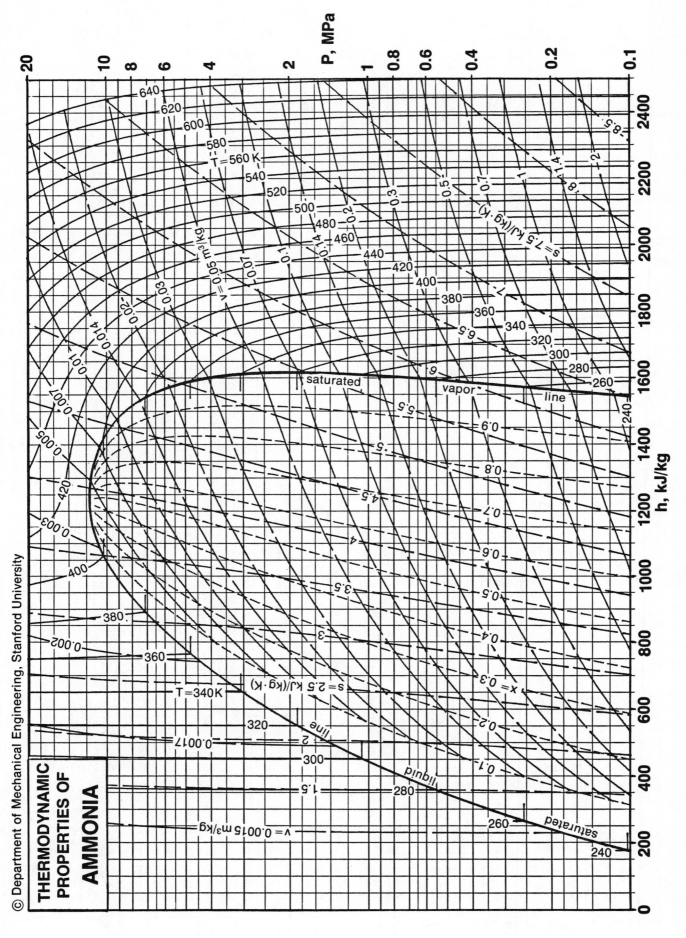

THERMODYNAMIC
PROPERTIES OF
AMMONIA

© Department of Mechanical Engineering, Stanford University

18

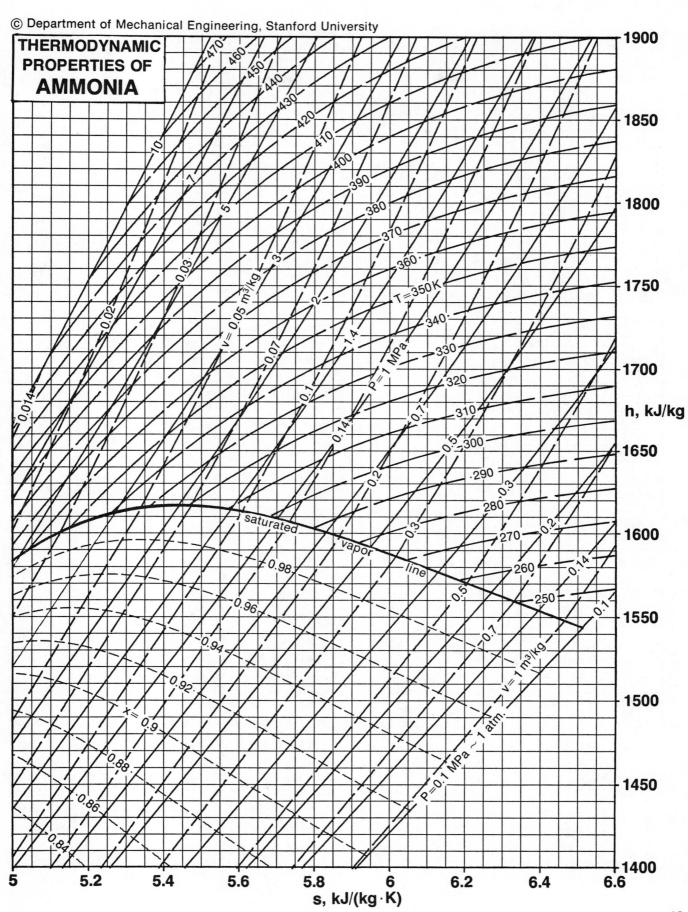

THERMODYNAMIC PROPERTIES OF AMMONIA

h, kJ/kg

s, kJ/(kg·K)

PROPERTIES OF SATURATED ARGON

T K	P MPa	volume, m³/kg v_f	v_g	enthalpy, kJ/kg h_f	h_{fg}	h_g	entropy, kJ/(kg·K) s_f	s_{fg}	s_g
83.80	0.06871	0.000708	0.2475	0.0	165.65	165.65	0.0	1.9767	1.9767
87.29	0.101325	0.000718	0.1734	4.83	162.17	167.00	0.0562	1.8578	1.9140
88	0.1092	0.000720	0.1619	5.77	161.49	167.26	0.0669	1.8351	1.9020
92	0.1624	0.000734	0.1124	10.88	157.75	168.63	0.1233	1.7146	1.8379
96	0.2331	0.000748	0.08054	15.70	154.13	169.83	0.1740	1.6055	1.7795
100	0.3245	0.000763	0.05925	20.37	150.45	170.82	0.2209	1.5046	1.7255
104	0.4400	0.000779	0.04455	25.01	146.58	171.59	0.2656	1.4094	1.6750
108	0.5833	0.000797	0.03412	29.73	142.39	172.12	0.3091	1.3184	1.6275
112	0.7577	0.000816	0.02654	34.58	137.79	172.37	0.3518	1.2303	1.5821
116	0.9670	0.000838	0.02092	39.57	132.74	172.31	0.3941	1.1443	1.5384
120	1.215	0.000862	0.01666	44.74	127.17	171.91	0.4361	1.0598	1.4959
124	1.505	0.000889	0.01337	50.11	120.99	171.10	0.4781	0.9757	1.4538
128	1.842	0.000920	0.01079	55.77	114.04	169.81	0.5205	0.8910	1.4115
132	2.228	0.000957	0.008737	61.83	106.10	167.93	0.5643	0.8039	1.3682
136	2.670	0.001002	0.007062	68.42	96.86	165.28	0.6104	0.7121	1.3225
140	3.170	0.001059	0.005666	75.76	85.78	161.54	0.6598	0.6127	1.2725
144	3.736	0.001141	0.004452	84.27	71.74	156.01	0.7153	0.4982	1.2135
148	4.378	0.001291	0.003279	95.82	50.47	146.29	0.7890	0.3410	1.1300
150.70	4.865	0.001949	0.001949	122.39	0.0	122.39	0.9615	0.0	0.9615

PROPERTIES OF GASEOUS ARGON

P,MPa (T_{sat},K)		sat	100	200	300	400	500	600	700	800
0.101325 (87.29)	v,m³/kg	0.1734	0.2008	0.4096	0.6158	0.8216	1.027	1.233	1.438	1.644
	h,kJ/kg	167.00	173.92	226.87	279.10	331.21	383.29	435.35	487.40	539.45
	s,kJ/(kg·K)	1.9140	1.9881	2.3557	2.5676	2.7175	2.8337	2.9286	3.0088	3.0783
0.20 (94.26)	v,m³/kg	0.09278	0.09931	0.2069	0.3118	0.4162	0.5205	0.6247	0.7289	0.8330
	h,kJ/kg	169.33	172.60	226.49	278.92	331.11	383.23	435.32	487.39	539.45
	s,kJ/(kg·K)	1.8043	1.8379	2.2129	2.4255	2.5757	2.6920	2.7870	2.8672	2.9368
0.30 (99.02)	v,m³/kg	0.06374	0.06451	0.1376	0.2077	0.2775	0.3471	0.4166	0.4860	0.5555
	h,kJ/kg	170.60	171.18	226.10	278.73	331.00	383.17	435.28	487.37	539.44
	s,kJ/(kg·K)	1.7383	1.7442	2.1272	2.3407	2.4911	2.6075	2.7025	2.7828	2.8523
0.40 (102.7)	v,m³/kg	0.04873		0.1029	0.1557	0.2081	0.2603	0.3125	0.3646	0.4167
	h,kJ/kg	171.37		225.71	278.54	330.90	383.10	435.25	487.35	539.44
	s,kJ/(kg·K)	1.6909		2.0660	2.2803	2.4309	2.5474	2.6425	2.7228	2.7924
0.50 (105.8)	v,m³/kg	0.03949		0.08205	0.1245	0.1665	0.2083	0.2501	0.2918	0.3335
	h,kJ/kg	171.86		225.32	278.36	330.79	383.04	435.21	487.34	539.44
	s,kJ/(kg·K)	1.6536		2.0182	2.2334	2.3842	2.5008	2.5959	2.6763	2.7459
0.60 (108.4)	v,m³/kg	0.03321		0.06818	0.1037	0.1387	0.1736	0.2084	0.2432	0.2780
	h,kJ/kg	172.16		224.93	278.17	330.68	382.98	435.18	487.32	539.44
	s,kJ/(kg·K)	1.6226		1.9789	2.1949	2.3460	2.4627	2.5579	2.6383	2.7079
0.80 (112.9)	v,m³/kg	0.02518		0.05083	0.07767	0.1040	0.1303	0.1564	0.1825	0.2086
	h,kJ/kg	172.39		224.15	277.80	330.47	382.85	435.11	487.29	539.44
	s,kJ/(kg·K)	1.5725		1.9163	2.1341	2.2856	2.4025	2.4978	2.5782	2.6479
10.	v,m³/kg			0.00297	0.00597	0.00836	0.01062	0.01281	0.01498	0.01712
	h,kJ/kg			181.09	261.74	321.76	377.84	432.39	486.18	539.50
	s,kJ/(kg·K)			1.2308	1.5649	1.7380	1.8633	1.9628	2.0457	2.1169
20.	v,m³/kg			0.00143	0.00297	0.00427	0.00545	0.00659	0.00770	0.00880
	h,kJ/kg			147.90	247.36	314.42	373.85	430.46	485.67	540.07
	s,kJ/(kg·K)			0.9681	1.3798	1.5736	1.7064	1.8097	1.8948	1.9675
30.	v,m³/kg			0.00116	0.00207	0.00295	0.00376	0.00454	0.00529	0.00603
	h,kJ/kg			140.03	237.65	309.30	371.31	429.55	485.91	541.19
	s,kJ/(kg·K)			0.8653	1.2657	1.4729	1.6115	1.7177	1.8047	1.8785
40.	v,m³/kg			0.00105	0.00167	0.00232	0.00294	0.00352	0.00410	0.00466
	h,kJ/kg			138.79	232.43	306.27	370.10	429.58	486.86	542.85
	s,kJ/(kg·K)			0.8042	1.1868	1.4002	1.5429	1.6515	1.7398	1.8146
50.	v,m³/kg			0.00098	0.00145	0.00196	0.00245	0.00292	0.00339	0.00384
	h,kJ/kg			139.98	230.35	304.99	370.04	430.47	488.47	545.03
	s,kJ/(kg·K)			0.7598	1.1283	1.3439	1.4893	1.5996	1.6890	1.7646

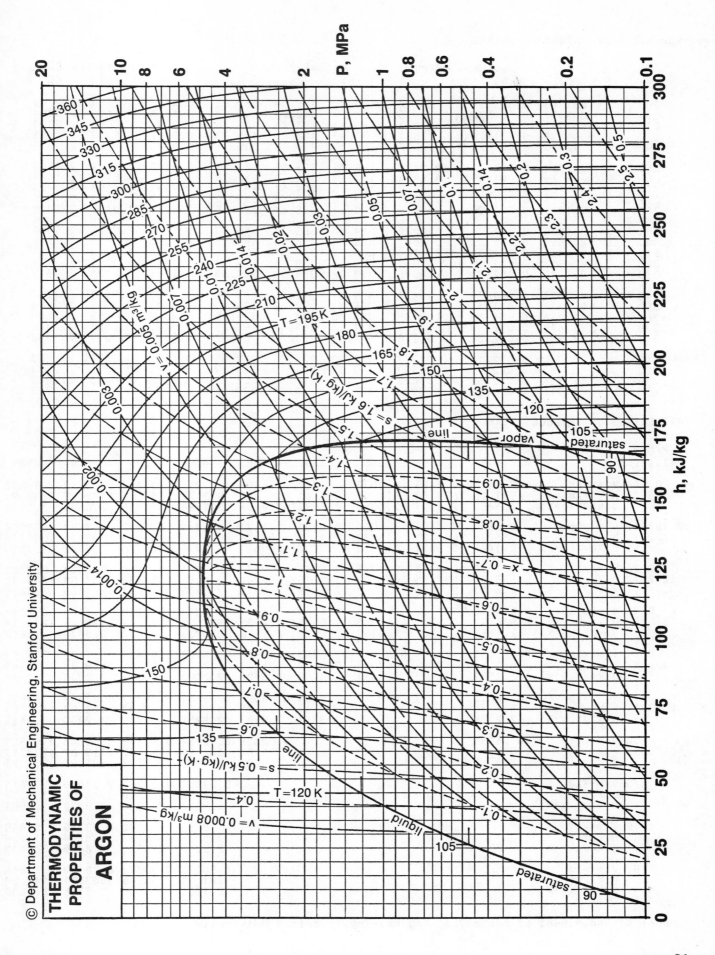

THERMODYNAMIC PROPERTIES OF **ARGON**

© Department of Mechanical Engineering, Stanford University

P, MPa

h, kJ/kg

PROPERTIES OF SATURATED BUTANE

T K	P MPa	volume, m³/kg v_f	v_g	enthalpy, kJ/kg h_f	h_fg	h_g	entropy, kJ/(kg·K) s_f	s_fg	s_g
200	0.001886	0.001511	15.14	0.0	455.99	455.99	0.0	2.2799	2.2799
210	0.003997	0.001532	7.486	24.97	444.06	469.03	0.1218	2.1146	2.2364
220	0.007791	0.001553	4.013	49.17	433.19	482.36	0.2344	1.9690	2.2034
230	0.01415	0.001575	2.301	72.97	422.96	495.93	0.3402	1.8389	2.1791
240	0.02420	0.001598	1.397	96.58	413.13	509.71	0.4405	1.7214	2.1619
250	0.03933	0.001621	0.8892	120.11	403.55	523.66	0.5365	1.6142	2.1507
260	0.06116	0.001645	0.5898	143.61	394.15	537.76	0.6286	1.5159	2.1445
270	0.09154	0.001666	0.4050	167.13	384.84	551.97	0.7171	1.4254	2.1425
272.66	0.101325	0.001677	0.3684	173.40	382.36	555.76	0.7402	1.4023	2.1425
280	0.1326	0.001696	0.2865	190.71	375.54	566.25	0.8026	1.3412	2.1438
290	0.1865	0.001724	0.2079	214.44	366.13	580.57	0.8856	1.2625	2.1481
300	0.2559	0.001753	0.1541	238.42	356.46	594.88	0.9665	1.1882	2.1547
310	0.3434	0.001784	0.1164	262.77	346.38	609.15	1.0458	1.1173	2.1631
320	0.4518	0.001818	0.08933	287.61	335.71	623.32	1.1240	1.0491	2.1731
330	0.5842	0.001854	0.06945	313.02	324.33	637.35	1.2015	0.9828	2.1843
340	0.7437	0.001894	0.05459	339.07	312.08	651.15	1.2783	0.9179	2.1962
350	0.9337	0.001938	0.04329	365.81	298.82	664.63	1.3548	0.8538	2.2086
360	1.158	0.001989	0.03455	393.30	284.36	677.66	1.4310	0.7899	2.2209
370	1.420	0.002049	0.02767	421.66	268.40	690.06	1.5072	0.7254	2.2326
380	1.726	0.002122	0.02216	451.22	250.30	701.52	1.5843	0.6587	2.2430
390	2.080	0.002215	0.01767	482.60	228.95	711.55	1.6639	0.5870	2.2509
400	2.488	0.002344	0.01390	517.08	202.19	719.27	1.7488	0.5055	2.2543
410	2.956	0.002552	0.01062	557.15	165.50	722.65	1.8449	0.4036	2.2485
423.95	3.718	0.004902	0.004902	679.56	0.0	679.56	2.1313	0.0	2.1313

PROPERTIES OF GASEOUS BUTANE

P,MPa (T_sat,K)		sat	300	340	380	420	460	500	540	580
0.050	v,m³/kg	0.7114	0.8456	0.9635	1.080	1.196	1.312	1.427	1.542	1.657
(255.3)	h,kJ/kg	531.15	604.62	677.01	755.89	841.33	933.29	1031.65	1136.26	1246.91
	s,kJ/(kg·K)	2.1469	2.4117	2.6380	2.8571	3.0708	3.2798	3.4848	3.6860	3.8836
0.101325	v,m³/kg	0.3684	0.4106	0.4706	0.5293	0.5873	0.6449	0.7023	0.7594	0.8164
(272.7)	h,kJ/kg	555.76	602.30	675.33	754.62	840.34	932.49	1030.99	1135.71	1246.44
	s,kJ/(kg·K)	2.1425	2.3051	2.5334	2.7537	2.9681	3.1775	3.3828	3.5842	3.7819
0.20	v,m³/kg	0.1946	0.2012	0.2335	0.2645	0.2947	0.3244	0.3539	0.3832	0.4123
(292.1)	h,kJ/kg	583.64	597.65	672.03	752.15	838.40	930.93	1029.71	1134.63	1245.52
	s,kJ/(kg·K)	2.1493	2.1966	2.4292	2.6518	2.8675	3.0778	3.2837	3.4855	3.6835
0.40	v,m³/kg	0.1005		0.1116	0.1284	0.1444	0.1599	0.1750	0.1900	0.2048
(315.5)	h,kJ/kg	616.93		664.95	746.95	834.39	927.72	1027.08	1132.43	1243.64
	s,kJ/(kg·K)	2.1685		2.3150	2.5429	2.7616	2.9737	3.1807	3.3834	3.5820
0.70	v,m³/kg	0.05802		0.05879	0.06987	0.07986	0.08928	0.09836	0.1072	0.1159
(337.4)	h,kJ/kg	647.63		653.05	738.62	828.11	922.77	1023.06	1129.08	1240.81
	s,kJ/(kg·K)	2.1931		2.2091	2.4469	2.6708	2.8860	3.0949	3.2988	3.4984
1.0	v,m³/kg	0.04032			0.04624	0.05396	0.06101	0.06767	0.07409	0.08036
(353.1)	h,kJ/kg	668.76			729.47	821.48	917.64	1018.93	1125.67	1237.93
	s,kJ/(kg·K)	2.2124			2.3781	2.6083	2.8269	3.0380	3.2433	3.4438
2.0	v,m³/kg	0.01855				0.02329	0.02784	0.03179	0.03543	0.03887
(387.9)	h,kJ/kg	709.57				795.65	898.93	1004.37	1113.87	1228.11
	s,kJ/(kg·K)	2.2495				2.4629	2.6978	2.9175	3.1281	3.3322
4.0	v,m³/kg						0.01061	0.01367	0.01606	0.01815
	h,kJ/kg						848.56	970.40	1088.00	1207.31
	s,kJ/(kg·K)						2.5126	2.7668	2.9930	3.2061
7.0	v,m³/kg						0.00354	0.00592	0.00785	0.00939
	h,kJ/kg						736.64	905.38	1044.04	1174.04
	s,kJ/(kg·K)						2.2303	2.5826	2.8496	3.0819
10.	v,m³/kg						0.00272	0.00375	0.00499	0.00615
	h,kJ/kg						701.91	855.86	1003.21	1142.24
	s,kJ/(kg·K)						2.1351	2.4559	2.7396	2.9880

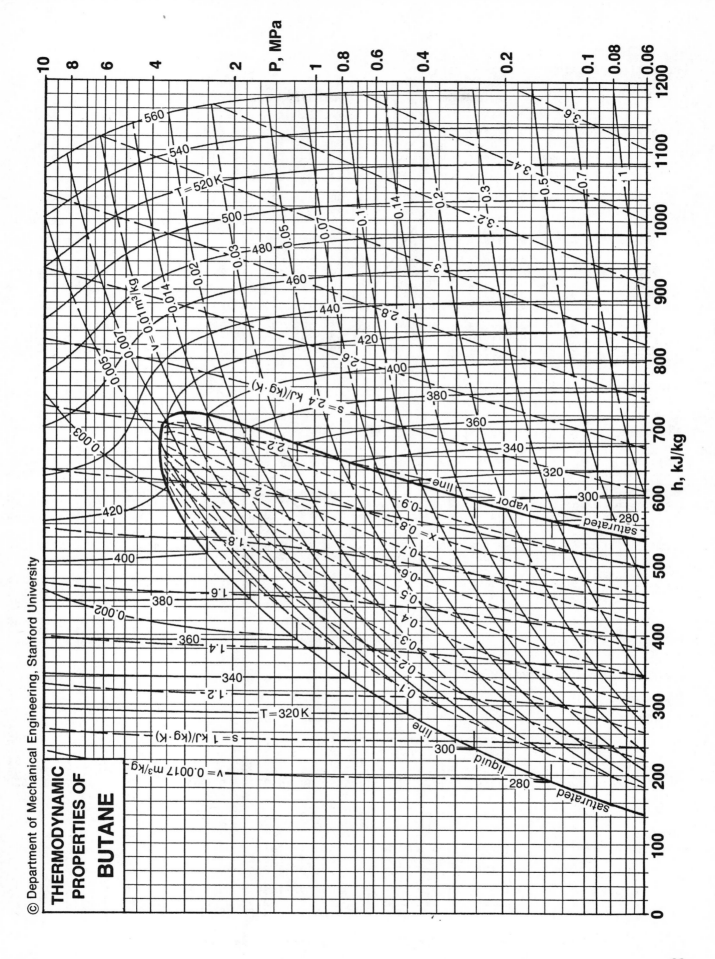

© Department of Mechanical Engineering, Stanford University

THERMODYNAMIC PROPERTIES OF
BUTANE

23

PROPERTIES OF SATURATED CARBON DIOXIDE

T K	P MPa	volume, m³/kg		enthalpy, kJ/kg			entropy, kJ/(kg·K)		
		v_f	v_g	h_f	h_{fg}	h_g	s_f	s_{fg}	s_g
216.54	0.5173	0.000847	0.07278	0.0	351.87	351.87	0.0	1.6250	1.6250
220	0.6000	0.000857	0.06314	7.00	346.12	353.12	0.0318	1.5732	1.6050
225	0.7366	0.000871	0.05181	17.52	337.21	354.73	0.0785	1.4987	1.5772
230	0.8949	0.000885	0.04287	28.07	328.02	356.09	0.1243	1.4262	1.5505
235	1.077	0.000901	0.03573	38.52	318.67	357.19	0.1685	1.3561	1.5246
240	1.285	0.000918	0.02997	48.90	309.10	358.00	0.2114	1.2879	1.4993
245	1.521	0.000936	0.02527	59.32	299.16	358.48	0.2535	1.2210	1.4745
250	1.788	0.000956	0.02140	69.85	288.74	358.59	0.2950	1.1550	1.4500
255	2.087	0.000977	0.01820	80.57	277.72	358.29	0.3363	1.0891	1.4254
260	2.421	0.001001	0.01552	91.49	266.04	357.53	0.3774	1.0233	1.4007
265	2.792	0.001027	0.01325	102.66	253.57	356.23	0.4186	0.9568	1.3754
270	3.204	0.001056	0.01133	114.16	240.13	354.29	0.4600	0.8893	1.3493
275	3.659	0.001090	0.009675	126.12	225.45	351.57	0.5020	0.8199	1.3219
280	4.160	0.001129	0.008242	138.72	209.16	347.88	0.5455	0.7470	1.2925
285	4.711	0.001177	0.006982	152.21	190.69	342.90	0.5910	0.6691	1.2601
290	5.314	0.001239	0.005854	166.95	169.14	336.09	0.6397	0.5832	1.2229
295	5.977	0.001324	0.004808	183.67	142.61	326.28	0.6939	0.4835	1.1774
300	6.706	0.001471	0.003749	205.06	104.89	309.95	0.7624	0.3496	1.1120
304.21	7.383	0.002155	0.002155	257.31	0.0	257.31	0.9312	0.0	0.9312

PROPERTIES OF GASEOUS CARBON DIOXIDE

P,MPa (T_{sat},K)		sat	300	400	500	600	700	800	900	1000
1.0 (233.0)	v,m³/kg	0.03844	0.05379	0.07418	0.09376	0.1130	0.1322	0.1513	0.1703	0.1893
	h,kJ/kg	356.78	419.95	513.65	613.22	718.90	829.90	945.34	1064.46	1186.61
	s,kJ/(kg·K)	1.5350	1.7737	2.0430	2.2649	2.4574	2.6284	2.7825	2.9228	3.0515
2.0 (253.6)	v,m³/kg	0.01903	0.02535	0.03640	0.04654	0.05638	0.06608	0.07571	0.08529	0.09484
	h,kJ/kg	358.42	409.41	508.45	610.01	716.73	828.37	944.25	1063.68	1186.07
	s,kJ/(kg·K)	1.4323	1.6174	1.9025	2.1289	2.3233	2.4954	2.6500	2.7907	2.9196
5.0 (287.5)	v,m³/kg	0.00641	0.00779	0.01374	0.01824	0.02241	0.02643	0.03039	0.03429	0.03817
	h,kJ/kg	339.84	366.98	492.26	600.43	710.37	823.93	941.10	1061.45	1184.53
	s,kJ/(kg·K)	1.2426	1.3351	1.6993	1.9407	2.1410	2.3160	2.4724	2.6141	2.7438
10.	v,m³/kg			0.00620	0.00885	0.01112	0.01325	0.01530	0.01731	0.01929
	h,kJ/kg			463.19	584.73	700.24	816.97	936.20	1058.02	1182.21
	s,kJ/(kg·K)			1.5127	1.7846	1.9952	2.1751	2.3343	2.4777	2.6086
20.	v,m³/kg			0.00262	0.00426	0.00554	0.00670	0.00779	0.00885	0.00988
	h,kJ/kg			403.03	555.30	681.94	804.67	927.73	1052.23	1178.42
	s,kJ/(kg·K)			1.2634	1.6054	1.8366	2.0258	2.1901	2.3367	2.4697

PROPERTIES OF LIQUID CARBON DIOXIDE

P MPa		220	230	240	250	260	270	280	290	300
	P_{sat},MPa	0.6000	0.8949	1.285	1.788	2.421	3.204	4.160	5.314	6.706
sat	ρ,kg/m³	1167.5	1129.5	1089.2	1046.2	999.36	946.94	885.60	807.37	680.04
	h,kJ/kg	7.00	28.07	48.90	69.85	91.49	114.16	138.72	166.95	205.06
	s,kJ/(kg·K)	0.0318	0.1243	0.2114	0.2950	0.3774	0.4600	0.5455	0.6397	0.7624
2.0	ρ,kg/m³	1170.7	1132.4	1091.6	1047.1					
	h,kJ/kg	7.36	28.25	48.93	69.83					
	s,kJ/(kg·K)	0.0279	0.1208	0.2088	0.2941					
5.0	ρ,kg/m³	1177.1	1140.1	1101.0	1059.1	1012.9	960.20	895.48		
	h,kJ/kg	8.15	28.81	49.18	69.64	90.67	112.85	137.37		
	s,kJ/(kg·K)	0.0199	0.1118	0.1984	0.2820	0.3644	0.4481	0.5373		
10.	ρ,kg/m³	1187.2	1152.0	1115.3	1076.7	1035.2	989.97	939.00	878.96	802.05
	h,kJ/kg	9.59	29.94	49.88	69.75	89.87	110.59	132.36	155.97	183.07
	s,kJ/(kg·K)	0.0073	0.0977	0.1826	0.2637	0.3426	0.4208	0.4999	0.5827	0.6746

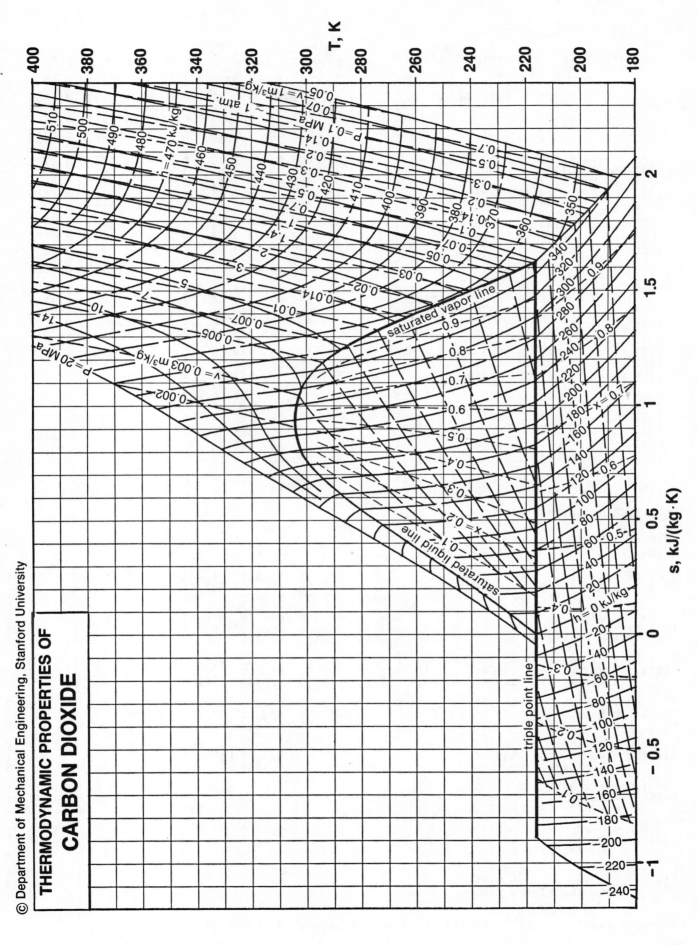

THERMODYNAMIC PROPERTIES OF
CARBON DIOXIDE

© Department of Mechanical Engineering, Stanford University

T, K

s, kJ/(kg·K)

saturated vapor line

saturated liquid line

triple point line

PROPERTIES OF SATURATED CESIUM

T K	P MPa	volume, m³/kg v_f	volume, m³/kg v_g	enthalpy, kJ/kg h_f	enthalpy, kJ/kg h_{fg}	enthalpy, kJ/kg h_g	entropy, kJ/(kg·K) s_f	entropy, kJ/(kg·K) s_{fg}	entropy, kJ/(kg·K) s_g
800	0.02024	0.000639	2.378	0.0	516.22	516.22	0.0	0.6453	0.6453
825	0.02801	0.000645	1.762	5.96	512.39	518.35	0.0073	0.6211	0.6284
850	0.03801	0.000652	1.330	11.99	508.37	520.36	0.0145	0.5981	0.6126
875	0.05066	0.000658	1.020	18.10	504.16	522.26	0.0216	0.5762	0.5978
900	0.06642	0.000665	0.7949	24.27	499.79	524.06	0.0285	0.5554	0.5839
925	0.08578	0.000672	0.6279	30.51	495.25	525.76	0.0354	0.5354	0.5708
942.05	0.101325	0.000677	0.5386	34.79	492.08	526.87	0.0399	0.5224	0.5623
950	0.1093	0.000679	0.5024	36.80	490.57	527.37	0.0421	0.5163	0.5584
975	0.1374	0.000686	0.4068	43.12	485.77	528.89	0.0486	0.4982	0.5468
1000	0.1708	0.000694	0.3329	49.49	480.85	530.34	0.0550	0.4809	0.5359
1025	0.2100	0.000702	0.2753	55.87	475.87	531.74	0.0613	0.4643	0.5256
1050	0.2556	0.000710	0.2297	62.26	470.82	533.08	0.0674	0.4484	0.5158
1075	0.3081	0.000718	0.1934	68.64	465.74	534.38	0.0734	0.4333	0.5067
1100	0.3682	0.000726	0.1642	75.02	460.64	535.66	0.0792	0.4188	0.4980
1125	0.4364	0.000735	0.1404	81.38	455.55	536.93	0.0849	0.4049	0.4898
1150	0.5133	0.000744	0.1210	87.72	450.48	538.20	0.0904	0.3917	0.4821
1175	0.5995	0.000753	0.1049	94.03	445.45	539.48	0.0958	0.3791	0.4749
1200	0.6954	0.000763	0.09160	100.32	440.46	540.78	0.1010	0.3671	0.4681
1225	0.8016	0.000773	0.08044	106.61	435.49	542.10	0.1062	0.3555	0.4617
1250	0.9187	0.000783	0.07102	112.90	430.55	543.45	0.1112	0.3444	0.4556
1275	1.047	0.000794	0.06303	119.23	425.59	544.82	0.1161	0.3338	0.4499
1300	1.187	0.000805	0.05621	125.61	420.58	546.19	0.1210	0.3235	0.4445
1325	1.339	0.000816	0.05034	132.09	415.47	547.56	0.1258	0.3136	0.4394
1350	1.504	0.000828	0.04527	138.69	410.22	548.91	0.1306	0.3039	0.4345
1375	1.681	0.000840	0.04085	145.45	404.75	550.20	0.1355	0.2944	0.4299
1400	1.872	0.000852	0.03699	152.38	399.02	551.40	0.1404	0.2850	0.4254
1425	2.076	0.000866	0.03358	159.51	392.98	552.49	0.1453	0.2758	0.4211
1450	2.293	0.000879	0.03057	166.81	386.61	553.42	0.1502	0.2667	0.4169
1475	2.525	0.000893	0.02790	174.21	379.97	554.18	0.1552	0.2576	0.4128
1500	2.770	0.000908	0.02553	181.56	373.20	554.76	0.1600	0.2488	0.4088
1525	3.030	0.000923	0.02344	188.62	366.58	555.20	0.1645	0.2403	0.4048
1550	3.304	0.000939	0.02162	195.02	360.57	555.59	0.1685	0.2326	0.4011

PROPERTIES OF GASEOUS CESIUM

P,MPa (T_{sat},K)		sat	1025	1100	1175	1250	1325	1400	1475	1550
0.050 (873.8)	v,m³/kg	1.033	1.252	1.353	1.452	1.549	1.645	1.741	1.836	1.931
	h,kJ/kg	522.18	555.60	569.52	582.65	595.32	607.71	619.92	632.03	644.08
	s,kJ/(kg·K)	0.5985	0.6339	0.6470	0.6585	0.6690	0.6786	0.6876	0.6960	0.7040
0.101325 (942.1)	v,m³/kg	0.5386	0.6023	0.6558	0.7070	0.7566	0.8053	0.8534	0.9011	0.9485
	h,kJ/kg	526.87	547.82	563.95	578.51	592.13	605.18	617.87	630.33	642.64
	s,kJ/(kg·K)	0.5623	0.5836	0.5988	0.6116	0.6229	0.6330	0.6423	0.6510	0.6591
0.20 (1019.)	v,m³/kg	0.2879	0.2905	0.3209	0.3491	0.3760	0.4018	0.4271	0.4519	0.4764
	h,kJ/kg	531.41	533.18	553.30	570.55	586.00	600.32	613.93	627.06	639.88
	s,kJ/(kg·K)	0.5280	0.5297	0.5487	0.5639	0.5766	0.5878	0.5977	0.6069	0.6154
0.40 (1112.)	v,m³/kg	0.1521			0.1657	0.1807	0.1948	0.2083	0.2214	0.2342
	h,kJ/kg	536.28			554.66	573.69	590.55	605.99	620.48	634.33
	s,kJ/(kg·K)	0.4940			0.5101	0.5258	0.5389	0.5502	0.5603	0.5695
0.70 (1201.)	v,m³/kg	0.09105				0.09728	0.1063	0.1147	0.1227	0.1305
	h,kJ/kg	540.84				555.77	576.17	594.26	610.74	626.11
	s,kJ/(kg·K)	0.4678				0.4800	0.4958	0.5091	0.5206	0.5308
1.0 (1266.)	v,m³/kg	0.06573					0.07103	0.07739	0.08339	0.08911
	h,kJ/kg	544.33					562.31	582.80	601.17	618.01
	s,kJ/(kg·K)	0.4519					0.4658	0.4808	0.4936	0.5048
2.0 (1416.)	v,m³/kg	0.03477							0.03755	0.04092
	h,kJ/kg	552.11							570.24	591.46
	s,kJ/(kg·K)	0.4226							0.4352	0.4492
3.0 (1522.)	v,m³/kg	0.02366								0.02461
	h,kJ/kg	555.15								564.03
	s,kJ/(kg·K)	0.4053								0.4111

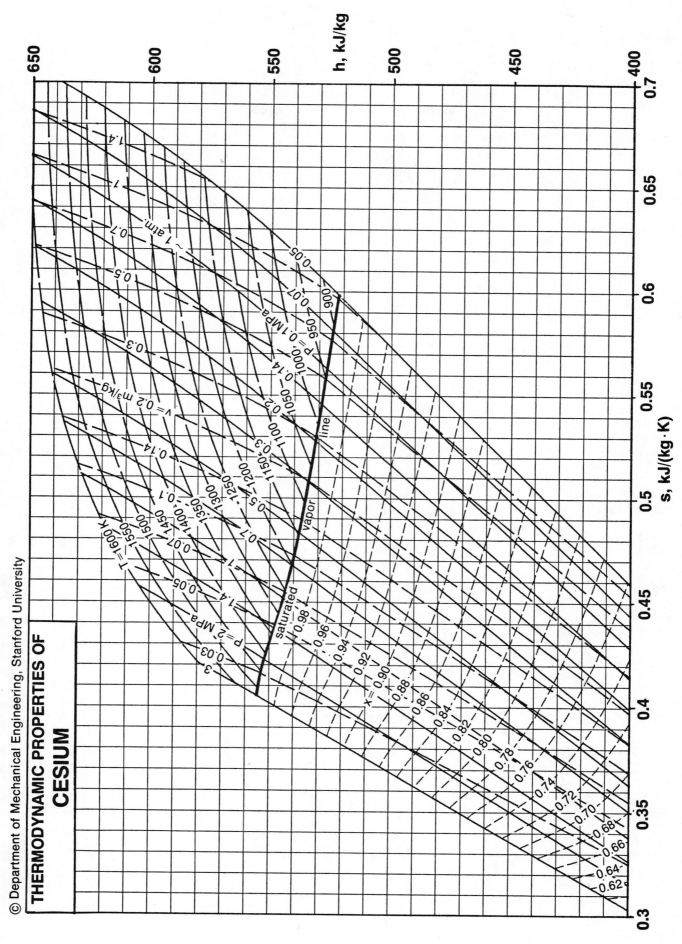

© Department of Mechanical Engineering, Stanford University

THERMODYNAMIC PROPERTIES OF CESIUM

27

PROPERTIES OF SATURATED ETHANE

T K	P MPa	v_f	v_g	h_f	h_fg	h_g	s_f	s_fg	s_g
150	0.009591	0.001693	4.299	0.0	539.18	539.18	0.0	3.5945	3.5945
160	0.02153	0.001735	2.031	27.17	523.99	551.16	0.1752	3.2750	3.4502
170	0.04329	0.001779	1.064	53.61	509.29	562.90	0.3353	2.9959	3.3312
180	0.07968	0.001823	0.6053	79.62	494.67	574.29	0.4836	2.7482	3.2318
184.32	0.101325	0.001843	0.4845	90.80	488.28	579.08	0.5448	2.6491	3.1939
190	0.1364	0.001869	0.3676	105.51	479.72	585.23	0.6230	2.5249	3.1479
200	0.2200	0.001918	0.2355	131.50	464.11	595.61	0.7555	2.3206	3.0761
210	0.3376	0.001969	0.1575	157.69	447.64	605.33	0.8822	2.1316	3.0138
220	0.4968	0.002023	0.1091	184.13	430.15	614.28	1.0037	1.9553	2.9590
230	0.7057	0.002082	0.07768	210.90	411.44	622.34	1.1208	1.7889	2.9097
240	0.9730	0.002147	0.05655	238.21	391.10	629.31	1.2346	1.6296	2.8642
250	1.308	0.002221	0.04184	266.47	368.49	634.96	1.3470	1.4739	2.8209
260	1.720	0.002308	0.03130	296.21	342.70	638.91	1.4599	1.3181	2.7780
270	2.221	0.002415	0.02352	327.97	312.59	640.56	1.5753	1.1577	2.7330
280	2.822	0.002555	0.01759	362.34	276.44	638.78	1.6948	0.9873	2.6821
290	3.541	0.002759	0.01286	400.71	230.25	630.96	1.8228	0.7939	2.6167
300	4.409	0.003142	0.008602	450.52	156.97	607.49	1.9828	0.5232	2.5060
305.88	5.010	0.004596	0.004596	532.03	0.0	532.03	2.2441	0.0	2.2441

PROPERTIES OF GASEOUS ETHANE

P,MPa (T_sat,K)		sat	300	340	380	420	460	500	540	580
0.070 (177.8)	v,m³/kg	0.6824	1.180	1.340	1.499	1.658	1.816	1.975	2.134	2.292
	h,kJ/kg	571.78	764.36	838.62	919.15	1006.11	1099.55	1199.46	1305.74	1418.27
	s,kJ/(kg·K)	3.2525	4.0686	4.3007	4.5245	4.7419	4.9543	5.1625	5.3669	5.5679
0.101325 (184.3)	v,m³/kg	0.4845	0.8132	0.9240	1.034	1.144	1.254	1.364	1.474	1.583
	h,kJ/kg	579.08	763.73	838.14	918.77	1005.80	1099.29	1199.24	1305.56	1418.11
	s,kJ/(kg·K)	3.1939	3.9648	4.1974	4.4214	4.6390	4.8516	5.0598	5.2643	5.4653
0.20 (197.9)	v,m³/kg	0.2575	0.4089	0.4658	0.5222	0.5783	0.6342	0.6901	0.7458	0.8014
	h,kJ/kg	593.49	761.74	836.62	917.58	1004.83	1098.49	1198.56	1304.98	1417.61
	s,kJ/(kg·K)	3.0902	3.7720	4.0061	4.2310	4.4492	4.6621	4.8706	5.0753	5.2765
0.40 (214.3)	v,m³/kg	0.1341	0.2012	0.2305	0.2592	0.2877	0.3160	0.3441	0.3721	0.4001
	h,kJ/kg	609.25	757.62	833.52	915.14	1002.86	1096.86	1197.19	1303.80	1416.60
	s,kJ/(kg·K)	2.9896	3.5706	3.8079	4.0347	4.2541	4.4677	4.6768	4.8818	5.0833
0.70 (229.8)	v,m³/kg	0.07829	0.1122	0.1296	0.1465	0.1632	0.1796	0.1958	0.2120	0.2281
	h,kJ/kg	622.15	751.24	828.77	911.44	999.88	1094.40	1195.12	1302.04	1415.07
	s,kJ/(kg·K)	2.9108	3.4008	3.6433	3.8730	4.0942	4.3090	4.5189	4.7245	4.9264
1.0 (240.9)	v,m³/kg	0.05502	0.07648	0.08926	0.1015	0.1133	0.1250	0.1365	0.1480	0.1593
	h,kJ/kg	629.87	744.60	823.91	907.68	996.87	1091.93	1193.05	1300.27	1413.55
	s,kJ/(kg·K)	2.8603	3.2865	3.5345	3.7673	3.9904	4.2064	4.4171	4.6234	4.8257
2.0 (265.8)	v,m³/kg	0.02651	0.03451	0.04205	0.04882	0.05520	0.06135	0.06736	0.07326	0.07910
	h,kJ/kg	640.20	720.03	806.77	894.73	986.63	1083.58	1186.08	1294.36	1408.47
	s,kJ/(kg·K)	2.7523	3.0353	3.3067	3.5512	3.7811	4.0015	4.2151	4.4233	4.6271
4.0 (295.5)	v,m³/kg	0.01051	0.01183	0.01813	0.02243	0.02614	0.02957	0.03283	0.03597	0.03904
	h,kJ/kg	621.42	644.02	766.56	866.58	965.16	1066.43	1171.98	1282.52	1398.37
	s,kJ/(kg·K)	2.5659	2.6418	3.0271	3.3054	3.5520	3.7823	4.0022	4.2148	4.4218
7.0	v,m³/kg			0.00727	0.01106	0.01374	0.01604	0.01812	0.02009	0.02197
	h,kJ/kg			678.32	817.80	930.66	1039.90	1150.64	1264.88	1383.51
	s,kJ/(kg·K)			2.6637	3.0531	3.3357	3.5841	3.8149	4.0347	4.2466
10.	v,m³/kg			0.00397	0.00672	0.00892	0.01074	0.01235	0.01383	0.01523
	h,kJ/kg			589.90	764.34	894.94	1013.29	1129.67	1247.78	1369.25
	s,kJ/(kg·K)			2.3579	2.8446	3.1719	3.4411	3.6837	3.9109	4.1279
20.	v,m³/kg			0.00277	0.00342	0.00429	0.00521	0.00609	0.00691	0.00769
	h,kJ/kg			532.36	668.78	808.21	941.97	1071.47	1199.79	1329.20
	s,kJ/(kg·K)			2.0966	2.4756	2.8246	3.1289	3.3989	3.6458	3.8769
30.	v,m³/kg			0.00252	0.00287	0.00332	0.00384	0.00438	0.00492	0.00544
	h,kJ/kg			526.36	646.92	774.99	905.97	1037.43	1169.40	1302.75
	s,kJ/(kg·K)			2.0017	2.3367	2.6570	2.9549	3.2290	3.4829	3.7211

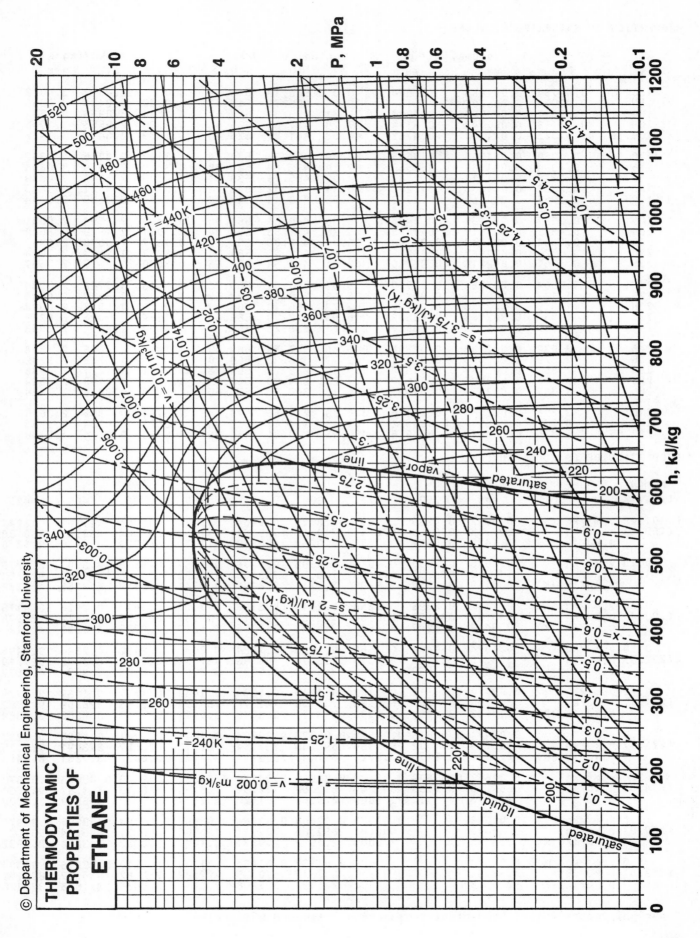

THERMODYNAMIC
PROPERTIES OF
ETHANE

© Department of Mechanical Engineering, Stanford University

P, MPa

h, kJ/kg

29

PROPERTIES OF SATURATED ETHYLENE

T K	P MPa	volume, m³/kg v_f	v_g	enthalpy, kJ/kg h_f	h_{fg}	h_g	entropy, kJ/(kg·K) s_f	s_{fg}	s_g
150	0.02734	0.001683	1.604	0.0	510.19	510.19	0.0	3.4012	3.4012
155	0.03973	0.001702	1.136	12.68	502.79	515.47	0.0830	3.2438	3.3268
160	0.05622	0.001722	0.8241	25.31	495.31	520.62	0.1631	3.0956	3.2587
165	0.07768	0.001743	0.6114	37.79	487.82	525.61	0.2396	2.9565	3.1961
169.38	0.101325	0.001762	0.4782	48.58	481.27	529.85	0.3039	2.8413	3.1452
170	0.1050	0.001765	0.4625	50.09	480.35	530.44	0.3127	2.8256	3.1383
175	0.1394	0.001788	0.3560	62.24	472.84	535.08	0.3829	2.7019	3.0848
180	0.1817	0.001811	0.2783	74.32	465.19	539.51	0.4505	2.5844	3.0349
185	0.2332	0.001836	0.2205	86.41	457.32	543.73	0.5162	2.4721	2.9883
190	0.2952	0.001862	0.1769	98.58	449.14	547.72	0.5805	2.3639	2.9444
195	0.3687	0.001890	0.1435	110.88	440.58	551.46	0.6437	2.2594	2.9031
200	0.4552	0.001919	0.1175	123.36	431.58	554.94	0.7061	2.1579	2.8640
205	0.5558	0.001949	0.09709	136.04	422.08	558.12	0.7677	2.0590	2.8267
210	0.6720	0.001982	0.08085	148.92	412.08	561.00	0.8287	1.9623	2.7910
215	0.8051	0.002016	0.06780	162.01	401.54	563.55	0.8890	1.8677	2.7567
220	0.9564	0.002053	0.05720	175.32	390.41	565.73	0.9488	1.7746	2.7234
225	1.127	0.002093	0.04851	188.88	378.62	567.50	1.0082	1.6827	2.6909
230	1.319	0.002136	0.04132	202.73	366.10	568.83	1.0672	1.5918	2.6590
235	1.534	0.002183	0.03532	216.94	352.70	569.64	1.1264	1.5008	2.6272
240	1.773	0.002235	0.03027	231.61	338.25	569.86	1.1859	1.4094	2.5953
245	2.037	0.002293	0.02598	246.85	322.55	569.40	1.2463	1.3165	2.5628
250	2.329	0.002359	0.02231	262.77	305.33	568.10	1.3079	1.2213	2.5292
255	2.650	0.002435	0.01914	279.50	286.28	565.78	1.3711	1.1227	2.4938
260	3.002	0.002525	0.01637	297.20	264.93	562.13	1.4364	1.0190	2.4554
265	3.387	0.002636	0.01391	316.13	240.53	556.66	1.5048	0.9076	2.4124
270	3.808	0.002781	0.01166	336.88	211.56	548.44	1.5781	0.7835	2.3616
275	4.271	0.002992	0.009522	361.13	174.17	535.30	1.6621	0.6334	2.2955
282.65	5.075	0.004615	0.004615	450.95	0.0	450.95	1.9730	0.0	1.9730

PROPERTIES OF GASEOUS ETHYLENE

P,MPa (T_sat,K)		sat	250	275	300	325	350	375	400	425
0.101325 (169.4)	v,m³/kg	0.4782	0.7239	0.7983	0.8725	0.9464	1.020	1.094	1.167	1.241
	h,kJ/kg	529.85	636.60	672.44	710.12	749.81	791.63	835.64	881.87	930.30
	s,kJ/(kg·K)	3.1452	3.6592	3.7958	3.9269	4.0539	4.1778	4.2993	4.4186	4.5360
0.20 (181.9)	v,m³/kg	0.2545	0.3630	0.4015	0.4395	0.4774	0.5151	0.5526	0.5901	0.6275
	h,kJ/kg	541.13	634.30	670.58	708.57	748.50	790.50	834.66	881.00	929.53
	s,kJ/(kg·K)	3.0169	3.4514	3.5896	3.7218	3.8496	3.9741	4.0959	4.2155	4.3332
0.30 (190.4)	v,m³/kg	0.1742	0.2395	0.2656	0.2913	0.3168	0.3422	0.3674	0.3925	0.4175
	h,kJ/kg	548.00	631.93	668.66	706.99	747.16	789.35	833.66	880.12	928.75
	s,kJ/(kg·K)	2.9414	3.3247	3.4647	3.5981	3.7266	3.8517	3.9739	4.0938	4.2117
0.50 (202.3)	v,m³/kg	0.1074	0.1406	0.1569	0.1728	0.1884	0.2039	0.2192	0.2344	0.2496
	h,kJ/kg	556.45	627.07	664.76	703.78	744.46	787.04	831.65	878.36	927.19
	s,kJ/(kg·K)	2.8465	3.1599	3.3036	3.4393	3.5695	3.6957	3.8188	3.9394	4.0577
0.70 (211.1)	v,m³/kg	0.07772	0.09813	0.1102	0.1219	0.1333	0.1446	0.1557	0.1667	0.1776
	h,kJ/kg	561.60	622.01	660.76	700.50	741.72	784.70	829.63	876.59	925.62
	s,kJ/(kg·K)	2.7833	3.0461	3.1938	3.3321	3.4640	3.5914	3.7153	3.8365	3.9554
1.0 (221.3)	v,m³/kg	0.05471	0.06616	0.07520	0.08377	0.09204	0.1001	0.1081	0.1159	0.1237
	h,kJ/kg	566.24	614.02	654.54	695.48	737.54	781.16	826.57	873.91	923.25
	s,kJ/(kg·K)	2.7147	2.9178	3.0723	3.2147	3.3494	3.4787	3.6039	3.7261	3.8458
2.0 (244.3)	v,m³/kg	0.02652	0.02809	0.03402	0.03912	0.04379	0.04822	0.05249	0.05665	0.06072
	h,kJ/kg	569.50	581.93	631.43	677.50	722.94	768.96	816.15	864.87	915.31
	s,kJ/(kg·K)	2.5673	2.6176	2.8065	2.9668	3.1123	3.2487	3.3789	3.5047	3.6270
3.0 (260.0)	v,m³/kg	0.01638		0.01978	0.02404	0.02764	0.03090	0.03397	0.03691	0.03976
	h,kJ/kg	562.15		602.41	657.05	707.11	756.09	805.37	855.64	907.27
	s,kJ/(kg·K)	2.4556		2.6063	2.7967	2.9571	3.1022	3.2382	3.3680	3.4932
5.0 (282.0)	v,m³/kg	0.00580			0.01137	0.01454	0.01700	0.01917	0.02116	0.02304
	h,kJ/kg	483.54			602.17	670.35	727.99	782.62	836.57	890.92
	s,kJ/(kg·K)	2.0898			2.5021	2.7208	2.8918	3.0425	3.1818	3.3136

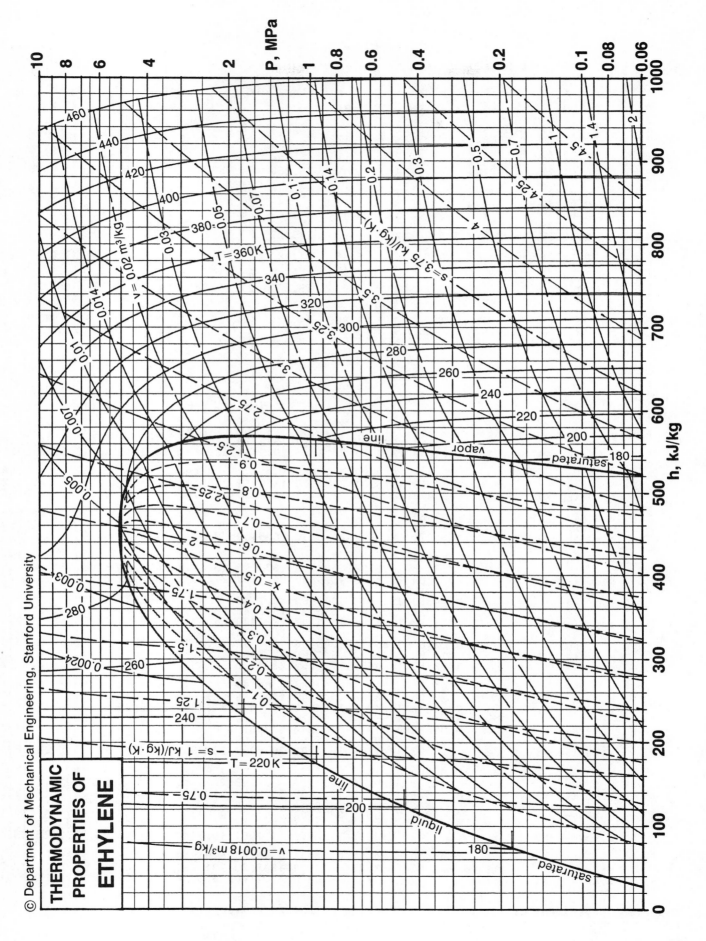

THERMODYNAMIC PROPERTIES OF ETHYLENE

© Department of Mechanical Engineering, Stanford University

P, MPa

h, kJ/kg

31

PROPERTIES OF SATURATED HELIUM-4

T K	P MPa	volume, m³/kg v_f	v_g	enthalpy, kJ/kg h_f	h_fg	h_g	entropy, kJ/(kg·K) s_f	s_fg	s_g
2.18	0.005102	0.006837	0.8376	0.0	22.661	22.661	0.0	10.4091	10.4091
2.2	0.005395	0.006841	0.7988	0.122	22.632	22.754	0.0548	10.2875	10.3423
2.4	0.008439	0.006883	0.5468	0.720	22.824	23.544	0.3074	9.5102	9.8176
2.6	0.01250	0.006937	0.3916	1.183	23.096	24.279	0.4813	8.8831	9.3644
2.8	0.01773	0.007004	0.2904	1.692	23.260	24.952	0.6564	8.3072	8.9636
3	0.02427	0.007084	0.2213	2.229	23.329	25.558	0.8256	7.7766	8.6022
3.2	0.03230	0.007179	0.1723	2.801	23.290	26.091	0.9919	7.2781	8.2700
3.4	0.04196	0.007289	0.1365	3.434	23.109	26.543	1.1623	6.7968	7.9591
3.6	0.05339	0.007419	0.1096	4.142	22.761	26.903	1.3406	6.3226	7.6632
3.8	0.06676	0.007572	0.08892	4.933	22.229	27.162	1.5273	5.8496	7.3769
4	0.08221	0.007753	0.07271	5.811	21.491	27.302	1.7221	5.3726	7.0947
4.2	0.09990	0.007972	0.05970	6.790	20.508	27.298	1.9269	4.8829	6.8098
4.22	0.101325	0.007991	0.05883	6.869	20.422	27.291	1.9428	4.8452	6.7880
4.4	0.1200	0.008246	0.04903	7.903	19.207	27.110	2.1478	4.3652	6.5130
4.6	0.1428	0.008602	0.04001	9.217	17.446	26.663	2.3971	3.7924	6.1895
4.8	0.1684	0.009103	0.03204	10.860	14.932	25.792	2.6982	3.1108	5.8090
5	0.1971	0.009915	0.02419	13.136	10.829	23.965	3.1064	2.1659	5.2723
5.2014	0.227	0.014360	0.01436	18.622	0.0	18.622	4.1124	0.0	4.1124

PROPERTIES OF GASEOUS HELIUM-4

P,MPa (T_sat,K)		sat	40	70	100	T,K 300	500	700	1000	1500
0.101325	v,m³/kg	0.05883	0.8219	1.438	2.053	6.153	10.25	14.35	20.50	30.75
(4.22)	h,kJ/kg	27.29	219.62	375.63	531.50	1570.19	2608.80	3647.41	5205.32	7801.84
	s,kJ/(kg·K)	6.7880	19.4650	22.3755	24.2286	29.9343	32.5871	34.3344	36.1866	38.2922
0.20	v,m³/kg	0.02336	0.4173	0.7298	1.042	3.119	5.196	7.273	10.39	15.58
(5.02)	h,kJ/kg	23.67	219.59	375.81	531.75	1570.51	2609.12	3647.72	5205.62	7802.12
	s,kJ/(kg·K)	5.1995	18.0470	20.9616	22.8157	28.5220	31.1747	32.9220	34.7742	36.8798
0.50	v,m³/kg		0.1681	0.2936	0.4184	1.249	2.080	2.911	4.157	6.234
	h,kJ/kg		219.49	376.35	532.51	1571.51	2610.10	3648.68	5206.54	7802.99
	s,kJ/(kg·K)		16.1271	19.0542	20.9110	26.6190	29.2717	31.0189	32.8711	34.9766
1.0	v,m³/kg		0.08500	0.1481	0.2107	0.6261	1.041	1.457	2.080	3.118
	h,kJ/kg		219.35	377.25	533.79	1573.16	2611.74	3650.27	5208.07	7804.45
	s,kJ/(kg·K)		14.6600	17.6076	19.4690	25.1797	27.8323	29.5795	31.4316	33.5371
2.0	v,m³/kg		0.04350	0.07544	0.1068	0.3146	0.5221	0.7296	1.041	1.560
	h,kJ/kg		219.24	379.06	536.33	1576.46	2615.00	3653.45	5211.14	7807.34
	s,kJ/(kg·K)		13.1690	16.1546	18.0247	23.7409	26.3935	28.1406	29.9925	32.0979
4.0	v,m³/kg		0.02288	0.03910	0.05490	0.1588	0.2624	0.3661	0.5216	0.7810
	h,kJ/kg		219.93	382.80	541.40	1583.04	2621.51	3659.80	5217.25	7813.13
	s,kJ/(kg·K)		11.6450	14.6897	16.5762	22.3032	24.9557	26.7025	28.5541	30.6592
7.0	v,m³/kg		0.01421	0.02355	0.03264	0.09197	0.1511	0.2103	0.2991	0.4471
	h,kJ/kg		223.35	388.84	549.09	1592.86	2631.24	3669.28	5226.37	7821.77
	s,kJ/(kg·K)		10.4014	13.4953	15.4016	21.1440	23.7962	25.5425	27.3938	29.4985
10.	v,m³/kg		0.01083	0.01735	0.02374	0.06525	0.1066	0.1480	0.2100	0.3136
	h,kJ/kg		228.94	395.47	556.93	1602.63	2640.91	3678.71	5235.45	7830.37
	s,kJ/(kg·K)		9.6173	12.7293	14.6502	20.4062	23.0583	24.8042	26.6550	28.7593
20.	v,m³/kg		0.00700	0.01017	0.01336	0.03405	0.05462	0.07521	0.1061	0.1578
	h,kJ/kg		255.08	420.70	584.25	1634.95	2672.86	3709.83	5265.41	7858.75
	s,kJ/(kg·K)		8.1528	11.2409	13.1866	18.9770	21.6282	23.3728	25.2222	27.3252
50.	v,m³/kg		0.00465	0.00583	0.00708	0.01527	0.02336	0.03149	0.04374	0.06421
	h,kJ/kg		350.04	506.54	670.41	1730.11	2766.57	3800.87	5352.83	7941.55
	s,kJ/(kg·K)		6.4042	9.3095	11.2572	17.1061	19.7540	21.4941	23.3392	25.4384
100.	v,m³/kg		0.00370	0.00427	0.00487	0.00890	0.01285	0.01683	0.02284	0.03294
	h,kJ/kg		504.52	653.87	814.00	1882.29	2917.30	3946.88	5492.26	8072.99
	s,kJ/(kg·K)		5.1517	7.9229	9.8246	15.7180	18.3630	20.0952	21.9324	24.0251

Copyright Department of Mechanical Engineering, Stanford University

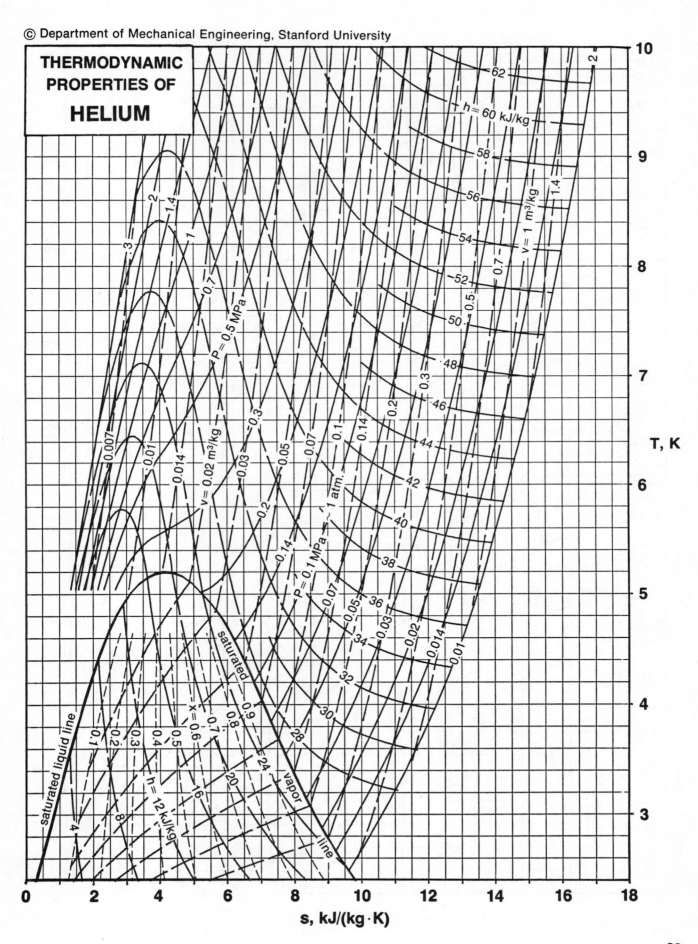

THERMODYNAMIC PROPERTIES OF HELIUM

T, K

s, kJ/(kg·K)

33

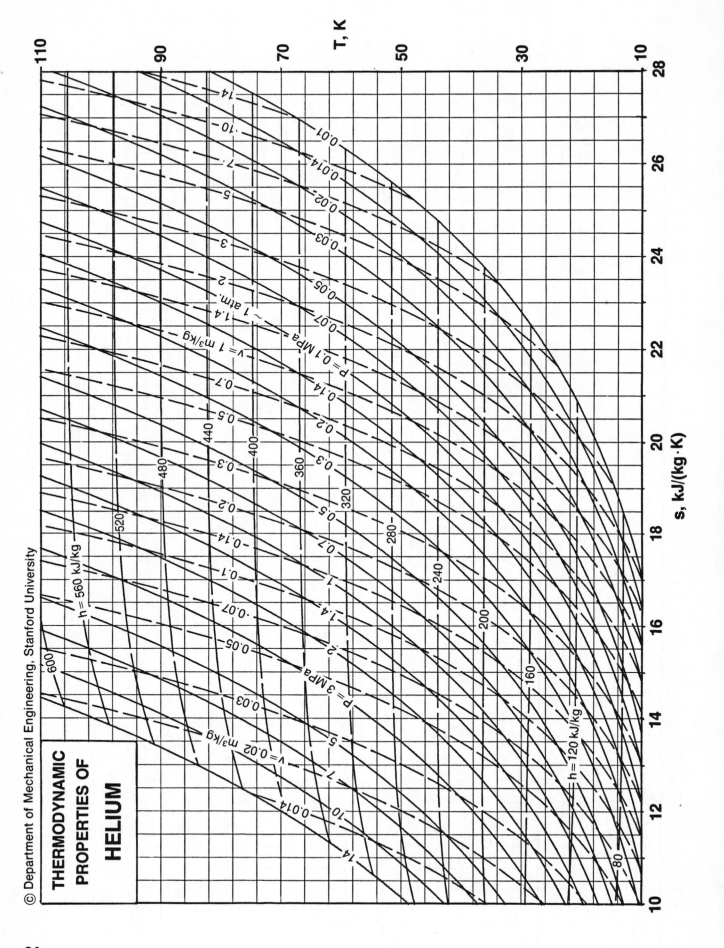

THERMODYNAMIC
PROPERTIES OF
HELIUM

© Department of Mechanical Engineering, Stanford University

T, K

s, kJ/(kg·K)

34

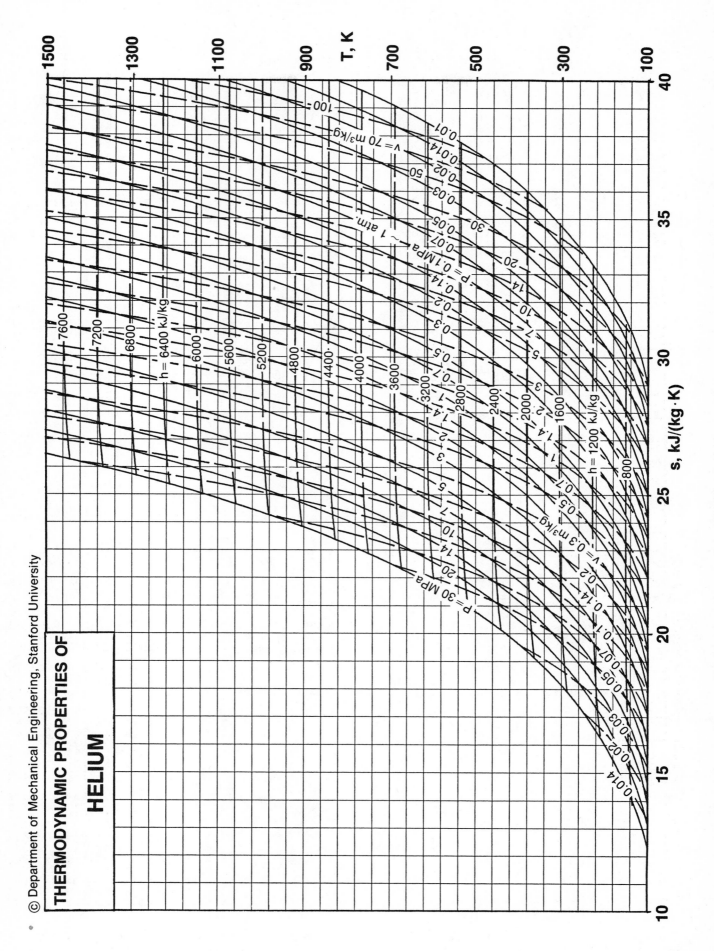

© Department of Mechanical Engineering, Stanford University

THERMODYNAMIC PROPERTIES OF
HELIUM

35

PROPERTIES OF SATURATED HEPTANE

T K	P MPa	volume, m³/kg v_f	v_g	enthalpy, kJ/kg h_f	h_fg	h_g	entropy, kJ/(kg·K) s_f	s_fg	s_g
300	0.006637	0.001476	3.728	0.0	364.96	364.96	0.0	1.2165	1.2165
310	0.01065	0.001496	2.393	22.32	359.23	381.55	0.0732	1.1588	1.2320
320	0.01650	0.001517	1.589	45.17	353.32	398.49	0.1457	1.1041	1.2498
330	0.02477	0.001539	1.087	68.68	347.07	415.75	0.2180	1.0517	1.2697
340	0.03613	0.001561	0.7632	92.84	340.47	433.31	0.2900	1.0014	1.2914
350	0.05134	0.001584	0.5491	117.61	333.55	451.16	0.3618	0.9530	1.3148
360	0.07124	0.001608	0.4036	142.88	326.40	469.28	0.4329	0.9066	1.3395
370	0.09677	0.001632	0.3024	168.60	319.03	487.63	0.5032	0.8623	1.3655
371.56	0.101325	0.001636	0.2895	172.66	317.86	490.52	0.5141	0.8555	1.3696
380	0.1289	0.001658	0.2305	194.70	311.52	506.22	0.5727	0.8198	1.3925
390	0.1688	0.001684	0.1783	221.17	303.83	525.00	0.6413	0.7790	1.4203
400	0.2175	0.001712	0.1398	248.01	295.95	543.96	0.7090	0.7399	1.4489
410	0.2764	0.001742	0.1109	275.25	287.81	563.06	0.7760	0.7020	1.4780
420	0.3466	0.001773	0.08887	302.96	279.33	582.29	0.8425	0.6651	1.5076
430	0.4295	0.001807	0.07183	331.16	270.43	601.59	0.9085	0.6289	1.5374
440	0.5267	0.001843	0.05849	359.91	261.02	620.93	0.9742	0.5932	1.5674
450	0.6395	0.001883	0.04792	389.21	251.04	640.25	1.0395	0.5579	1.5974
460	0.7696	0.001926	0.03945	419.07	240.42	659.49	1.1046	0.5227	1.6273
470	0.9187	0.001975	0.03257	449.51	229.06	678.57	1.1695	0.4873	1.6568
480	1.089	0.002031	0.02692	480.57	216.78	697.35	1.2342	0.4516	1.6858
490	1.282	0.002096	0.02222	512.43	203.21	715.64	1.2990	0.4147	1.7137
500	1.502	0.002177	0.01824	545.43	187.73	733.16	1.3647	0.3755	1.7402
510	1.751	0.002282	0.01481	580.26	169.11	749.37	1.4326	0.3316	1.7642
520	2.032	0.002434	0.01176	618.28	144.94	763.22	1.5051	0.2788	1.7839
530	2.350	0.002720	0.008817	662.90	108.73	771.63	1.5885	0.2052	1.7937
537.68	2.620	0.005061	0.005061	747.84	0.0	747.84	1.7456	0.0	1.7456

PROPERTIES OF GASEOUS HEPTANE

P,MPa (T_sat,K)		sat	400	440	480	520	560	600	640	680
0.101325 (371.6)	v,m³/kg	0.2895	0.3153	0.3507	0.3853	0.4195	0.4534	0.4870	0.5205	0.5538
	h,kJ/kg	490.52	549.17	637.13	731.41	831.87	938.29	1050.40	1167.90	1290.48
	s,kJ/(kg·K)	1.3696	1.5217	1.7311	1.9361	2.1371	2.3342	2.5275	2.7170	2.9028
0.20 (396.6)	v,m³/kg	0.1516	0.1533	0.1727	0.1912	0.2093	0.2270	0.2445	0.2618	0.2790
	h,kJ/kg	537.54	544.78	633.72	728.68	829.63	936.41	1048.80	1166.53	1289.29
	s,kJ/(kg·K)	1.4392	1.4573	1.6691	1.8756	2.0775	2.2753	2.4691	2.6590	2.8450
0.40 (426.6)	v,m³/kg	0.07712		0.08086	0.09138	0.1013	0.1107	0.1200	0.1290	0.1379
	h,kJ/kg	595.06		626.22	722.83	824.91	932.51	1045.51	1163.71	1286.85
	s,kJ/(kg·K)	1.5273		1.5992	1.8093	2.0135	2.2128	2.4076	2.5983	2.7849
0.70 (454.8)	v,m³/kg	0.04361			0.04820	0.05477	0.06081	0.06654	0.07204	0.07740
	h,kJ/kg	649.55			713.04	817.30	926.35	1040.39	1159.37	1283.12
	s,kJ/(kg·K)	1.6119			1.7477	1.9563	2.1583	2.3549	2.5468	2.7344
1.0 (474.9)	v,m³/kg	0.02965			0.03044	0.03597	0.04074	0.04512	0.04924	0.05319
	h,kJ/kg	687.89			701.37	808.85	919.75	1035.02	1154.89	1279.30
	s,kJ/(kg·K)	1.6712			1.6994	1.9145	2.1199	2.3187	2.5120	2.7006
2.0 (518.9)	v,m³/kg	0.01208				0.01227	0.01681	0.01992	0.02255	0.02493
	h,kJ/kg	761.89				765.80	892.97	1014.87	1138.72	1265.86
	s,kJ/(kg·K)	1.7820				1.7896	2.0253	2.2356	2.4354	2.6281
4.0	v,m³/kg						0.00340	0.00675	0.00908	0.01082
	h,kJ/kg						774.78	956.10	1099.31	1235.68
	s,kJ/(kg·K)						1.7846	2.0980	2.3292	2.5359
7.0	v,m³/kg						0.00245	0.00316	0.00421	0.00529
	h,kJ/kg						737.76	888.80	1041.80	1190.19
	s,kJ/(kg·K)						1.7040	1.9643	2.2112	2.4362
10.	v,m³/kg						0.00226	0.00261	0.00313	0.00374
	h,kJ/kg						729.89	868.71	1014.34	1161.60
	s,kJ/(kg·K)						1.6773	1.9167	2.1516	2.3748
20.	v,m³/kg						0.00202	0.00216	0.00234	0.00254
	h,kJ/kg						725.59	854.88	989.63	1129.26
	s,kJ/(kg·K)						1.6318	1.8548	2.0722	2.2837

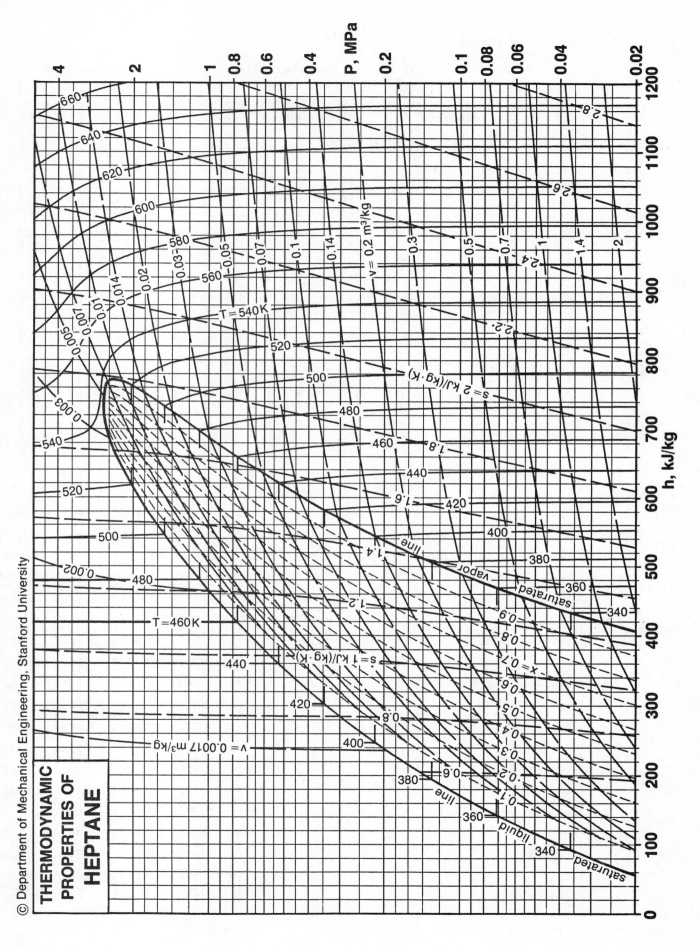

THERMODYNAMIC PROPERTIES OF HEPTANE

© Department of Mechanical Engineering, Stanford University

PROPERTIES OF SATURATED HEXANE

T	P	volume, m³/kg		enthalpy, kJ/kg			entropy, kJ/(kg·K)		
K	MPa	v_f	v_g	h_f	h_{fg}	h_g	s_f	s_{fg}	s_g
250	0.001520	0.001407	15.83	0.0	408.29	408.29	0.0	1.6331	1.6331
260	0.002891	0.001428	8.646	27.31	395.66	422.97	0.1071	1.5218	1.6289
270	0.005159	0.001450	5.020	52.78	385.21	437.99	0.2033	1.4267	1.6300
280	0.008728	0.001473	3.068	77.20	376.13	453.33	0.2921	1.3433	1.6354
290	0.01411	0.001496	1.959	101.10	367.87	468.97	0.3759	1.2685	1.6444
300	0.02192	0.001520	1.298	124.78	360.12	484.90	0.4561	1.2005	1.6566
310	0.03289	0.001545	0.8882	148.40	352.71	501.11	0.5335	1.1378	1.6713
320	0.04789	0.001571	0.6251	172.05	345.51	517.56	0.6086	1.0797	1.6883
330	0.06787	0.001597	0.4509	195.78	338.45	534.23	0.6815	1.0256	1.7071
340	0.09392	0.001625	0.3322	219.62	331.49	551.11	0.7525	0.9750	1.7275
342.44	0.101325	0.001632	0.3093	225.46	329.79	555.25	0.7696	0.9631	1.7327
350	0.1273	0.001653	0.2494	243.65	324.52	568.17	0.8220	0.9272	1.7492
360	0.1692	0.001683	0.1903	267.95	317.43	585.38	0.8903	0.8817	1.7720
370	0.2213	0.001714	0.1472	292.61	310.10	602.71	0.9576	0.8381	1.7957
380	0.2850	0.001746	0.1153	317.75	302.37	620.12	1.0243	0.7958	1.8201
390	0.3619	0.001781	0.09133	343.45	294.14	637.59	1.0907	0.7542	1.8449
400	0.4540	0.001817	0.07299	369.77	285.29	655.06	1.1569	0.7133	1.8702
410	0.5630	0.001857	0.05880	396.72	275.77	672.49	1.2230	0.6726	1.8956
420	0.6909	0.001900	0.04767	424.32	265.49	689.81	1.2889	0.6321	1.9210
430	0.8400	0.001948	0.03883	452.56	254.37	706.93	1.3547	0.5916	1.9463
440	1.013	0.002004	0.03173	481.50	242.25	723.75	1.4204	0.5506	1.9710
450	1.211	0.002070	0.02595	511.32	228.78	740.10	1.4865	0.5084	1.9949
460	1.439	0.002152	0.02119	542.42	213.30	755.72	1.5538	0.4637	2.0175
470	1.700	0.002261	0.01719	575.57	194.67	770.24	1.6239	0.4142	2.0381
480	1.995	0.002418	0.01379	612.02	170.96	782.98	1.6992	0.3561	2.0553
490	2.326	0.002684	0.01080	653.94	138.71	792.65	1.7838	0.2831	2.0669
500	2.690	0.003311	0.007969	707.11	88.16	795.27	1.8890	0.1764	2.0654
506.13	2.927	0.005218	0.005218	772.01	0.0	772.01	2.0160	0.0	2.0160

PROPERTIES OF GASEOUS HEXANE

P,MPa (T_{sat},K)		sat	400	440	480	520	560	600	640	680
0.101325 (342.4)	v,m³/kg	0.3093	0.3701	0.4107	0.4505	0.4900	0.5291	0.5680	0.6067	0.6453
	h,kJ/kg	555.25	671.13	759.34	853.87	954.60	1061.32	1173.79	1291.71	1414.79
	s,kJ/(kg·K)	1.7327	2.0450	2.2551	2.4606	2.6621	2.8597	3.0537	3.2439	3.4304
0.20 (366.2)	v,m³/kg	0.1622	0.1818	0.2038	0.2249	0.2456	0.2659	0.2860	0.3059	0.3258
	h,kJ/kg	596.04	666.98	756.17	851.38	952.59	1059.67	1172.41	1290.54	1413.79
	s,kJ/(kg·K)	1.7865	1.9717	2.1842	2.3912	2.5936	2.7919	2.9863	3.1769	3.3636
0.40 (394.3)	v,m³/kg	0.08277	0.08468	0.09733	0.1090	0.1201	0.1308	0.1412	0.1515	0.1617
	h,kJ/kg	645.18	657.78	749.40	846.15	948.42	1056.26	1169.57	1288.15	1411.74
	s,kJ/(kg·K)	1.8559	1.8876	2.1058	2.3162	2.5207	2.7205	2.9159	3.1072	3.2944
0.70 (420.7)	v,m³/kg	0.04703		0.05128	0.05910	0.06617	0.07281	0.07917	0.08535	0.09139
	h,kJ/kg	690.93		738.03	837.73	941.86	1050.98	1165.22	1284.50	1408.64
	s,kJ/(kg·K)	1.9227		2.0322	2.2490	2.4573	2.6594	2.8564	3.0488	3.2369
1.0 (439.3)	v,m³/kg	0.03217		0.03230	0.03894	0.04452	0.04958	0.05433	0.05887	0.06327
	h,kJ/kg	722.62		724.40	828.45	934.89	1045.48	1160.75	1280.78	1405.50
	s,kJ/(kg·K)	1.9694		1.9734	2.1997	2.4127	2.6175	2.8163	3.0099	3.1989
2.0 (480.2)	v,m³/kg	0.01374			0.01880	0.02230	0.02528	0.02796	0.03047	
	h,kJ/kg	783.18			907.21	1025.18	1144.83	1267.83	1394.71	
	s,kJ/(kg·K)	2.0556			2.3040	2.5226	2.7289	2.9273	3.1196	
4.0	v,m³/kg				0.00347	0.00807	0.01061	0.01251	0.01413	
	h,kJ/kg				768.76	968.38	1107.08	1239.23	1371.81	
	s,kJ/(kg·K)				2.0011	2.3723	2.6117	2.8249	3.0258	
7.0	v,m³/kg				0.00249	0.00336	0.00476	0.00615	0.00735	
	h,kJ/kg				729.35	883.40	1043.14	1192.95	1336.27	
	s,kJ/(kg·K)				1.9093	2.1945	2.4701	2.7119	2.9292	
10.	v,m³/kg				0.00229	0.00271	0.00336	0.00416	0.00498	
	h,kJ/kg				720.54	858.94	1007.27	1157.55	1305.96	
	s,kJ/(kg·K)				1.8787	2.1350	2.3907	2.6332	2.8582	

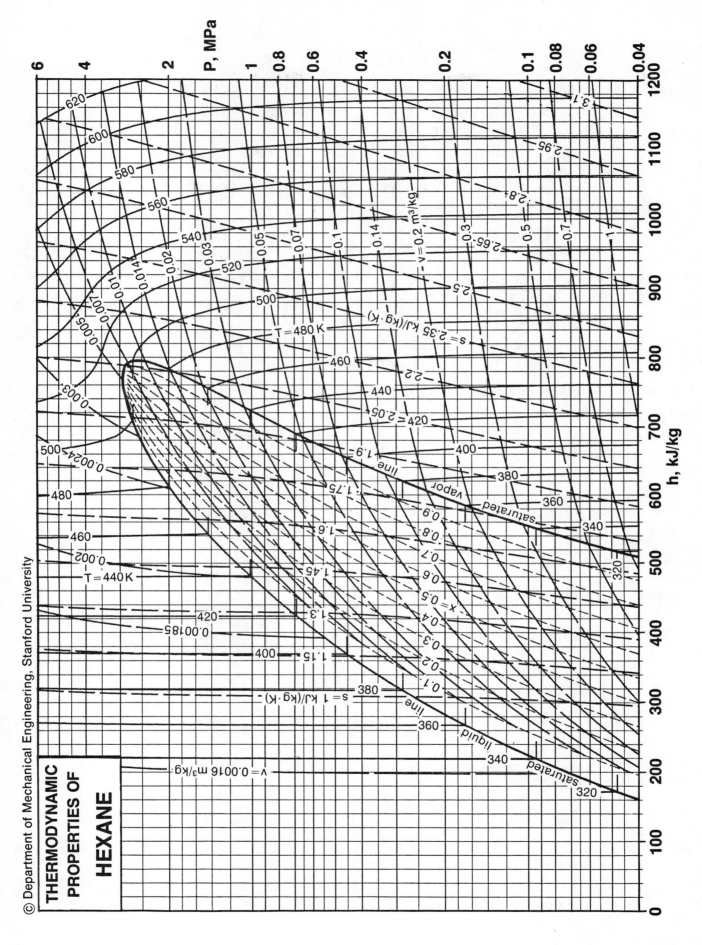

THERMODYNAMIC
PROPERTIES OF
HEXANE

© Department of Mechanical Engineering, Stanford University

39

PROPERTIES OF SATURATED HYDROGEN (PARA)

T K	P MPa	volume, m³/kg v_f	v_g	enthalpy, kJ/kg h_f	h_{fg}	h_g	entropy, kJ/(kg·K) s_f	s_{fg}	s_g
13.80	0.007042	0.012983	7.952	0.0	447.2	447.2	0.0	32.408	32.408
14	0.007896	0.013011	7.185	1.2	447.9	449.1	0.082	31.994	32.076
15	0.01343	0.013158	4.491	7.4	450.6	458.0	0.508	30.042	30.550
16	0.02153	0.013314	2.960	14.4	452.2	466.6	0.950	28.264	29.214
17	0.03284	0.013481	2.038	21.9	452.7	474.6	1.400	26.628	28.028
18	0.04807	0.013660	1.454	30.1	452.0	482.1	1.856	25.110	26.966
19	0.06796	0.013854	1.068	38.9	450.0	488.9	2.316	23.686	26.002
20	0.09326	0.014065	0.8045	48.3	446.8	495.1	2.781	22.337	25.118
20.28	0.101325	0.014127	0.7466	51.0	445.6	496.6	2.910	21.975	24.885
21	0.1247	0.014296	0.6185	58.4	442.0	500.4	3.251	21.047	24.298
22	0.1632	0.014550	0.4837	69.2	435.7	504.9	3.728	19.801	23.529
23	0.2094	0.014831	0.3837	80.8	427.5	508.3	4.214	18.586	22.800
24	0.2642	0.015147	0.3081	93.3	417.4	510.7	4.709	17.391	22.100
25	0.3284	0.015503	0.2496	106.7	405.1	511.8	5.216	16.202	21.418
26	0.4029	0.015911	0.2038	121.2	390.2	511.4	5.740	15.006	20.746
27	0.4885	0.016386	0.1672	137.0	372.3	509.3	6.284	13.787	20.071
28	0.5861	0.016951	0.1374	154.4	350.7	505.1	6.855	12.525	19.380
29	0.6967	0.017644	0.1129	173.7	324.4	498.1	7.467	11.186	18.653
30	0.8214	0.018532	0.09207	195.8	291.6	487.4	8.140	9.719	17.859
31	0.9615	0.019760	0.07387	222.2	248.6	470.8	8.916	8.020	16.936
32.94	1.284	0.031888	0.03189	346.5	0.0	346.5	12.536	0.0	12.536

PROPERTIES OF GASEOUS HYDROGEN (PARA)

P,MPa (T_{sat},K)		sat	100	200	300	400	600	800	1200	1500
0.101325 (20.28)	v,m³/kg	0.7466	4.070	8.147	12.22	16.29	24.43	32.57	48.85	61.06
	h,kJ/kg	496.6	1399.8	2971.3	4509.6	5976.6	8880.9	11806.0	17833.5	22547.2
	s,kJ/(kg·K)	24.885	42.689	53.475	59.729	63.952	69.840	74.046	80.146	83.650
0.20 (22.81)	v,m³/kg	0.4006	2.061	4.130	6.194	8.257	12.38	16.51	24.75	30.94
	h,kJ/kg	507.7	1398.3	2971.3	4510.1	5977.3	8881.7	11806.9	17834.3	22548.0
	s,kJ/(kg·K)	22.936	39.869	50.667	56.924	61.147	67.035	71.242	77.342	80.846
0.50 (27.12)	v,m³/kg	0.1631	0.8241	1.656	2.482	3.307	4.957	6.607	9.906	12.38
	h,kJ/kg	508.9	1393.6	2971.5	4511.6	5979.4	8884.2	11809.5	17836.9	22550.6
	s,kJ/(kg·K)	19.986	36.046	46.880	53.143	57.367	63.257	67.463	73.563	77.067
1.0 (31.26)	v,m³/kg	0.06946	0.4119	0.8308	1.245	1.658	2.483	3.307	4.957	6.194
	h,kJ/kg	465.1	1386.0	2971.7	4514.1	5982.8	8888.4	11813.8	17841.3	22554.9
	s,kJ/(kg·K)	16.664	33.114	44.008	50.280	54.507	60.398	64.605	70.705	74.209
2.0	v,m³/kg		0.2059	0.4184	0.6261	0.8328	1.245	1.658	2.482	3.101
	h,kJ/kg		1371.4	2972.3	4519.1	5989.7	8896.7	11822.6	17850.1	22563.5
	s,kJ/(kg·K)		30.114	41.122	47.413	51.645	57.539	61.747	67.847	71.351
4.0	v,m³/kg		0.1034	0.2123	0.3168	0.4204	0.6268	0.8329	1.245	1.554
	h,kJ/kg		1345.2	2974.1	4529.3	6003.5	8913.3	11840.0	17867.6	22580.8
	s,kJ/(kg·K)		26.993	38.213	44.538	48.781	54.681	58.890	64.990	68.494
7.0	v,m³/kg		0.06019	0.1240	0.1843	0.2436	0.3616	0.4793	0.7146	0.8911
	h,kJ/kg		1313.9	2978.3	4544.9	6024.2	8938.1	11866.0	17893.8	22606.6
	s,kJ/(kg·K)		24.349	35.834	42.207	46.465	52.374	56.584	62.685	66.188
10.	v,m³/kg		0.04345	0.08877	0.1312	0.1729	0.2556	0.3379	0.5025	0.6260
	h,kJ/kg		1292.9	2984.2	4561.0	6045.1	8962.9	11892.0	17920.0	22632.3
	s,kJ/(kg·K)		22.615	34.299	40.715	44.987	50.904	55.116	61.217	64.720
20.	v,m³/kg		0.02528	0.04795	0.06945	0.09043	0.1318	0.1729	0.2551	0.3167
	h,kJ/kg		1281.7	3015.9	4617.9	6115.4	9045.0	11978.2	18007.0	22718.0
	s,kJ/(kg·K)		19.291	31.274	37.794	42.105	48.047	52.265	58.367	61.869
50.	v,m³/kg		0.01551	0.02401	0.03257	0.04097	0.05751	0.07391	0.1066	0.1311
	h,kJ/kg		1456.2	3185.6	4816.6	6336.4	9290.7	12233.9	18265.8	22973.9
	s,kJ/(kg·K)		15.362	27.268	33.906	38.282	44.275	48.508	54.614	58.113
100.	v,m³/kg		0.01192	0.01608	0.02031	0.02448	0.03272	0.04086	0.05708	0.06923
	h,kJ/kg		1850.1	3553.2	5192.3	6725.3	9700.6	12655.0	18692.0	23396.7
	s,kJ/(kg·K)		12.618	24.314	30.983	35.397	41.433	45.682	51.794	55.291

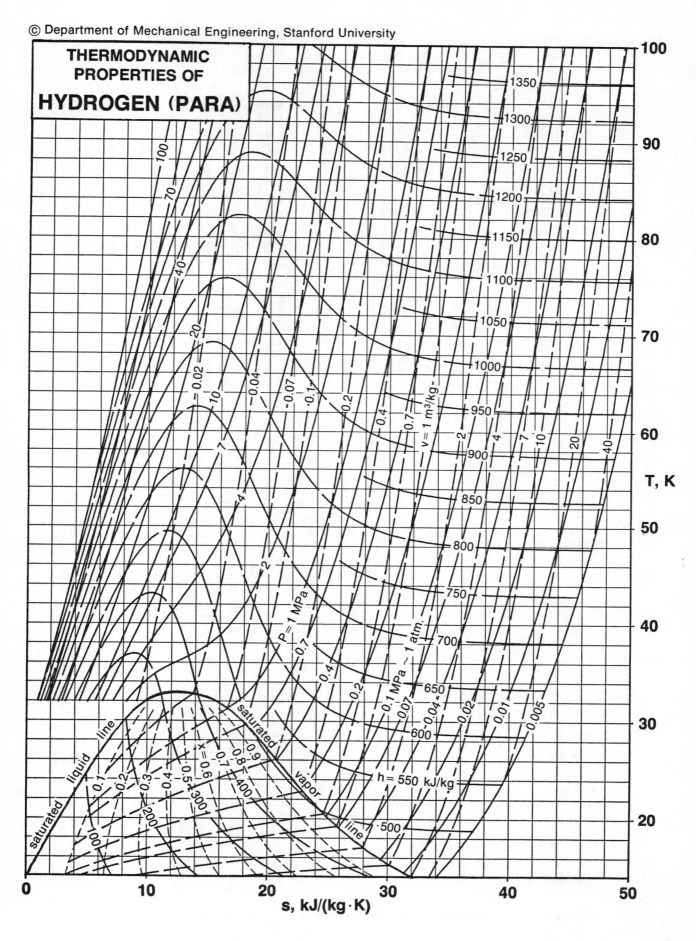

THERMODYNAMIC
PROPERTIES OF
HYDROGEN (PARA)

s, kJ/(kg·K)

T, K

PROPERTIES OF SATURATED ISOBUTANE

T K	P MPa	volume, m³/kg		enthalpy, kJ/kg			entropy, kJ/(kg·K)		
		v_f	v_g	h_f	h_{fg}	h_g	s_f	s_{fg}	s_g
200	0.003750	0.001524	7.603	0.0	421.70	421.70	0.0	2.1085	2.1085
210	0.007527	0.001548	3.968	22.40	411.50	433.90	0.1093	1.9595	2.0688
220	0.01400	0.001571	2.227	44.26	402.11	446.37	0.2109	1.8278	2.0387
230	0.02442	0.001596	1.328	65.88	393.20	459.08	0.3069	1.7096	2.0165
240	0.04034	0.001622	0.8337	87.47	384.55	472.02	0.3987	1.6023	2.0010
250	0.06360	0.001648	0.5463	109.18	375.98	485.16	0.4872	1.5039	1.9911
260	0.09632	0.001677	0.3713	131.14	367.33	498.47	0.5731	1.4128	1.9859
261.28	0.101325	0.001681	0.3542	133.99	366.20	500.19	0.5840	1.4015	1.9855
270	0.1409	0.001707	0.2604	153.44	358.46	511.90	0.6570	1.3276	1.9846
280	0.1999	0.001739	0.1875	176.17	349.27	525.44	0.7393	1.2474	1.9867
290	0.2762	0.001774	0.1381	199.41	339.61	539.02	0.8203	1.1711	1.9914
300	0.3727	0.001813	0.1037	223.26	329.35	552.61	0.9006	1.0979	1.9985
310	0.4927	0.001855	0.07916	247.81	318.33	566.14	0.9804	1.0269	2.0073
320	0.6395	0.001904	0.06125	273.18	306.37	579.55	1.0600	0.9575	2.0175
330	0.8166	0.001959	0.04792	299.47	293.27	592.74	1.1399	0.8887	2.0286
340	1.027	0.002025	0.03781	326.87	278.72	605.59	1.2204	0.8198	2.0402
350	1.276	0.002103	0.03002	355.58	262.36	617.94	1.3022	0.7496	2.0518
360	1.566	0.002202	0.02390	385.97	243.59	629.56	1.3860	0.6766	2.0626
370	1.901	0.002330	0.01902	418.58	221.51	640.09	1.4732	0.5987	2.0719
380	2.284	0.002508	0.01504	454.31	194.63	648.94	1.5660	0.5122	2.0782
390	2.718	0.002780	0.01171	494.74	160.22	654.96	1.6681	0.4108	2.0789
400	3.204	0.003289	0.008751	543.73	111.39	655.12	1.7883	0.2785	2.0668
409.07	3.685	0.005141	0.005141	623.01	0.0	623.01	1.9793	0.0	1.9793

PROPERTIES OF GASEOUS ISOBUTANE

P,MPa (T_sat,K)		sat	300	340	380	T,K 420	460	500	540	580
0.101325 (261.3)	v,m³/kg	0.3542	0.4129	0.4720	0.5303	0.5880	0.6454	0.7026	0.7597	0.8166
	h,kJ/kg	500.19	562.86	634.57	713.55	799.68	892.71	992.32	1098.16	1209.89
	s,kJ/(kg·K)	1.9855	2.2089	2.4331	2.6525	2.8679	3.0793	3.2869	3.4905	3.6900
0.20 (280.0)	v,m³/kg	0.1874	0.2036	0.2350	0.2655	0.2954	0.3249	0.3543	0.3835	0.4125
	h,kJ/kg	525.46	559.30	631.95	711.52	798.05	891.37	991.19	1097.20	1209.06
	s,kJ/(kg·K)	1.9867	2.1034	2.3305	2.5516	2.7679	2.9800	3.1880	3.3919	3.5917
0.40 (302.5)	v,m³/kg	0.09689		0.1132	0.1294	0.1451	0.1604	0.1754	0.1903	0.2051
	h,kJ/kg	555.95		626.38	707.28	794.69	888.62	988.89	1095.24	1207.37
	s,kJ/(kg·K)	2.0005		2.2198	2.4446	2.6632	2.8767	3.0856	3.2902	3.4904
0.70 (323.6)	v,m³/kg	0.05597		0.06060	0.07098	0.08060	0.08981	0.09876	0.1075	0.1162
	h,kJ/kg	584.36		617.21	700.55	789.45	884.38	985.38	1092.27	1204.81
	s,kJ/(kg·K)	2.0214		2.1204	2.3520	2.5743	2.7901	3.0006	3.2062	3.4072
1.0 (338.8)	v,m³/kg	0.03890		0.03918	0.04745	0.05475	0.06156	0.06808	0.07441	0.08062
	h,kJ/kg	604.05		606.65	693.28	783.95	880.01	981.78	1089.24	1202.22
	s,kJ/(kg·K)	2.0388		2.0464	2.2872	2.5140	2.7324	2.9444	3.1511	3.3529
2.0 (372.7)	v,m³/kg	0.01786			0.01907	0.02428	0.02848	0.03225	0.03578	0.03915
	h,kJ/kg	642.70			662.11	763.09	864.25	969.18	1078.83	1193.41
	s,kJ/(kg·K)	2.0740			2.1256	2.3784	2.6084	2.8270	3.0379	3.2426
4.0	v,m³/kg					0.00709	0.01160	0.01426	0.01648	0.01848
	h,kJ/kg					684.71	824.61	940.64	1056.42	1175.03
	s,kJ/(kg·K)					2.1237	2.4432	2.6851	2.9078	3.1197
7.0	v,m³/kg					0.00283	0.00456	0.00671	0.00839	0.00980
	h,kJ/kg					575.94	742.33	890.12	1020.08	1146.62
	s,kJ/(kg·K)					1.8389	2.2171	2.5256	2.7758	3.0019
10.	v,m³/kg					0.00251	0.00326	0.00436	0.00553	0.00659
	h,kJ/kg					560.78	702.81	848.49	986.96	1120.35
	s,kJ/(kg·K)					1.7839	2.1067	2.4105	2.6770	2.9153
20.	v,m³/kg					0.00215	0.00242	0.00277	0.00318	0.00362
	h,kJ/kg					548.46	670.39	799.93	933.75	1069.65
	s,kJ/(kg·K)					1.7000	1.9772	2.2471	2.5045	2.7473

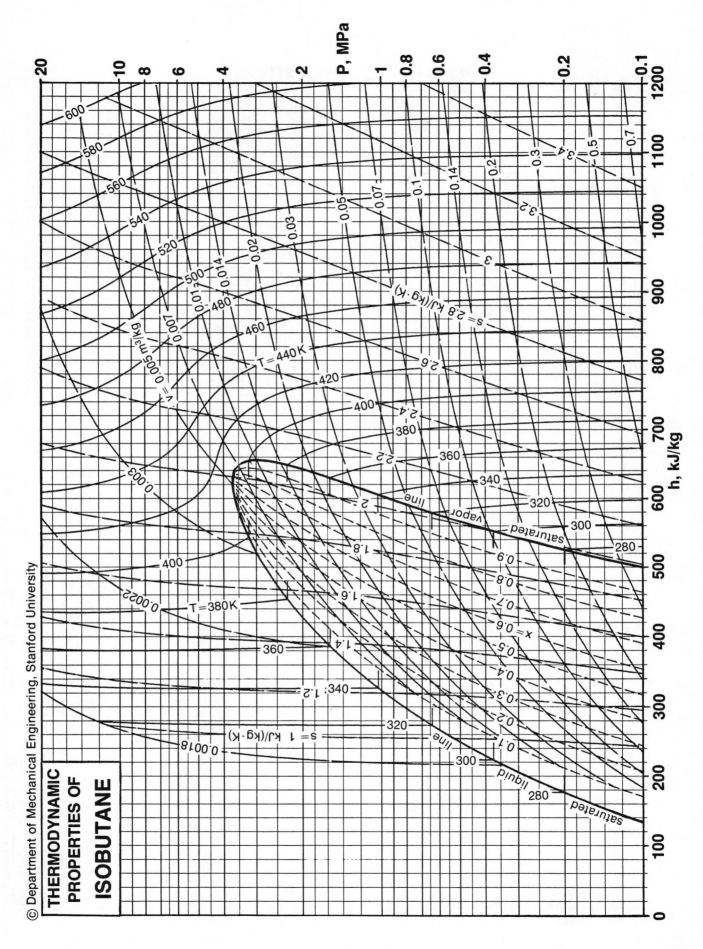

© Department of Mechanical Engineering, Stanford University

THERMODYNAMIC PROPERTIES OF ISOBUTANE

43

PROPERTIES OF SATURATED ISOPENTANE

T K	P MPa	volume, m³/kg v_f	volume, m³/kg v_g	enthalpy, kJ/kg h_f	enthalpy, kJ/kg h_{fg}	enthalpy, kJ/kg h_g	entropy, kJ/(kg·K) s_f	entropy, kJ/(kg·K) s_{fg}	entropy, kJ/(kg·K) s_g
200	0.0003494	0.001398	65.95	0.0	410.41	410.41	0.0	2.0521	2.0521
210	0.0008130	0.001419	29.74	16.05	406.32	422.37	0.0783	1.9348	2.0131
220	0.001738	0.001440	14.56	33.60	401.18	434.78	0.1599	1.8235	1.9834
230	0.003447	0.001462	7.662	52.36	395.26	447.62	0.2432	1.7186	1.9618
240	0.006404	0.001484	4.294	72.06	388.81	460.87	0.3271	1.6200	1.9471
250	0.01123	0.001507	2.543	92.52	381.98	474.50	0.4105	1.5280	1.9385
260	0.01873	0.001530	1.579	113.57	374.91	488.48	0.4931	1.4419	1.9350
270	0.02986	0.001554	1.023	135.15	367.64	502.79	0.5744	1.3617	1.9361
280	0.04580	0.001578	0.6869	157.16	360.24	517.40	0.6544	1.2865	1.9409
290	0.06788	0.001604	0.4761	179.60	352.67	532.27	0.7330	1.2161	1.9491
300	0.09759	0.001630	0.3392	202.46	344.91	547.37	0.8103	1.1497	1.9600
301.08	0.101325	0.001633	0.3275	204.96	344.06	549.02	0.8186	1.1428	1.9614
310	0.1366	0.001657	0.2475	225.75	336.93	562.68	0.8865	1.0868	1.9733
320	0.1866	0.001686	0.1844	249.50	328.66	578.16	0.9616	1.0271	1.9887
330	0.2497	0.001716	0.1399	273.74	320.05	593.79	1.0359	0.9698	2.0057
340	0.3277	0.001747	0.1078	298.52	311.00	609.52	1.1094	0.9147	2.0241
350	0.4229	0.001781	0.08423	323.86	301.46	625.32	1.1824	0.8613	2.0437
360	0.5374	0.001818	0.06658	349.80	291.35	641.15	1.2549	0.8093	2.0642
370	0.6736	0.001858	0.05314	376.39	280.55	656.94	1.3270	0.7583	2.0853
380	0.8340	0.001903	0.04275	403.66	268.97	672.63	1.3990	0.7078	2.1068
390	1.021	0.001953	0.03459	431.69	256.45	688.14	1.4708	0.6576	2.1284
400	1.238	0.002010	0.02810	460.61	242.71	703.32	1.5430	0.6067	2.1497
410	1.487	0.002078	0.02286	490.61	227.40	718.01	1.6158	0.5546	2.1704
420	1.773	0.002162	0.01856	522.02	209.90	731.92	1.6900	0.4997	2.1897
430	2.098	0.002270	0.01495	555.41	189.15	744.56	1.7669	0.4398	2.2067
440	2.468	0.002423	0.01185	591.83	163.17	755.00	1.8486	0.3708	2.2194
450	2.887	0.002676	0.009026	633.77	127.11	760.88	1.9404	0.2825	2.2229
460.98	3.409	0.004622	0.004622	728.67	0.0	728.67	2.1444	0.0	2.1444

PROPERTIES OF GASEOUS ISOPENTANE

P,MPa (T_{sat},K)		sat	300	340	380	420	460	500	540	580
0.050 (282.2)	v,m³/kg	0.6331	0.6767	0.7728	0.8676	0.9616	1.055	1.148	1.241	1.334
	h,kJ/kg	520.58	549.88	620.72	698.67	783.61	875.33	973.61	1078.20	1188.83
	s,kJ/(kg·K)	1.9424	2.0431	2.2645	2.4811	2.6935	2.9020	3.1067	3.3079	3.5055
0.101325 (301.1)	v,m³/kg	0.3275		0.3757	0.4238	0.4711	0.5179	0.5643	0.6105	0.6566
	h,kJ/kg	549.02		618.78	697.21	782.47	874.41	972.86	1077.57	1188.29
	s,kJ/(kg·K)	1.9614		2.1791	2.3970	2.6101	2.8191	3.0243	3.2257	3.4234
0.20 (322.3)	v,m³/kg	0.1727		0.1846	0.2104	0.2353	0.2597	0.2837	0.3075	0.3311
	h,kJ/kg	581.77		614.89	694.33	780.23	872.63	971.40	1076.35	1187.25
	s,kJ/(kg·K)	1.9925		2.0925	2.3132	2.5280	2.7381	2.9439	3.1457	3.3438
0.50 (356.9)	v,m³/kg	0.07149			0.07852	0.08983	0.1005	0.1107	0.1207	0.1305
	h,kJ/kg	636.28			684.88	773.11	867.02	966.84	1072.56	1184.05
	s,kJ/(kg·K)	2.0578			2.1897	2.4104	2.6238	2.8318	3.0352	3.2343
1.0 (388.9)	v,m³/kg	0.03537				0.04094	0.04722	0.05296	0.05839	0.06363
	h,kJ/kg	686.51				759.73	856.92	958.84	1066.01	1178.57
	s,kJ/(kg·K)	2.1261				2.3072	2.5282	2.7406	2.9467	3.1477
2.0 (427.1)	v,m³/kg	0.01593					0.02006	0.02386	0.02715	0.03016
	h,kJ/kg	741.08					832.42	940.82	1051.84	1166.97
	s,kJ/(kg·K)	2.2022					2.4083	2.6342	2.8478	3.0534
5.0	v,m³/kg							0.00526	0.00813	0.01006
	h,kJ/kg							847.92	996.83	1126.56
	s,kJ/(kg·K)							2.3764	2.6634	2.8952
10.	v,m³/kg							0.00265	0.00339	0.00428
	h,kJ/kg							771.71	917.46	1061.98
	s,kJ/(kg·K)							2.1909	2.4713	2.7295
20.	v,m³/kg							0.00221	0.00245	0.00274
	h,kJ/kg							754.34	883.40	1018.40
	s,kJ/(kg·K)							2.1087	2.3569	2.5980

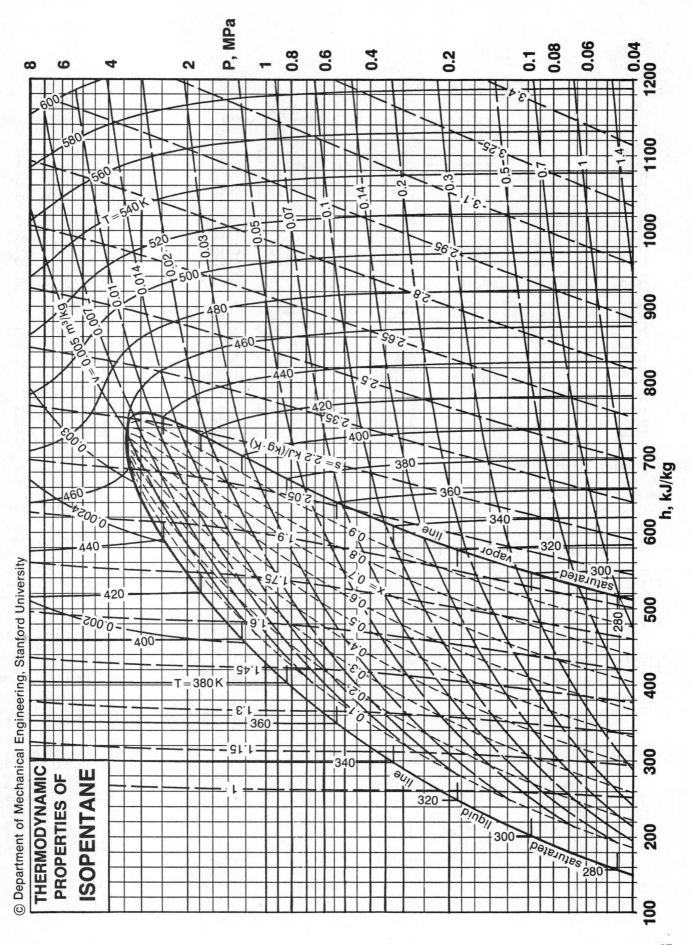

THERMODYNAMIC PROPERTIES OF ISOPENTANE

© Department of Mechanical Engineering, Stanford University

P, MPa

h, kJ/kg

PROPERTIES OF SATURATED LITHIUM

T	P	volume, m³/kg		enthalpy, kJ/kg			entropy, kJ/(kg·K)		
K	MPa	v_f	v_g	h_f	h_{fg}	h_g	s_f	s_{fg}	s_g
1200	0.002029	0.002268	675.3	0.0	20830.7	20830.7	0.0	17.359	17.359
1240	0.003315	0.002290	424.4	111.7	20749.2	20860.9	0.092	16.733	16.825
1280	0.005258	0.002312	274.3	245.0	20637.8	20882.8	0.197	16.124	16.321
1320	0.008115	0.002334	181.9	396.7	20500.2	20896.9	0.314	15.530	15.844
1360	0.01221	0.002357	123.6	563.3	20341.4	20904.7	0.438	14.957	15.395
1400	0.01794	0.002379	85.85	741.3	20166.6	20907.9	0.567	14.405	14.972
1440	0.02581	0.002403	60.90	926.7	19982.5	20909.2	0.698	13.877	14.575
1480	0.03638	0.002426	44.06	1116.1	19795.8	20911.9	0.827	13.376	14.203
1520	0.05034	0.002450	32.47	1306.4	19613.0	20919.4	0.954	12.904	13.858
1560	0.06845	0.002474	24.35	1495.8	19439.6	20935.4	1.077	12.462	13.539
1600	0.09158	0.002499	18.57	1683.9	19279.0	20962.9	1.196	12.050	13.246
1614.40	0.101325	0.002508	16.91	1751.6	19224.5	20976.1	1.238	11.909	13.147
1640	0.1207	0.002524	14.38	1872.3	19131.8	21004.1	1.313	11.665	12.978
1680	0.1569	0.002549	11.30	2063.8	18995.7	21059.5	1.428	11.307	12.735
1720	0.2012	0.002574	8.994	2263.1	18864.9	21128.0	1.545	10.968	12.513
1760	0.2549	0.002600	7.245	2475.7	18731.0	21206.7	1.667	10.643	12.310
1800	0.3192	0.002627	5.899	2706.5	18584.3	21290.8	1.797	10.324	12.121
1840	0.3954	0.002653	4.849	2958.9	18415.2	21374.1	1.935	10.008	11.943
1880	0.4848	0.002680	4.018	3231.3	18217.9	21449.2	2.082	9.690	11.772
1920	0.5889	0.002708	3.356	3516.4	17991.4	21507.8	2.231	9.371	11.602
1960	0.7088	0.002736	2.825	3793.7	17748.7	21542.4	2.374	9.056	11.430
2000	0.8460	0.002764	2.400	4025.2	17524.2	21549.4	2.491	8.762	11.253
2040	1.002	0.002793	2.064	4155.2	17379.9	21535.1	2.555	8.520	11.075

PROPERTIES OF GASEOUS LITHIUM

P,MPa (T_{sat},K)		sat	1500	1600	1700	1800	1900	2000	2100	2200
0.010 (1340.)	v,m³/kg	149.3	175.3	188.9	201.8	214.4	226.7	239.0	251.1	263.2
	h,kJ/kg	20901.5	22132.2	22589.0	22970.3	23316.2	23644.1	23962.2	24274.8	24584.4
	s,kJ/(kg·K)	15.615	16.489	16.784	17.016	17.213	17.391	17.554	17.707	17.851
0.020 (1412.)	v,m³/kg	77.49	85.53	93.14	100.0	106.6	112.9	119.2	125.3	131.4
	h,kJ/kg	20908.3	21756.6	22371.9	22833.6	23224.7	23579.8	23915.2	24239.4	24557.0
	s,kJ/(kg·K)	14.853	15.437	15.835	16.116	16.339	16.531	16.703	16.862	17.009
0.050 (1519.)	v,m³/kg	32.68		35.76	39.00	41.92	44.65	47.28	49.84	52.36
	h,kJ/kg	20919.1		21745.1	22438.8	22959.1	23392.2	23777.5	24135.2	24475.9
	s,kJ/(kg·K)	13.865		14.395	14.817	15.114	15.349	15.546	15.721	15.880
0.101325 (1614.)	v,m³/kg	16.91			18.50	20.14	21.62	23.02	24.36	25.66
	h,kJ/kg	20976.1			21826.3	22538.7	23090.4	23553.1	23963.3	24341.1
	s,kJ/(kg·K)	13.147			13.660	14.068	14.367	14.604	14.805	14.980
0.20 (1719.)	v,m³/kg	9.042				9.771	10.61	11.38	12.12	12.82
	h,kJ/kg	21126.3				21866.0	22582.4	23161.9	23656.0	24095.2
	s,kJ/(kg·K)	12.518				12.939	13.327	13.624	13.865	14.070
0.40 (1842.)	v,m³/kg	4.797					5.041	5.455	5.855	6.239
	h,kJ/kg	21378.6					21833.9	22527.2	23124.4	23649.9
	s,kJ/(kg·K)	11.934					12.177	12.533	12.825	13.069
0.70 (1957.)	v,m³/kg	2.858						2.967	3.208	3.439
	h,kJ/kg	21540.9						21856.5	22519.6	23108.1
	s,kJ/(kg·K)	11.442						11.601	11.925	12.199
1.0 (2040.)	v,m³/kg	2.067							2.186	2.357
	h,kJ/kg	21535.3							22027.8	22691.9
	s,kJ/(kg·K)	11.077							11.315	11.624

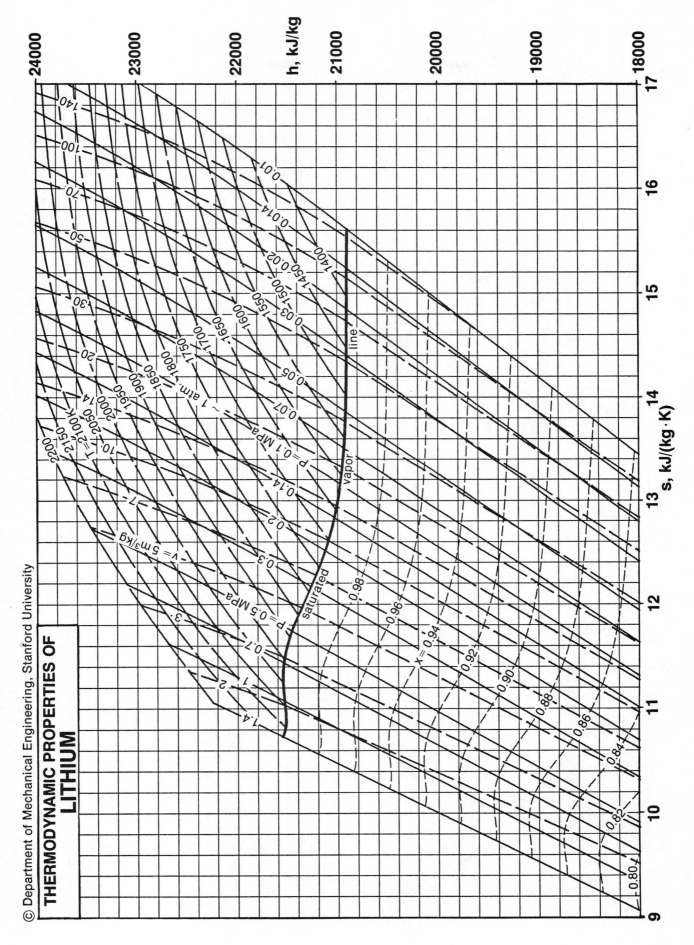

© Department of Mechanical Engineering, Stanford University

THERMODYNAMIC PROPERTIES OF LITHIUM

h, kJ/kg

s, kJ/(kg·K)

47

PROPERTIES OF SATURATED MERCURY

T K	P MPa	volume, m³/kg v_f	v_g	enthalpy, kJ/kg h_f	h_{fg}	h_g	entropy, kJ/(kg·K) s_f	s_{fg}	s_g
400	0.0001397	0.0000752	118.7	0.0	301.91	301.91	0.0	0.7548	0.7548
425	0.0004071	0.0000756	43.27	3.43	301.07	304.50	0.0083	0.7084	0.7167
450	0.001051	0.0000759	17.75	6.79	300.30	307.09	0.0160	0.6673	0.6833
475	0.002450	0.0000762	8.033	10.08	299.60	309.68	0.0231	0.6308	0.6539
500	0.005241	0.0000766	3.953	13.34	298.92	312.26	0.0298	0.5978	0.6276
525	0.01041	0.0000769	2.089	16.56	298.28	314.84	0.0361	0.5681	0.6042
550	0.01941	0.0000773	1.174	19.77	297.64	317.41	0.0421	0.5411	0.5832
575	0.03424	0.0000777	0.6952	22.97	297.01	319.98	0.0478	0.5165	0.5643
600	0.05757	0.0000780	0.4312	26.19	296.34	322.53	0.0532	0.4939	0.5471
625	0.09278	0.0000784	0.2785	29.42	295.64	325.06	0.0585	0.4730	0.5315
629.85	0.101325	0.0000785	0.2569	30.06	295.49	325.55	0.0595	0.4692	0.5287
650	0.1440	0.0000788	0.1864	32.69	294.88	327.57	0.0636	0.4537	0.5173
675	0.2163	0.0000792	0.1287	36.01	294.05	330.06	0.0686	0.4357	0.5043
700	0.3154	0.0000796	0.09139	39.38	293.14	332.52	0.0735	0.4188	0.4923
725	0.4479	0.0000800	0.06653	42.81	292.13	334.94	0.0783	0.4029	0.4812
750	0.6212	0.0000804	0.04952	46.30	291.02	337.32	0.0830	0.3881	0.4711
775	0.8431	0.0000808	0.03760	49.88	289.78	339.66	0.0877	0.3739	0.4616
800	1.122	0.0000812	0.02907	53.52	288.42	341.94	0.0923	0.3605	0.4528
825	1.468	0.0000816	0.02284	57.25	286.93	344.18	0.0968	0.3478	0.4446
850	1.890	0.0000821	0.01822	61.06	285.30	346.36	0.1014	0.3356	0.4370
875	2.397	0.0000825	0.01472	64.95	283.52	348.47	0.1058	0.3240	0.4298
900	2.999	0.0000830	0.01205	68.92	281.61	350.53	0.1102	0.3129	0.4231
925	3.708	0.0000834	0.009967	72.97	279.55	352.52	0.1146	0.3022	0.4168
950	4.532	0.0000839	0.008330	77.10	277.34	354.44	0.1189	0.2920	0.4109
975	5.481	0.0000843	0.007029	81.31	274.98	356.29	0.1232	0.2821	0.4053
1000	6.565	0.0000848	0.005982	85.59	272.48	358.07	0.1275	0.2725	0.4000
1025	7.794	0.0000853	0.005131	89.94	269.84	359.78	0.1317	0.2632	0.3949
1050	9.177	0.0000858	0.004434	94.35	267.06	361.41	0.1358	0.2543	0.3901
1075	10.72	0.0000863	0.003859	98.83	264.14	362.97	0.1399	0.2457	0.3856
1100	12.44	0.0000868	0.003379	103.36	261.10	364.46	0.1439	0.2374	0.3813
1125	14.33	0.0000873	0.002976	107.95	257.93	365.88	0.1479	0.2293	0.3772

PROPERTIES OF GASEOUS MERCURY

P,MPa (T_{sat},K)		sat	900	1000	1100	T,K 1200	1300	1400	1500	1600
0.20 (670.0)	v,m³/kg	0.1382	0.1861	0.2069	0.2277	0.2484	0.2692	0.2899	0.3107	0.3314
	h,kJ/kg	329.57	353.51	363.91	374.29	384.68	395.05	405.43	415.80	426.17
	s,kJ/(kg·K)	0.5068	0.5375	0.5484	0.5583	0.5674	0.5757	0.5834	0.5905	0.5972
0.50 (733.2)	v,m³/kg	0.06024	0.07422	0.08258	0.09091	0.09924	0.1076	0.1159	0.1242	0.1325
	h,kJ/kg	335.72	353.20	363.65	374.07	384.48	394.89	405.28	415.67	426.06
	s,kJ/(kg·K)	0.4778	0.4993	0.5103	0.5202	0.5293	0.5376	0.5453	0.5525	0.5592
1.0 (789.7)	v,m³/kg	0.03225	0.03692	0.04113	0.04532	0.04951	0.05368	0.05785	0.06202	0.06618
	h,kJ/kg	341.01	352.68	363.21	373.70	384.16	394.61	405.04	415.46	425.87
	s,kJ/(kg·K)	0.4564	0.4702	0.4813	0.4913	0.5004	0.5087	0.5165	0.5237	0.5304
2.0 (855.8)	v,m³/kg	0.01731	0.01827	0.02040	0.02253	0.02464	0.02674	0.02884	0.03093	0.03302
	h,kJ/kg	346.86	351.62	362.32	372.95	383.52	394.05	404.55	415.02	425.48
	s,kJ/(kg·K)	0.4353	0.4407	0.4520	0.4621	0.4713	0.4797	0.4875	0.4948	0.5015
5.0 (962.8)	v,m³/kg	0.00763		0.00796	0.00885	0.00972	0.01058	0.01143	0.01228	0.01313
	h,kJ/kg	355.39		359.56	370.63	381.54	392.34	403.06	413.71	424.32
	s,kJ/(kg·K)	0.4080		0.4122	0.4228	0.4323	0.4409	0.4489	0.4562	0.4630
10. (1064.)	v,m³/kg	0.00411			0.00428	0.00474	0.00518	0.00563	0.00606	0.00650
	h,kJ/kg	362.27			366.56	378.11	389.40	400.51	411.48	422.34
	s,kJ/(kg·K)	0.3876			0.3916	0.4017	0.4107	0.4189	0.4265	0.4335

Copyright Department of Mechanical Engineering, Stanford University

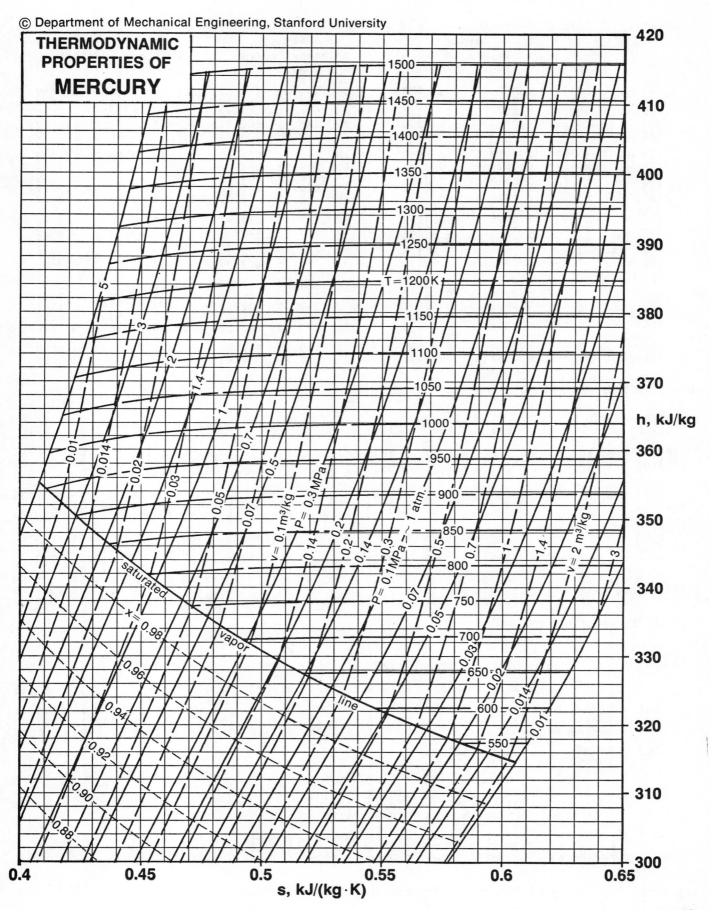

THERMODYNAMIC PROPERTIES OF MERCURY

s, kJ/(kg·K)

h, kJ/kg

49

PROPERTIES OF SATURATED METHANE

T K	P MPa	volume, m³/kg v_f	volume, m³/kg v_g	enthalpy, kJ/kg h_f	enthalpy, kJ/kg h_{fg}	enthalpy, kJ/kg h_g	entropy, kJ/(kg·K) s_f	entropy, kJ/(kg·K) s_{fg}	entropy, kJ/(kg·K) s_g
90.68	0.01174	0.002215	3.972	0.0	543.01	543.01	0.0	5.9882	5.9882
95	0.01991	0.002243	2.445	14.19	537.20	551.39	0.1526	5.6548	5.8074
100	0.03451	0.002278	1.477	30.89	529.95	560.84	0.3236	5.2996	5.6232
105	0.05657	0.002314	0.9393	47.85	522.12	569.97	0.4886	4.9726	5.4612
110	0.08840	0.002353	0.6241	65.04	513.69	578.73	0.6478	4.6699	5.3177
111.63	0.101325	0.002366	0.5507	70.70	510.79	581.49	0.6987	4.5756	5.2743
115	0.1326	0.002394	0.4303	82.46	504.57	587.03	0.8018	4.3876	5.1894
120	0.1919	0.002438	0.3061	100.14	494.69	594.83	0.9511	4.1224	5.0735
125	0.2694	0.002485	0.2236	118.11	483.94	602.05	1.0962	3.8715	4.9677
130	0.3681	0.002536	0.1670	136.39	472.21	608.60	1.2376	3.6324	4.8700
135	0.4913	0.002591	0.1272	155.04	459.37	614.41	1.3760	3.4028	4.7788
140	0.6423	0.002652	0.09842	174.10	445.27	619.37	1.5117	3.1806	4.6923
145	0.8245	0.002718	0.07718	193.64	429.72	623.36	1.6455	2.9636	4.6091
150	1.041	0.002792	0.06118	213.74	412.52	626.26	1.7777	2.7501	4.5278
155	1.297	0.002875	0.04890	234.52	393.35	627.87	1.9092	2.5377	4.4469
160	1.594	0.002971	0.03932	256.12	371.84	627.96	2.0408	2.3240	4.3648
165	1.937	0.003083	0.03171	278.75	347.45	626.20	2.1737	2.1058	4.2795
170	2.331	0.003218	0.02557	302.73	319.38	622.11	2.3094	1.8787	4.1881
175	2.780	0.003388	0.02050	328.62	286.25	614.87	2.4509	1.6357	4.0866
180	3.289	0.003618	0.01621	357.50	245.43	602.93	2.6036	1.3634	3.9670
185	3.865	0.003979	0.01235	392.30	189.97	582.27	2.7822	1.0268	3.8090
190.55	4.599	0.006233	0.006233	490.61	0.0	490.61	3.2853	0.0	3.2853

PROPERTIES OF GASEOUS METHANE

P,MPa (T_{sat},K)		sat	150	175	T,K 200	225	250	300	350	400
0.101325 (111.6)	v,m³/kg	0.5507	0.7559	0.8866	1.016	1.146	1.275	1.532	1.788	2.045
	h,kJ/kg	581.49	663.98	716.70	769.30	822.08	875.36	984.69	1099.70	1222.25
	s,kJ/(kg·K)	5.2743	5.9102	6.2353	6.5162	6.7649	6.9894	7.3878	7.7421	8.0692
0.20 (120.6)	v,m³/kg	0.2946	0.3772	0.4450	0.5117	0.5779	0.6437	0.7748	0.9053	1.035
	h,kJ/kg	595.71	660.72	714.27	767.37	820.51	874.05	983.74	1099.01	1221.75
	s,kJ/(kg·K)	5.0606	5.5435	5.8737	6.1574	6.4077	6.6333	7.0331	7.3882	7.7158
0.50 (135.3)	v,m³/kg	0.1251	0.1435	0.1727	0.2007	0.2280	0.2550	0.3083	0.3611	0.4136
	h,kJ/kg	614.75	650.00	706.57	761.38	815.65	870.02	980.87	1096.92	1220.23
	s,kJ/(kg·K)	4.7731	5.0206	5.3696	5.6625	5.9181	6.1473	6.5513	6.9088	7.2379
1.0 (149.1)	v,m³/kg	0.06373	0.06441	0.08157	0.09685	0.1114	0.1254	0.1529	0.1797	0.2063
	h,kJ/kg	625.83	628.36	692.55	750.92	807.33	863.19	976.05	1093.43	1217.69
	s,kJ/(kg·K)	4.5422	4.5592	4.9558	5.2677	5.5335	5.7689	6.1803	6.5420	6.8736

PROPERTIES OF LIQUID METHANE

P MPa		100	110	120	T,K 130	140	150	160	170	180
	P_{sat},MPa	0.03451	0.08840	0.1919	0.3681	0.6423	1.041	1.594	2.331	3.289
sat	ρ,kg/m³	439.05	425.00	410.15	394.30	377.13	358.16	336.58	310.77	276.41
	h,kJ/kg	30.89	65.04	100.14	136.39	174.10	213.75	256.12	302.73	357.50
	s,kJ/(kg·K)	0.3236	0.6478	0.9511	1.2376	1.5118	1.7777	2.0408	2.3094	2.6035
0.101325	ρ,kg/m³	439.10	425.01							
	h,kJ/kg	31.01	65.06							
	s,kJ/(kg·K)	0.3232	0.6478							
0.50	ρ,kg/m³	439.39	425.36	410.49	394.48					
	h,kJ/kg	31.65	65.72	100.64	136.58					
	s,kJ/(kg·K)	0.3206	0.6453	0.9490	1.2366					
2.0	ρ,kg/m³	440.50	426.69	412.10	396.51	379.51	360.46	338.04		
	h,kJ/kg	34.02	68.01	102.78	138.52	175.48	214.19	255.86		
	s,kJ/(kg·K)	0.3102	0.6341	0.9366	1.2226	1.4963	1.7632	2.0318		

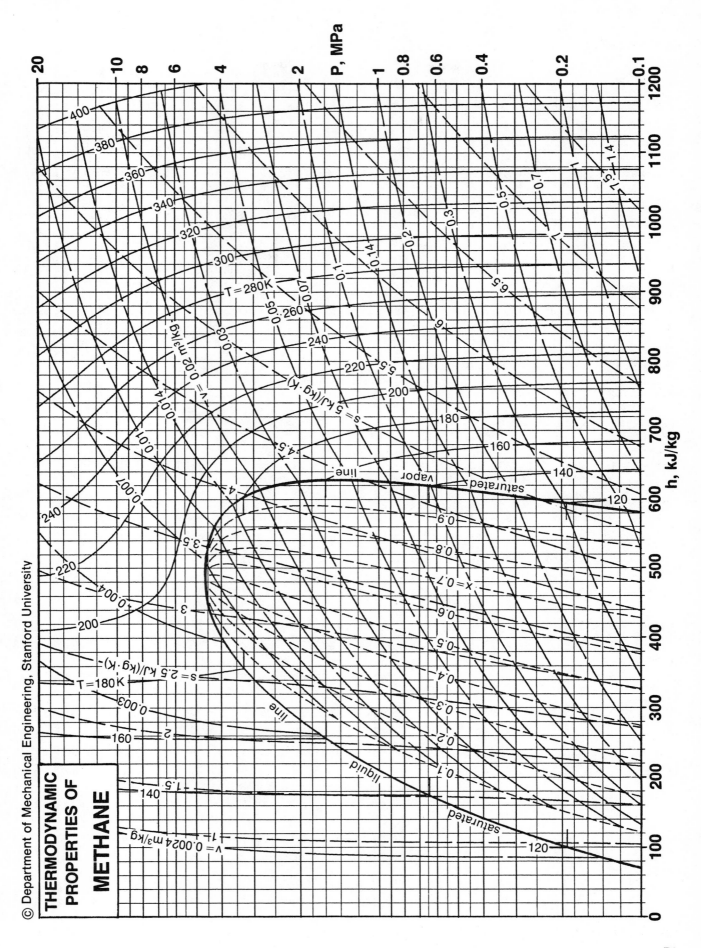

THERMODYNAMIC
PROPERTIES OF
METHANE

© Department of Mechanical Engineering, Stanford University

P, MPa

h, kJ/kg

PROPERTIES OF SATURATED NEON

T K	P MPa	volume, m³/kg v_f	v_g	enthalpy, kJ/kg h_f	h_{fg}	h_g	entropy, kJ/(kg·K) s_f	s_{fg}	s_g
24.54	0.04319	0.000801	0.2281	0.0	89.13	89.13	0.0	3.6320	3.6320
26	0.07184	0.000817	0.1434	2.81	87.47	90.28	0.1102	3.3644	3.4746
27	0.09854	0.000829	0.1073	4.81	86.18	90.99	0.1848	3.1919	3.3767
27.09	0.101325	0.000830	0.1046	4.99	86.06	91.05	0.1916	3.1765	3.3681
28	0.1321	0.000842	0.08196	6.86	84.76	91.62	0.2586	3.0269	3.2855
29	0.1735	0.000855	0.06365	8.98	83.18	92.16	0.3316	2.8681	3.1997
30	0.2238	0.000869	0.05016	11.15	81.44	92.59	0.4037	2.7148	3.1185
31	0.2840	0.000885	0.04004	13.37	79.55	92.92	0.4748	2.5662	3.0410
32	0.3553	0.000901	0.03231	15.64	77.49	93.13	0.5449	2.4213	2.9662
33	0.4386	0.000919	0.02631	17.96	75.23	93.19	0.6139	2.2797	2.8936
34	0.5352	0.000938	0.02160	20.33	72.78	93.11	0.6819	2.1405	2.8224
35	0.6462	0.000959	0.01785	22.75	70.10	92.85	0.7489	2.0029	2.7518
36	0.7728	0.000982	0.01482	25.21	67.19	92.40	0.8149	1.8664	2.6813
37	0.9164	0.001008	0.01236	27.73	64.02	91.75	0.8800	1.7301	2.6101
38	1.078	0.001038	0.01033	30.31	60.54	90.85	0.9445	1.5931	2.5376
39	1.260	0.001072	0.008651	32.98	56.71	89.69	1.0087	1.4543	2.4630
40	1.463	0.001113	0.007243	35.77	52.46	88.23	1.0738	1.3115	2.3853
41	1.688	0.001164	0.006049	38.78	47.61	86.39	1.1417	1.1614	2.3031
42	1.939	0.001231	0.005013	42.20	41.85	84.05	1.2170	0.9963	2.2133
43	2.216	0.001329	0.004066	46.54	34.27	80.81	1.3107	0.7969	2.1076
44.40	2.654	0.002070	0.002070	64.50	0.0	64.50	1.7040	0.0	1.7040

PROPERTIES OF GASEOUS NEON

P,MPa (T_{sat},K)		sat	40	80	120	T,K 160	200	240	280	320
0.070 (25.92)	v,m³/kg	0.1468	0.2324	0.4701	0.7061	0.9418	1.177	1.413	1.648	1.884
	h,kJ/kg	90.22	105.03	146.57	187.86	229.10	270.31	311.52	352.72	393.91
	s,kJ/(kg·K)	3.4826	3.9390	4.6593	5.0780	5.3745	5.6045	5.7923	5.9510	6.0886
0.101325 (27.09)	v,m³/kg	0.1046	0.1596	0.3245	0.4878	0.6508	0.8135	0.9763	1.139	1.302
	h,kJ/kg	91.05	104.78	146.48	187.82	229.08	270.31	311.52	352.72	393.92
	s,kJ/(kg·K)	3.3681	3.7828	4.5062	4.9253	5.2220	5.4520	5.6399	5.7987	5.9362
0.20 (29.55)	v,m³/kg	0.05574	0.07931	0.1641	0.2471	0.3298	0.4124	0.4949	0.5773	0.6598
	h,kJ/kg	92.41	103.97	146.20	187.70	229.02	270.29	311.52	352.74	393.95
	s,kJ/(kg·K)	3.1546	3.4901	4.2234	4.6441	4.9414	5.1716	5.3595	5.5184	5.6560
0.40 (32.56)	v,m³/kg	0.02879	0.03804	0.08170	0.1236	0.1651	0.2064	0.2477	0.2890	0.3302
	h,kJ/kg	93.18	102.24	145.64	187.44	228.90	270.24	311.53	352.78	394.01
	s,kJ/(kg·K)	2.9257	3.1766	3.9326	4.3565	4.6547	4.8854	5.0736	5.2325	5.3702
0.70 (35.44)	v,m³/kg	0.01643	0.02023	0.04640	0.07060	0.09443	0.1181	0.1418	0.1654	0.1890
	h,kJ/kg	92.68	99.30	144.81	187.06	228.72	270.18	311.53	352.83	394.11
	s,kJ/(kg·K)	2.7208	2.8969	3.6943	4.1229	4.4226	4.6539	4.8424	5.0015	5.1393
1.0 (37.53)	v,m³/kg	0.01123	0.01297	0.03229	0.04942	0.06619	0.08283	0.09942	0.1160	0.1325
	h,kJ/kg	91.30	95.80	143.99	186.69	228.55	270.11	311.54	352.89	394.20
	s,kJ/(kg·K)	2.5718	2.6881	3.5396	3.9729	4.2741	4.5059	4.6948	4.8541	4.9920
2.0 (42.23)	v,m³/kg	0.00479		0.01587	0.02472	0.03324	0.04164	0.04998	0.05829	0.06658
	h,kJ/kg	83.41		141.34	185.50	228.00	269.92	311.57	353.08	394.50
	s,kJ/(kg·K)	2.1909		3.2288	3.6775	3.9833	4.2172	4.4071	4.5670	4.7053
4.0	v,m³/kg			0.00772	0.01240	0.01677	0.02104	0.02526	0.02944	0.03362
	h,kJ/kg			136.42	183.34	227.01	269.58	311.66	353.47	395.10
	s,kJ/(kg·K)			2.8959	3.3737	3.6880	3.9256	4.1174	4.2785	4.4175
7.0	v,m³/kg			0.00430	0.00715	0.00972	0.01221	0.01465	0.01707	0.01947
	h,kJ/kg			129.72	180.61	225.79	269.23	311.87	354.08	396.02
	s,kJ/(kg·K)			2.5991	3.1188	3.4442	3.6866	3.8810	4.0437	4.1837
10.	v,m³/kg			0.00298	0.00507	0.00691	0.00868	0.01041	0.01212	0.01381
	h,kJ/kg			123.77	178.37	224.85	269.03	312.17	354.73	396.94
	s,kJ/(kg·K)			2.3914	2.9506	3.2855	3.5321	3.7288	3.8928	4.0337
20.	v,m³/kg			0.00169	0.00271	0.00367	0.00457	0.00545	0.00632	0.00718
	h,kJ/kg			113.86	173.73	223.42	269.44	313.81	357.28	400.19
	s,kJ/(kg·K)			1.9984	2.6110	2.9693	3.2263	3.4286	3.5962	3.7394

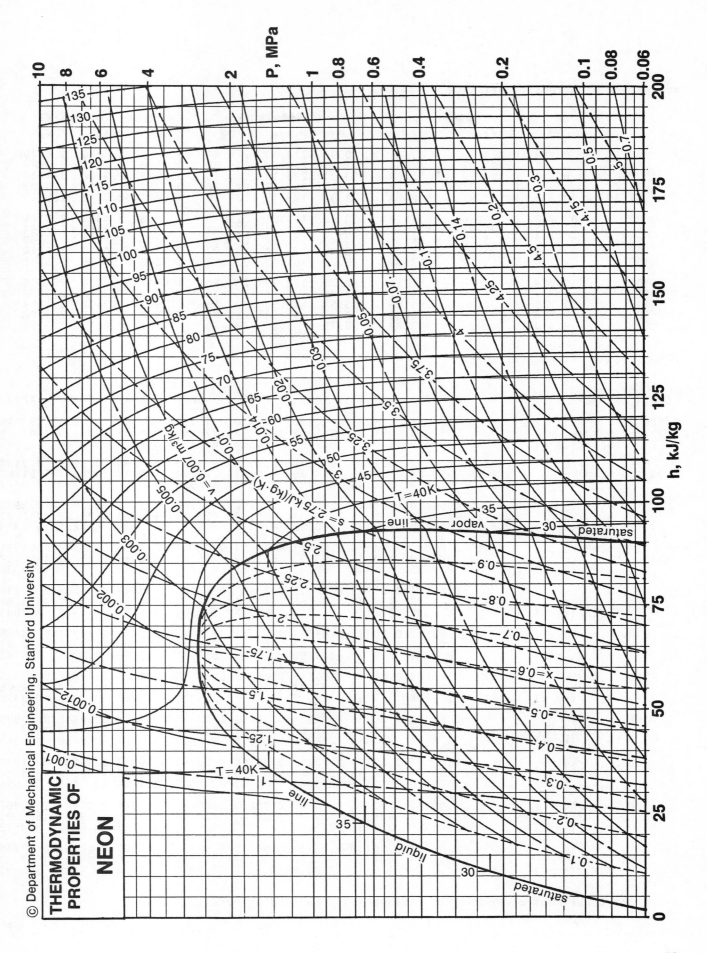

© Department of Mechanical Engineering, Stanford University

THERMODYNAMIC
PROPERTIES OF
NEON

P, MPa

h, kJ/kg

PROPERTIES OF SATURATED NITROGEN

T K	P MPa	volume, m³/kg v_f	v_g	enthalpy, kJ/kg h_f	h_{fg}	h_g	entropy, kJ/(kg·K) s_f	s_{fg}	s_g
63.15	0.01254	0.001153	1.481	0.0	214.83	214.83	0.0	3.4019	3.4019
65	0.01742	0.001162	1.094	3.27	213.32	216.59	0.0510	3.2817	3.3327
70	0.03858	0.001190	0.5269	13.01	208.14	221.15	0.1948	2.9734	3.1682
75	0.07612	0.001221	0.2822	23.23	202.13	225.36	0.3352	2.6951	3.0303
77.35	0.101325	0.001237	0.2168	28.05	199.15	227.20	0.3981	2.5748	2.9729
80	0.1370	0.001256	0.1641	33.50	195.65	229.15	0.4668	2.4457	2.9125
85	0.2291	0.001295	0.1017	43.84	188.58	232.42	0.5908	2.2186	2.8094
90	0.3608	0.001340	0.06629	54.43	180.64	235.07	0.7098	2.0071	2.7169
95	0.5411	0.001392	0.04490	65.39	171.58	236.97	0.8256	1.8062	2.6318
100	0.7790	0.001452	0.03131	76.79	161.19	237.98	0.9392	1.6119	2.5511
105	1.084	0.001524	0.02228	88.71	149.17	237.88	1.0510	1.4206	2.4716
110	1.467	0.001613	0.01602	101.40	134.88	236.28	1.1634	1.2262	2.3896
115	1.940	0.001729	0.01149	115.55	116.98	232.53	1.2822	1.0172	2.2994
120	2.513	0.001904	0.008033	132.46	92.60	225.06	1.4171	0.7717	2.1888
126.20	3.400	0.003184	0.003184	180.78	0.0	180.78	1.7903	0.0	1.7903

PROPERTIES OF GASEOUS NITROGEN

P,MPa (T$_{sat}$,K)		sat	200	300	400	T,K 500	600	800	1000	1200
0.101325 (77.35)	v,m³/kg	0.2168	0.5845	0.8786	1.172	1.465	1.758	2.344	2.930	3.516
	h,kJ/kg	227.20	357.00	461.14	565.30	670.20	776.59	995.91	1224.55	1461.29
	s,kJ/(kg·K)	2.9729	3.9829	4.4051	4.7048	4.9388	5.1327	5.4479	5.7028	5.9185
0.50 (93.98)	v,m³/kg	0.04848	0.1174	0.1779	0.2378	0.2974	0.3569	0.4758	0.5946	0.7134
	h,kJ/kg	236.65	355.05	460.25	564.89	670.03	776.59	996.10	1224.84	1461.63
	s,kJ/(kg·K)	2.6487	3.5019	3.9286	4.2297	4.4643	4.6585	4.9739	5.2289	5.4447
1.0 (103.7)	v,m³/kg	0.02425	0.05810	0.08890	0.1191	0.1490	0.1788	0.2384	0.2978	0.3572
	h,kJ/kg	238.02	352.58	459.16	564.37	669.84	776.60	996.33	1225.20	1462.07
	s,kJ/(kg·K)	2.4918	3.2870	3.7195	4.0222	4.2575	4.4521	4.7679	5.0231	5.2389
2.0 (115.6)	v,m³/kg	0.01105	0.02844	0.04440	0.05971	0.07481	0.08980	0.1197	0.1494	0.1791
	h,kJ/kg	231.91	347.60	457.00	563.37	669.47	776.62	996.81	1225.92	1462.94
	s,kJ/(kg·K)	2.2881	3.0626	3.5070	3.8131	4.0499	4.2452	4.5616	4.8170	5.0330
5.0	v,m³/kg		0.01071	0.01775	0.02413	0.03031	0.03640	0.04843	0.06038	0.07230
	h,kJ/kg		332.45	450.83	560.56	668.48	776.77	998.29	1228.12	1465.57
	s,kJ/(kg·K)		2.7330	3.2154	3.5314	3.7722	3.9696	4.2880	4.5442	4.7606
10.	v,m³/kg		0.00502	0.00895	0.01232	0.01551	0.01861	0.02470	0.03071	0.03669
	h,kJ/kg		308.56	441.78	556.63	667.31	777.34	1000.90	1231.86	1470.01
	s,kJ/(kg·K)		2.4341	2.9797	3.3106	3.5576	3.7582	4.0796	4.3371	4.5541
20.	v,m³/kg		0.00269	0.00470	0.00649	0.00815	0.00975	0.01285	0.01588	0.01889
	h,kJ/kg		280.28	428.93	551.48	666.60	779.54	1006.65	1239.64	1479.06
	s,kJ/(kg·K)		2.1168	2.7261	3.0795	3.3365	3.5425	3.8690	4.1288	4.3470
40.	v,m³/kg		0.00188	0.00278	0.00368	0.00453	0.00535	0.00694	0.00848	0.00999
	h,kJ/kg		272.71	421.05	550.24	670.61	787.47	1019.85	1256.13	1497.70
	s,kJ/(kg·K)		1.8614	2.4664	2.8389	3.1078	3.3209	3.6551	3.9186	4.1387
70.	v,m³/kg		0.00156	0.00204	0.00254	0.00302	0.00350	0.00442	0.00531	0.00618
	h,kJ/kg		287.71	431.56	562.23	685.58	805.40	1042.66	1282.44	1526.54
	s,kJ/(kg·K)		1.6820	2.2676	2.6442	2.9197	3.1382	3.4794	3.7469	3.9694
100.	v,m³/kg		0.00142	0.00175	0.00209	0.00243	0.00276	0.00341	0.00404	0.00466
	h,kJ/kg		309.67	451.53	582.06	706.35	827.54	1067.65	1309.89	1555.93
	s,kJ/(kg·K)		1.5689	2.1461	2.5222	2.7997	3.0208	3.3662	3.6363	3.8606
200.	v,m³/kg		0.00121	0.00138	0.00155	0.00172	0.00189	0.00222	0.00254	0.00286
	h,kJ/kg		393.11	534.36	664.90	790.06	912.85	1157.26	1404.11	1654.43
	s,kJ/(kg·K)		1.3371	1.9118	2.2878	2.5673	2.7912	3.1428	3.4181	3.6462

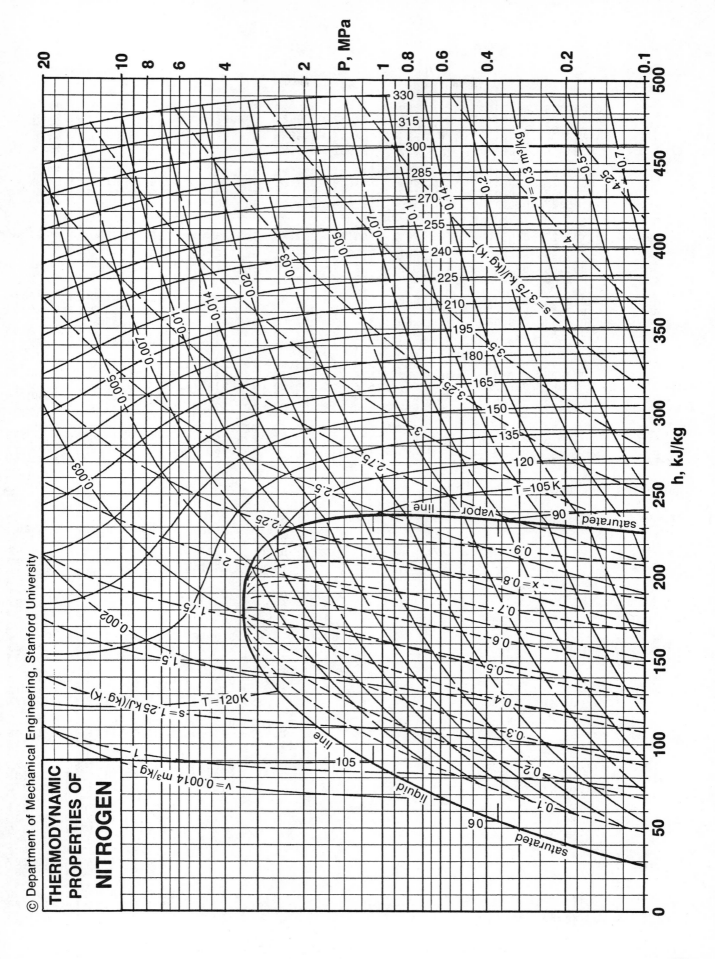

THERMODYNAMIC
PROPERTIES OF
NITROGEN

© Department of Mechanical Engineering, Stanford University

P, MPa

h, kJ/kg

55

PROPERTIES OF SATURATED OCTANE

T K	P MPa	volume, m³/kg v_f	v_g	enthalpy, kJ/kg h_f	h_fg	h_g	entropy, kJ/(kg·K) s_f	s_fg	s_g
300	0.002055	0.001440	10.59	0.0	366.29	366.29	0.0	1.2210	1.2210
310	0.003522	0.001455	6.378	22.72	360.20	382.92	0.0745	1.1619	1.2364
320	0.005792	0.001470	3.994	46.10	353.86	399.96	0.1487	1.1058	1.2545
330	0.009176	0.001486	2.593	69.99	347.39	417.38	0.2222	1.0527	1.2749
340	0.01406	0.001502	1.737	94.32	340.85	435.17	0.2948	1.0025	1.2973
350	0.02089	0.001518	1.197	119.02	334.29	453.31	0.3664	0.9551	1.3215
360	0.03022	0.001535	0.8467	144.09	327.68	471.77	0.4369	0.9103	1.3472
370	0.04265	0.001552	0.6123	169.53	321.01	490.54	0.5066	0.8676	1.3742
380	0.05887	0.001570	0.4519	195.34	314.25	509.59	0.5754	0.8269	1.4023
390	0.07965	0.001588	0.3395	221.53	307.36	528.89	0.6433	0.7881	1.4314
398.44	0.101325	0.001604	0.2701	243.92	301.44	545.36	0.7000	0.7566	1.4566
400	0.1058	0.001607	0.2592	248.10	300.33	548.43	0.7105	0.7508	1.4613
410	0.1383	0.001627	0.2008	275.03	293.15	568.18	0.7768	0.7150	1.4918
420	0.1780	0.001648	0.1575	302.32	285.80	588.12	0.8424	0.6805	1.5229
430	0.2260	0.001671	0.1249	329.96	278.25	608.21	0.9073	0.6471	1.5544
440	0.2834	0.001695	0.1000	357.94	270.48	628.42	0.9714	0.6147	1.5861
450	0.3514	0.001722	0.08077	386.26	262.46	648.72	1.0348	0.5832	1.6180
460	0.4314	0.001753	0.06569	414.97	254.08	669.05	1.0975	0.5524	1.6499
470	0.5247	0.001788	0.05373	444.12	245.26	689.38	1.1599	0.5218	1.6817
480	0.6328	0.001829	0.04414	473.84	235.78	709.62	1.2220	0.4913	1.7133
490	0.7574	0.001879	0.03638	504.31	225.40	729.71	1.2844	0.4600	1.7444
500	0.9000	0.001941	0.03002	535.79	213.72	749.51	1.3474	0.4275	1.7749
510	1.062	0.002023	0.02477	568.61	200.30	768.91	1.4118	0.3927	1.8045
520	1.246	0.002135	0.02040	603.22	184.47	787.69	1.4783	0.3547	1.8330
530	1.451	0.002300	0.01672	640.22	165.35	805.57	1.5479	0.3119	1.8598
540	1.678	0.002567	0.01357	680.60	141.50	822.10	1.6223	0.2620	1.8843
550	1.926	0.003082	0.01082	726.67	109.72	836.39	1.7055	0.1995	1.9050
560	2.192	0.004575	0.008265	789.60	56.36	845.96	1.8171	0.1006	1.9177
567.51	2.400	0.005523	0.005523	834.22	0.0	834.22	1.8944	0.0	1.8944

PROPERTIES OF GASEOUS OCTANE

P,MPa (T_sat,K)		sat	400	440	480	520	560	600	640	680
0.101325 (398.4)	v,m³/kg	0.2701	0.2714	0.3040	0.3354	0.3661	0.3963	0.4261	0.4558	0.4853
	h,kJ/kg	545.36	548.71	637.59	732.66	833.78	940.74	1053.28	1171.14	1294.01
	s,kJ/(kg·K)	1.4566	1.4650	1.6766	1.8833	2.0856	2.2837	2.4778	2.6679	2.8541
0.20 (424.8)	v,m³/kg	0.1406		0.1476	0.1650	0.1816	0.1977	0.2134	0.2289	0.2442
	h,kJ/kg	597.79		632.80	728.96	830.83	938.34	1051.29	1169.46	1292.57
	s,kJ/(kg·K)	1.5380		1.6190	1.8281	2.0319	2.2310	2.4258	2.6164	2.8029
0.40 (456.3)	v,m³/kg	0.07092			0.07712	0.08670	0.09563	0.1041	0.1124	0.1204
	h,kJ/kg	661.45			720.79	824.51	933.28	1047.14	1165.99	1289.63
	s,kJ/(kg·K)	1.6380			1.7648	1.9723	2.1737	2.3700	2.5618	2.7491
0.70 (485.6)	v,m³/kg	0.03963				0.04565	0.05171	0.05721	0.06239	0.06733
	h,kJ/kg	720.82				813.90	925.11	1040.60	1160.61	1285.12
	s,kJ/(kg·K)	1.7306				1.9158	2.1218	2.3210	2.5146	2.7032
1.0 (506.3)	v,m³/kg	0.02660				0.02874	0.03395	0.03836	0.04235	0.04608
	h,kJ/kg	761.80				801.16	916.06	1033.61	1154.99	1280.46
	s,kJ/(kg·K)	1.7937				1.8704	2.0833	2.2860	2.4818	2.6719
2.0 (552.8)	v,m³/kg	0.01009					0.01157	0.01590	0.01880	0.02123
	h,kJ/kg	839.77					869.93	1005.49	1134.07	1263.86
	s,kJ/(kg·K)	1.9098					1.9640	2.1980	2.4055	2.6022
4.0	v,m³/kg							0.00374	0.00660	0.00871
	h,kJ/kg							900.25	1076.15	1224.65
	s,kJ/(kg·K)							1.9954	2.2795	2.5046
7.0	v,m³/kg							0.00238	0.00308	0.00402
	h,kJ/kg							860.81	1012.59	1168.07
	s,kJ/(kg·K)							1.9155	2.1603	2.3960
10.	v,m³/kg							0.00210	0.00243	0.00290
	h,kJ/kg							851.52	992.54	1140.88
	s,kJ/(kg·K)							1.8889	2.1164	2.3412

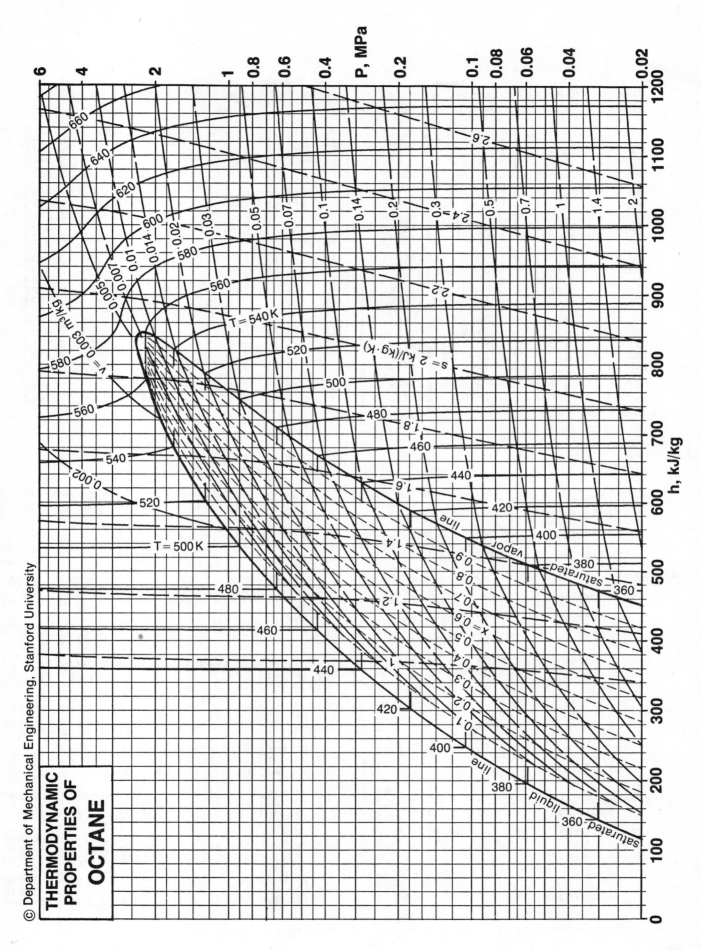

THERMODYNAMIC PROPERTIES OF
OCTANE

© Department of Mechanical Engineering, Stanford University

P, MPa

h, kJ/kg

$v = 0.003\ m^3/kg$

$s = 2\ kJ/(kg\cdot K)$

T = 540 K

T = 500 K

saturated vapor line

saturated liquid line

PROPERTIES OF SATURATED OXYGEN

T K	P MPa	volume, m³/kg v_f	volume, m³/kg v_g	enthalpy, kJ/kg h_f	enthalpy, kJ/kg h_{fg}	enthalpy, kJ/kg h_g	entropy, kJ/(kg·K) s_f	entropy, kJ/(kg·K) s_{fg}	entropy, kJ/(kg·K) s_g
54.34	0.0001453	0.000764	97.12	0.0	242.37	242.37	0.0	4.4602	4.4602
60	0.0007249	0.000780	21.49	9.23	238.26	247.49	0.1615	3.9710	4.1325
65	0.002331	0.000794	7.229	17.54	234.43	251.97	0.2945	3.6066	3.9011
70	0.006253	0.000808	2.896	25.88	230.50	256.38	0.4182	3.2928	3.7110
75	0.01453	0.000824	1.331	34.22	226.47	260.69	0.5331	3.0196	3.5527
80	0.03009	0.000840	0.6813	42.56	222.30	264.86	0.6405	2.7788	3.4193
85	0.05679	0.000857	0.3805	50.92	217.92	268.84	0.7417	2.5637	3.3054
90	0.09932	0.000876	0.2279	59.36	213.23	272.59	0.8377	2.3692	3.2069
90.19	0.101325	0.000877	0.2237	59.69	213.03	272.72	0.8413	2.3621	3.2034
95	0.1631	0.000896	0.1444	67.91	208.14	276.05	0.9296	2.1909	3.1205
100	0.2540	0.000917	0.09590	76.61	202.57	279.18	1.0179	2.0258	3.0437
105	0.3785	0.000940	0.06612	85.47	196.45	281.92	1.1033	1.8709	2.9742
110	0.5434	0.000966	0.04701	94.52	189.69	284.21	1.1860	1.7244	2.9104
115	0.7554	0.000994	0.03426	103.79	182.17	285.96	1.2666	1.5840	2.8506
120	1.022	0.001027	0.02546	113.34	173.75	287.09	1.3455	1.4480	2.7935
125	1.351	0.001064	0.01921	123.24	164.24	287.48	1.4236	1.3139	2.7375
130	1.749	0.001108	0.01463	133.65	153.30	286.95	1.5018	1.1793	2.6811
135	2.225	0.001161	0.01120	144.77	140.50	285.27	1.5817	1.0407	2.6224
140	2.788	0.001230	0.008562	156.91	125.11	282.02	1.6650	0.8937	2.5587
145	3.448	0.001324	0.006458	170.52	105.93	276.45	1.7547	0.7305	2.4852
150	4.216	0.001479	0.004671	186.90	79.53	266.43	1.8583	0.5302	2.3885
154.58	5.043	0.002293	0.002293	226.53	0.0	226.53	2.1080	0.0	2.1080

PROPERTIES OF GASEOUS OXYGEN

P,MPa (T_{sat},K)		sat	200	300	400	T,K 500	600	700	800	1000
0.020 (77.11)	v,m³/kg	0.9916	2.597	3.897	5.196	6.496	7.795	9.094	10.39	12.99
	h,kJ/kg	262.47	374.80	466.17	559.04	654.65	753.40	855.13	959.42	1174.07
	s,kJ/(kg·K)	3.4938	4.3661	4.7365	5.0035	5.2167	5.3967	5.5534	5.6926	5.9320
0.050 (83.94)	v,m³/kg	0.4276	1.038	1.558	2.079	2.598	3.118	3.638	4.158	5.197
	h,kJ/kg	268.02	374.65	466.10	559.00	654.63	753.40	855.13	959.43	1174.09
	s,kJ/(kg·K)	3.3281	4.1275	4.4982	4.7653	4.9786	5.1586	5.3153	5.4546	5.6939
0.101325 (90.19)	v,m³/kg	0.2237	0.5113	0.7688	1.026	1.282	1.539	1.795	2.052	2.565
	h,kJ/kg	272.72	374.39	465.97	558.94	654.60	753.39	855.14	959.45	1174.11
	s,kJ/(kg·K)	3.2034	3.9431	4.3143	4.5816	4.7950	4.9750	5.1318	5.2710	5.5104
0.20 (97.24)	v,m³/kg	0.1196	0.2583	0.3893	0.5197	0.6498	0.7798	0.9098	1.040	1.300
	h,kJ/kg	277.50	373.89	465.73	558.82	654.54	753.38	855.15	959.48	1174.17
	s,kJ/(kg·K)	3.0851	3.7647	4.1370	4.4047	4.6181	4.7982	4.9551	5.0944	5.3337
0.50 (108.8)	v,m³/kg	0.05087	0.1024	0.1554	0.2079	0.2601	0.3122	0.3642	0.4162	0.5201
	h,kJ/kg	283.71	372.35	464.99	558.44	654.37	753.33	855.19	959.57	1174.33
	s,kJ/(kg·K)	2.9252	3.5212	3.8969	4.1656	4.3796	4.5599	4.7169	4.8562	5.0957
1.0 (119.6)	v,m³/kg	0.02602	0.05039	0.07749	0.1039	0.1302	0.1563	0.1823	0.2083	0.2603
	h,kJ/kg	287.03	369.73	463.76	557.81	654.09	753.25	855.25	959.73	1174.59
	s,kJ/(kg·K)	2.7977	3.3320	3.7135	3.9840	4.1987	4.3794	4.5366	4.6760	4.9156
2.0 (132.7)	v,m³/kg	0.01264	0.02439	0.03853	0.05198	0.06520	0.07832	0.09137	0.1044	0.1304
	h,kJ/kg	286.19	364.33	461.29	556.57	653.52	753.11	855.38	960.04	1175.13
	s,kJ/(kg·K)	2.6493	3.1328	3.5266	3.8007	4.0169	4.1984	4.3560	4.4958	4.7356
5.0 (154.4)	v,m³/kg	0.00276	0.00876	0.01516	0.02082	0.02624	0.03156	0.03681	0.04204	0.05244
	h,kJ/kg	239.04	346.74	453.93	552.90	651.86	752.69	855.78	961.00	1176.75
	s,kJ/(kg·K)	2.1897	2.8310	3.2684	3.5533	3.7740	3.9578	4.1167	4.2571	4.4977
10.	v,m³/kg		0.00361	0.00743	0.01046	0.01327	0.01598	0.01864	0.02126	0.02647
	h,kJ/kg		313.19	442.21	547.14	649.30	752.12	856.53	962.66	1179.50
	s,kJ/(kg·K)		2.5239	3.0559	3.3582	3.5861	3.7736	3.9345	4.0762	4.3180
20.	v,m³/kg		0.00173	0.00370	0.00534	0.00682	0.00822	0.00957	0.01089	0.01350
	h,kJ/kg		268.46	422.72	537.55	645.22	751.58	858.40	966.22	1185.16
	s,kJ/(kg·K)		2.1834	2.8202	3.1515	3.3919	3.5858	3.7505	3.8944	4.1386

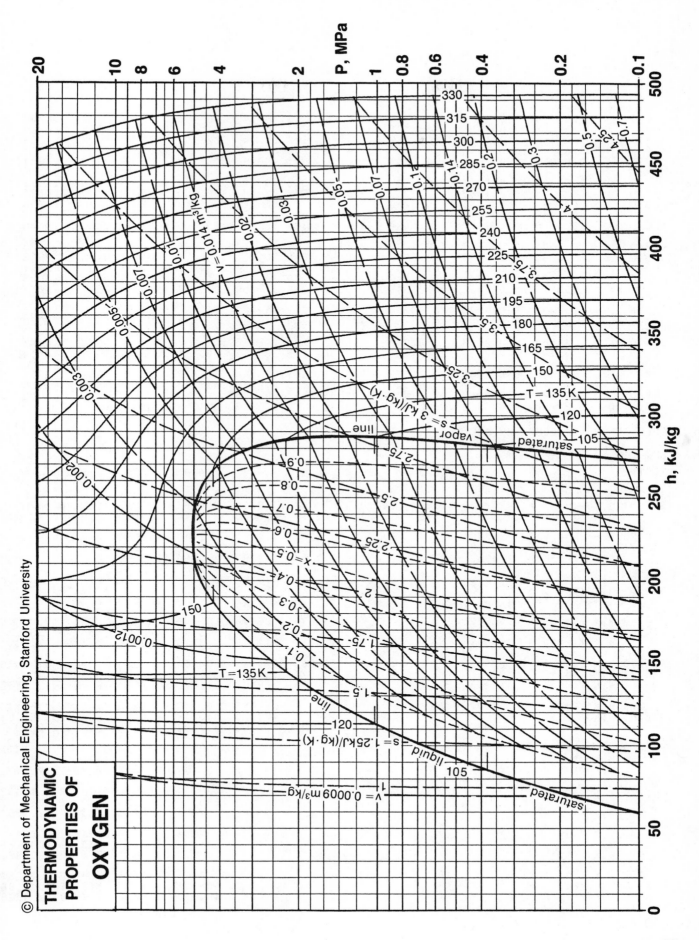

© Department of Mechanical Engineering, Stanford University

THERMODYNAMIC PROPERTIES OF OXYGEN

P, MPa

h, kJ/kg

59

PROPERTIES OF SATURATED PENTANE

T K	P MPa	v_f	v_g	h_f	h_{fg}	h_g	s_f	s_{fg}	s_g
250	0.007604	0.001509	3.764	0.0	406.46	406.46	0.0	1.6258	1.6258
260	0.01306	0.001531	2.271	23.85	397.16	421.01	0.0935	1.5275	1.6210
270	0.02136	0.001553	1.436	47.54	388.28	435.82	0.1829	1.4380	1.6209
280	0.03346	0.001576	0.9452	71.24	379.63	450.87	0.2690	1.3558	1.6248
290	0.05050	0.001600	0.6441	95.00	371.15	466.15	0.3523	1.2798	1.6321
300	0.07376	0.001625	0.4523	118.83	362.79	481.62	0.4329	1.2093	1.6422
309.04	0.101325	0.001649	0.3360	140.44	355.32	495.76	0.5038	1.1497	1.6535
310	0.1047	0.001651	0.3259	142.75	354.52	497.27	0.5112	1.1436	1.6548
320	0.1449	0.001678	0.2402	166.82	346.25	513.07	0.5874	1.0820	1.6694
330	0.1960	0.001707	0.1804	191.13	337.86	528.99	0.6619	1.0239	1.6858
340	0.2601	0.001737	0.1379	215.77	329.23	545.00	0.7352	0.9683	1.7035
350	0.3390	0.001769	0.1068	240.86	320.20	561.06	0.8075	0.9148	1.7223
360	0.4349	0.001804	0.08384	266.52	310.61	577.13	0.8793	0.8628	1.7421
370	0.5501	0.001841	0.06649	292.81	300.34	593.15	0.9507	0.8118	1.7625
380	0.6869	0.001882	0.05318	319.76	289.31	609.07	1.0219	0.7614	1.7833
390	0.8478	0.001928	0.04284	347.40	277.41	624.81	1.0929	0.7113	1.8042
400	1.036	0.001980	0.03467	375.74	264.51	640.25	1.1637	0.6613	1.8250
410	1.253	0.002041	0.02813	404.91	250.32	655.23	1.2347	0.6105	1.8452
420	1.505	0.002115	0.02281	435.22	234.29	669.51	1.3065	0.5578	1.8643
430	1.794	0.002210	0.01841	467.34	215.36	682.70	1.3806	0.5008	1.8814
440	2.124	0.002340	0.01470	502.43	191.70	694.13	1.4595	0.4357	1.8952
450	2.500	0.002542	0.01146	542.58	159.87	702.45	1.5476	0.3553	1.9029
460	2.921	0.002962	0.008427	592.55	111.20	703.75	1.6549	0.2417	1.8966
467.00	3.240	0.005085	0.005085	673.30	0.0	673.30	1.8263	0.0	1.8263

PROPERTIES OF GASEOUS PENTANE

P,MPa (T_sat,K)		sat	320	360	400	440	480	520	560	600
0.101325 (309.0)	v,m³/kg	0.3360	0.3498	0.3989	0.4468	0.4939	0.5407	0.5871	0.6334	0.6795
	h,kJ/kg	495.76	515.28	590.46	672.08	760.26	854.93	955.93	1063.06	1176.06
	s,kJ/(kg·K)	1.6535	1.7156	1.9368	2.1516	2.3616	2.5674	2.7695	2.9679	3.1627
0.20 (330.7)	v,m³/kg	0.1770		0.1966	0.2221	0.2469	0.2713	0.2953	0.3191	0.3427
	h,kJ/kg	530.09		586.76	669.27	758.03	853.12	954.43	1061.79	1174.97
	s,kJ/(kg·K)	1.6869		1.8511	2.0683	2.2796	2.4864	2.6890	2.8879	3.0830
0.40 (356.6)	v,m³/kg	0.09099		0.09228	0.1066	0.1200	0.1329	0.1454	0.1577	0.1698
	h,kJ/kg	571.62		578.65	663.27	753.37	849.36	951.33	1059.18	1172.74
	s,kJ/(kg·K)	1.7352		1.7548	1.9776	2.1922	2.4009	2.6049	2.8046	3.0004
0.70 (380.9)	v,m³/kg	0.05217			0.05674	0.06545	0.07348	0.08111	0.08849	0.09570
	h,kJ/kg	610.47			653.34	745.92	843.49	946.54	1055.18	1169.34
	s,kJ/(kg·K)	1.7851			1.8950	2.1155	2.3276	2.5338	2.7350	2.9318
1.0 (398.2)	v,m³/kg	0.03599			0.03635	0.04345	0.04964	0.05536	0.06080	0.06605
	h,kJ/kg	637.52			641.77	737.80	837.28	941.56	1051.07	1165.87
	s,kJ/(kg·K)	1.8213			1.8320	2.0608	2.2771	2.4857	2.6885	2.8865
2.0 (436.4)	v,m³/kg	0.01597				0.01655	0.02143	0.02516	0.02843	0.03145
	h,kJ/kg	690.26				701.10	813.15	923.36	1036.52	1153.83
	s,kJ/(kg·K)	1.8907				1.9154	2.1593	2.3798	2.5894	2.7917
4.0	v,m³/kg						0.00423	0.00954	0.01212	0.01415
	h,kJ/kg						688.44	874.48	1002.41	1127.35
	s,kJ/(kg·K)						1.8509	2.2255	2.4627	2.6782
7.0	v,m³/kg						0.00256	0.00376	0.00546	0.00699
	h,kJ/kg						625.29	787.04	942.55	1084.07
	s,kJ/(kg·K)						1.7008	2.0243	2.3126	2.5568
10.	v,m³/kg						0.00234	0.00288	0.00372	0.00465
	h,kJ/kg						614.09	755.36	903.48	1048.76
	s,kJ/(kg·K)						1.6623	1.9448	2.2192	2.4698
20.	v,m³/kg						0.00208	0.00228	0.00255	0.00287
	h,kJ/kg						606.02	730.27	862.32	1000.06
	s,kJ/(kg·K)						1.6000	1.8485	2.0930	2.3306

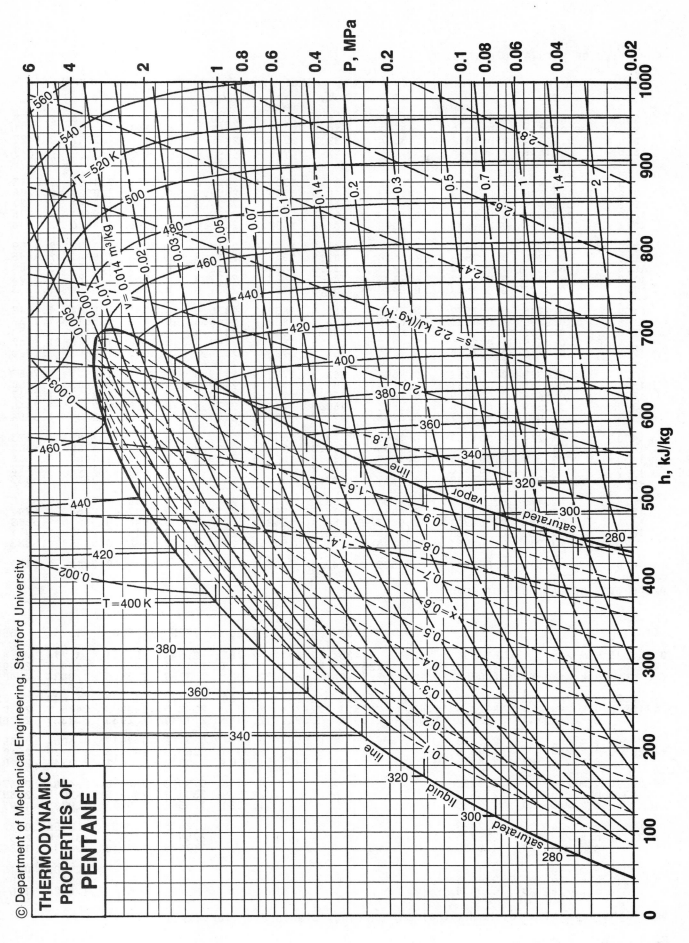

THERMODYNAMIC
PROPERTIES OF
PENTANE

© Department of Mechanical Engineering, Stanford University

P, MPa

h, kJ/kg

61

PROPERTIES OF SATURATED POTASSIUM

T K	P MPa	volume, m³/kg v_f	v_g	enthalpy, kJ/kg h_f	h_{fg}	h_g	entropy, kJ/(kg·K) s_f	s_{fg}	s_g
800	0.006363	0.001389	25.97	0.0	2060.7	2060.7	0.0	2.5758	2.5758
825	0.009283	0.001400	18.27	19.5	2048.6	2068.1	0.0240	2.4831	2.5071
850	0.01324	0.001412	13.14	39.2	2035.9	2075.1	0.0475	2.3952	2.4427
875	0.01849	0.001425	9.630	59.1	2022.6	2081.7	0.0706	2.3115	2.3821
900	0.02535	0.001437	7.187	79.3	2008.5	2087.8	0.0933	2.2317	2.3250
925	0.03414	0.001450	5.452	99.5	1994.1	2093.6	0.1155	2.1558	2.2713
950	0.04526	0.001463	4.199	119.9	1979.2	2099.1	0.1372	2.0834	2.2206
975	0.05911	0.001476	3.279	140.5	1963.8	2104.3	0.1586	2.0141	2.1727
1000	0.07614	0.001490	2.593	161.1	1948.1	2109.2	0.1794	1.9481	2.1275
1025	0.09686	0.001504	2.076	181.8	1932.1	2113.9	0.1998	1.8850	2.0848
1029.83	0.101325	0.001507	1.991	185.8	1929.0	2114.8	0.2037	1.8732	2.0769
1050	0.1218	0.001518	1.680	202.5	1916.0	2118.5	0.2198	1.8247	2.0445
1075	0.1514	0.001533	1.373	223.3	1899.6	2122.9	0.2393	1.7671	2.0064
1100	0.1864	0.001548	1.134	244.1	1883.2	2127.3	0.2583	1.7120	1.9703
1125	0.2272	0.001563	0.9444	264.8	1866.8	2131.6	0.2769	1.6594	1.9363
1150	0.2746	0.001579	0.7932	285.5	1850.5	2136.0	0.2951	1.6091	1.9042
1175	0.3290	0.001595	0.6715	306.2	1834.2	2140.4	0.3128	1.5610	1.8738
1200	0.3913	0.001611	0.5727	326.9	1818.1	2145.0	0.3301	1.5151	1.8452
1225	0.4619	0.001628	0.4918	347.5	1802.2	2149.7	0.3470	1.4712	1.8182
1250	0.5416	0.001645	0.4251	368.1	1786.4	2154.5	0.3636	1.4291	1.7927
1275	0.6309	0.001663	0.3697	388.7	1770.9	2159.6	0.3798	1.3889	1.7687
1300	0.7305	0.001681	0.3234	409.4	1755.4	2164.8	0.3957	1.3503	1.7460
1325	0.8409	0.001699	0.2844	430.1	1740.2	2170.3	0.4113	1.3134	1.7247
1350	0.9629	0.001718	0.2515	450.9	1724.9	2175.8	0.4268	1.2777	1.7045
1375	1.097	0.001737	0.2233	472.0	1709.6	2181.6	0.4420	1.2434	1.6854
1400	1.244	0.001757	0.1993	493.2	1694.2	2187.4	0.4572	1.2101	1.6673
1425	1.403	0.001778	0.1785	514.8	1678.6	2193.4	0.4722	1.1780	1.6502
1450	1.577	0.001798	0.1605	536.7	1662.6	2199.3	0.4873	1.1465	1.6338
1475	1.765	0.001820	0.1449	559.2	1645.9	2205.1	0.5024	1.1158	1.6182
1500	1.967	0.001842	0.1311	582.2	1628.5	2210.7	0.5176	1.0857	1.6033
1525	2.185	0.001864	0.1191	605.9	1610.0	2215.9	0.5330	1.0558	1.5888
1550	2.418	0.001888	0.1083	630.5	1590.3	2220.8	0.5487	1.0260	1.5747
1575	2.667	0.001911	0.09879	656.1	1568.8	2224.9	0.5648	0.9961	1.5609
1600	2.932	0.001936	0.09023	683.0	1545.1	2228.1	0.5815	0.9656	1.5471
1625	3.214	0.001961	0.08248	711.5	1518.5	2230.0	0.5988	0.9345	1.5333
1650	3.512	0.001987	0.07539	742.1	1488.0	2230.1	0.6171	0.9018	1.5189

PROPERTIES OF GASEOUS POTASSIUM

P,MPa (T_{sat},K)		sat	1125	1200	1275	1350	1425	1500	1575	1650
0.101325 (1030.)	v,m³/kg	1.991	2.251	2.435	2.611	2.781	2.947	3.111	3.274	3.435
	h,kJ/kg	2114.8	2209.1	2267.6	2319.2	2366.9	2412.1	2455.8	2498.5	2540.6
	s,kJ/(kg·K)	2.0769	2.1647	2.2150	2.2568	2.2931	2.3257	2.3556	2.3834	2.4095
0.20 (1109.)	v,m³/kg	1.062	1.087	1.194	1.291	1.384	1.472	1.558	1.643	1.727
	h,kJ/kg	2128.8	2148.3	2225.1	2288.1	2343.2	2393.5	2440.9	2486.3	2530.3
	s,kJ/(kg·K)	1.9582	1.9756	2.0418	2.0927	2.1348	2.1711	2.2035	2.2330	2.2603
0.40 (1203.)	v,m³/kg	0.5612			0.6154	0.6671	0.7155	0.7617	0.8064	0.8501
	h,kJ/kg	2145.6			2226.7	2296.4	2356.8	2411.3	2461.9	2510.0
	s,kJ/(kg·K)	1.8416			1.9071	1.9603	2.0038	2.0411	2.0741	2.1039
0.70 (1293.)	v,m³/kg	0.3362				0.3616	0.3923	0.4210	0.4484	0.4747
	h,kJ/kg	2163.3				2229.9	2304.1	2368.6	2426.7	2480.3
	s,kJ/(kg·K)	1.7526				1.8030	1.8566	1.9007	1.9385	1.9718
1.0 (1357.)	v,m³/kg	0.2429					0.2638	0.2853	0.3056	0.3249
	h,kJ/kg	2177.5					2254.8	2328.2	2393.0	2451.9
	s,kJ/(kg·K)	1.6989					1.7545	1.8048	1.8470	1.8835
2.0 (1504.)	v,m³/kg	0.1292							0.1403	0.1512
	h,kJ/kg	2211.5							2291.2	2364.9
	s,kJ/(kg·K)	1.6010							1.6528	1.6985

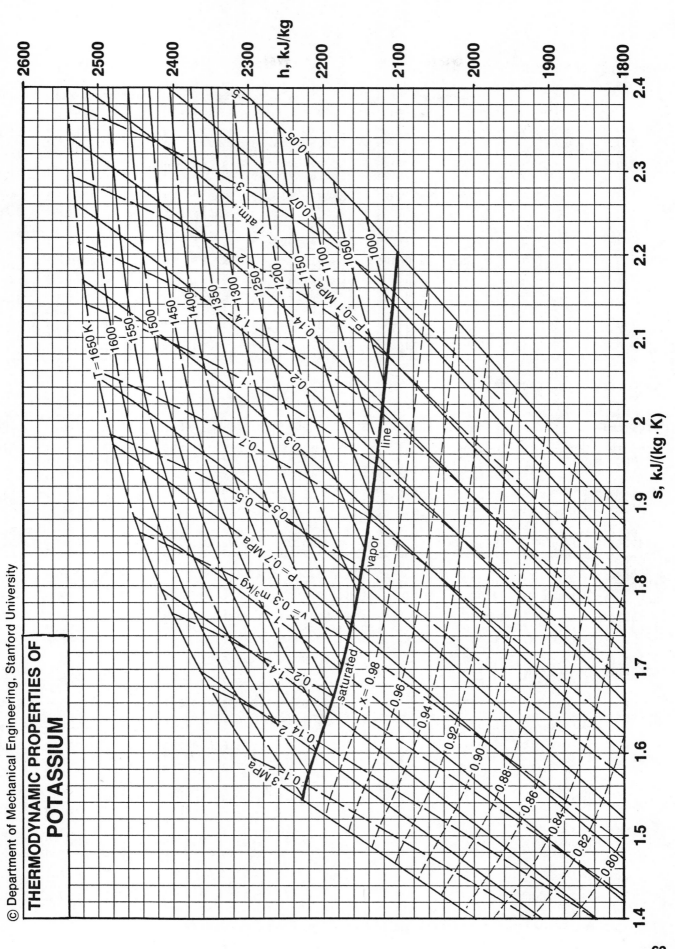

© Department of Mechanical Engineering, Stanford University

THERMODYNAMIC PROPERTIES OF
POTASSIUM

h, kJ/kg

s, kJ/(kg·K)

63

PROPERTIES OF SATURATED PROPANE

T K	P MPa	volume, m³/kg		enthalpy, kJ/kg			entropy, kJ/(kg·K)		
		v$_f$	v$_g$	h$_f$	h$_{fg}$	h$_g$	s$_f$	s$_{fg}$	s$_g$
200	0.01997	0.001661	1.865	0.0	456.24	456.24	0.0	2.2812	2.2812
210	0.03566	0.001689	1.089	21.65	446.46	468.11	0.1055	2.1260	2.2315
220	0.05998	0.001719	0.6721	43.69	436.25	479.94	0.2078	1.9830	2.1908
230	0.09586	0.001751	0.4346	66.12	425.57	491.69	0.3073	1.8502	2.1575
231.25	0.101325	0.001755	0.4127	68.96	424.19	493.15	0.3195	1.8343	2.1538
240	0.1467	0.001784	0.2922	88.90	414.42	503.32	0.4038	1.7268	2.1306
250	0.2161	0.001819	0.2031	111.98	402.82	514.80	0.4975	1.6113	2.1088
260	0.3081	0.001857	0.1452	135.43	390.63	526.06	0.5888	1.5024	2.0912
270	0.4272	0.001897	0.1062	159.37	377.69	537.06	0.6783	1.3989	2.0772
280	0.5779	0.001941	0.07924	183.98	363.74	547.72	0.7668	1.2990	2.0658
290	0.7650	0.001990	0.06006	209.42	348.53	557.95	0.8547	1.2019	2.0566
300	0.9935	0.002044	0.04612	235.79	331.84	567.63	0.9426	1.1061	2.0487
310	1.269	0.002107	0.03576	263.18	313.43	576.61	1.0305	1.0110	2.0415
320	1.596	0.002183	0.02790	291.73	292.88	584.61	1.1189	0.9152	2.0341
330	1.983	0.002277	0.02180	321.82	269.42	591.24	1.2088	0.8164	2.0252
340	2.435	0.002403	0.01695	354.44	241.34	595.78	1.3030	0.7098	2.0128
350	2.961	0.002595	0.01297	391.67	205.14	596.81	1.4071	0.5861	1.9932
360	3.566	0.002956	0.009517	438.37	152.37	590.74	1.5339	0.4232	1.9571
369.82	4.236	0.005066	0.005066	539.78	0.0	539.78	1.8042	0.0	1.8042

PROPERTIES OF GASEOUS PROPANE

P,MPa (T$_{sat}$,K)		sat	250	300	350	T,K 400	450	500	550	600
0.050 (216.4)	v,m³/kg	0.7958	0.9291	1.123	1.315	1.505	1.695	1.885	2.074	2.263
	h,kJ/kg	475.66	523.67	603.16	693.61	795.32	908.02	1031.20	1164.24	1306.49
	s,kJ/(kg·K)	2.2046	2.4106	2.6999	2.9783	3.2496	3.5148	3.7742	4.0277	4.2751
0.101325 (231.3)	v,m³/kg	0.4127	0.4509	0.5494	0.6455	0.7404	0.8347	0.9286	1.022	1.116
	h,kJ/kg	493.15	521.02	601.52	692.49	794.51	907.40	1030.72	1163.85	1306.17
	s,kJ/(kg·K)	2.1538	2.2697	2.5627	2.8427	3.1149	3.3806	3.6402	3.8938	4.1414
0.20 (247.9)	v,m³/kg	0.2185	0.2208	0.2736	0.3238	0.3728	0.4211	0.4691	0.5169	0.5645
	h,kJ/kg	512.44	515.70	598.29	690.32	792.93	906.21	1029.78	1163.09	1305.54
	s,kJ/(kg·K)	2.1129	2.1260	2.4267	2.7100	2.9837	3.2503	3.5105	3.7645	4.0123
0.40 (267.9)	v,m³/kg	0.1132		0.1318	0.1586	0.1840	0.2088	0.2332	0.2574	0.2814
	h,kJ/kg	534.80		591.44	685.79	789.70	903.77	1027.87	1161.55	1304.27
	s,kJ/(kg·K)	2.0798		2.2794	2.5700	2.8472	3.1157	3.3770	3.6317	3.8799
0.70 (286.8)	v,m³/kg	0.06561		0.07064	0.08763	0.1031	0.1178	0.1321	0.1462	0.1601
	h,kJ/kg	554.69		580.20	678.70	784.73	900.06	1024.98	1159.23	1302.36
	s,kJ/(kg·K)	2.0594		2.1464	2.4498	2.7327	3.0042	3.2672	3.5230	3.7720
1.0 (300.3)	v,m³/kg	0.04581			0.05915	0.07065	0.08135	0.09163	0.1017	0.1116
	h,kJ/kg	567.88			671.19	779.59	896.28	1022.05	1156.89	1300.45
	s,kJ/(kg·K)	2.0485			2.3669	2.6562	2.9308	3.1957	3.4526	3.7023
2.0 (330.4)	v,m³/kg	0.02158			0.02534	0.03268	0.03882	0.04444	0.04979	0.05497
	h,kJ/kg	591.47			641.60	761.13	883.12	1012.06	1148.99	1294.01
	s,kJ/(kg·K)	2.0248			2.1723	2.4916	2.7788	3.0504	3.3113	3.5635
4.0 (366.5)	v,m³/kg	0.00724				0.01316	0.01745	0.02085	0.02389	0.02673
	h,kJ/kg	576.24				714.17	853.84	990.91	1132.70	1280.98
	s,kJ/(kg·K)	1.9072				2.2702	2.5994	2.8882	3.1584	3.4164
7.0	v,m³/kg					0.00418	0.00822	0.01080	0.01288	0.01473
	h,kJ/kg					591.69	800.86	956.60	1107.49	1261.33
	s,kJ/(kg·K)					1.9064	2.4019	2.7303	3.0179	3.2856
10.	v,m³/kg					0.00298	0.00495	0.00697	0.00862	0.01005
	h,kJ/kg					544.14	746.96	921.77	1082.57	1242.27
	s,kJ/(kg·K)					1.7619	2.2400	2.6088	2.9154	3.1933
20.	v,m³/kg					0.00238	0.00287	0.00355	0.00431	0.00506
	h,kJ/kg					517.85	678.63	849.71	1021.44	1192.46
	s,kJ/(kg·K)					1.6314	2.0098	2.3702	2.6976	2.9952

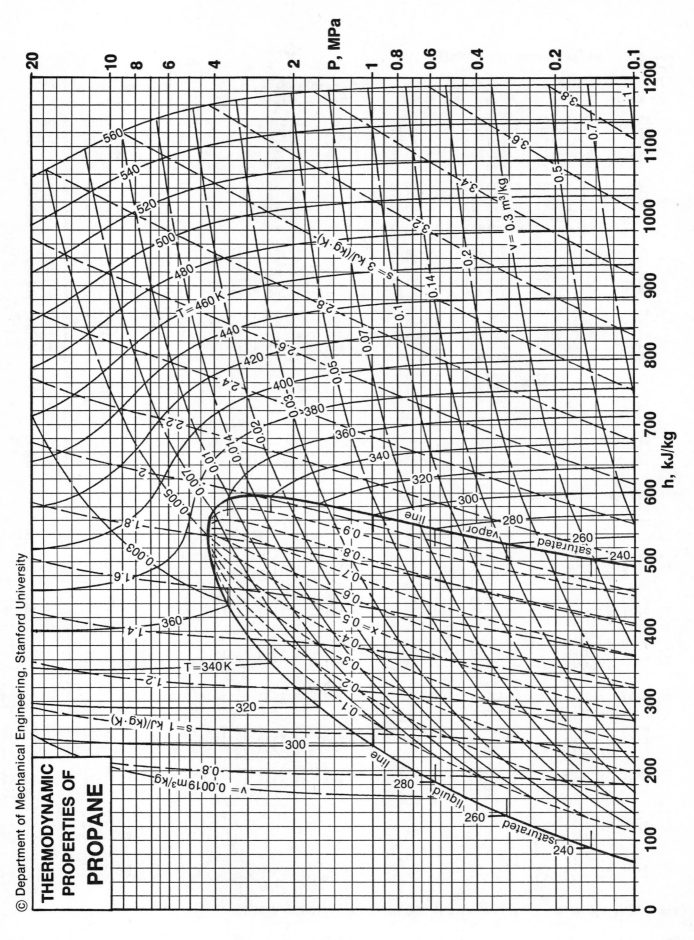

© Department of Mechanical Engineering, Stanford University

THERMODYNAMIC PROPERTIES OF PROPANE

P, MPa

h, kJ/kg

65

PROPERTIES OF SATURATED PROPYL ALCOHOL

T K	P MPa	volume, m³/kg v_f	v_g	enthalpy, kJ/kg h_f	h_{fg}	h_g	entropy, kJ/(kg·K) s_f	s_{fg}	s_g
275	0.0004998	0.001225	76.08	0.0	832.75	832.75	0.0	3.0282	3.0282
285	0.001072	0.001235	36.74	25.18	820.95	846.13	0.0899	2.8806	2.9705
295	0.002163	0.001246	18.84	51.05	808.84	859.89	0.1791	2.7419	2.9210
305	0.004128	0.001258	10.19	77.68	796.31	873.99	0.2679	2.6108	2.8787
315	0.007497	0.001270	5.785	105.13	783.26	888.39	0.3564	2.4866	2.8430
325	0.01302	0.001283	3.428	133.48	769.56	903.04	0.4450	2.3679	2.8129
335	0.02170	0.001298	2.112	162.79	755.10	917.89	0.5338	2.2540	2.7878
345	0.03487	0.001313	1.347	193.11	739.75	932.86	0.6229	2.1442	2.7671
355	0.05417	0.001330	0.8867	224.53	723.36	947.89	0.7126	2.0376	2.7502
365	0.08163	0.001348	0.6003	257.07	705.84	962.91	0.8029	1.9338	2.7367
370.57	0.101325	0.001358	0.4885	275.71	695.53	971.24	0.8535	1.8769	2.7304
375	0.1196	0.001367	0.4169	290.76	687.08	977.84	0.8938	1.8322	2.7260
385	0.1708	0.001388	0.2962	325.61	667.00	992.61	0.9853	1.7325	2.7178
395	0.2382	0.001411	0.2148	361.60	645.54	1007.14	1.0774	1.6342	2.7116
405	0.3251	0.001436	0.1586	398.70	622.66	1021.36	1.1698	1.5374	2.7072
415	0.4350	0.001463	0.1191	436.88	598.32	1035.20	1.2625	1.4418	2.7043
425	0.5715	0.001493	0.09070	476.06	572.52	1048.58	1.3553	1.3472	2.7025
435	0.7383	0.001525	0.06996	516.18	545.24	1061.42	1.4480	1.2535	2.7015
445	0.9390	0.001562	0.05456	557.15	516.46	1073.61	1.5405	1.1606	2.7011
455	1.177	0.001602	0.04294	598.89	486.16	1085.05	1.6324	1.0685	2.7009
465	1.457	0.001648	0.03405	641.31	454.27	1095.58	1.7236	0.9769	2.7005
475	1.782	0.001700	0.02713	684.34	420.66	1105.00	1.8140	0.8856	2.6996
485	2.155	0.001761	0.02167	727.92	385.08	1113.00	1.9035	0.7939	2.6974
495	2.581	0.001834	0.01729	772.05	347.04	1119.09	1.9920	0.7011	2.6931
505	3.064	0.001923	0.01371	816.84	305.60	1122.44	2.0797	0.6052	2.6849
515	3.610	0.002041	0.01069	862.74	258.62	1121.36	2.1676	0.5022	2.6698
525	4.229	0.002217	0.007988	911.30	200.13	1111.43	2.2585	0.3812	2.6397
536.85	5.075	0.003658	0.003658	1022.82	0.0	1022.82	2.4638	0.0	2.4638

PROPERTIES OF GASEOUS PROPYL ALCOHOL

P,MPa (T_{sat},K)		sat	400	425	450	475	500	525	550	575
0.101325 (370.6)	v,m³/kg	0.4885	0.5326	0.5691	0.6051	0.6407	0.6760	0.7111	0.7460	0.7807
	h,kJ/kg	971.24	1025.14	1073.08	1122.99	1174.84	1228.60	1284.21	1341.62	1400.77
	s,kJ/(kg·K)	2.7304	2.8703	2.9865	3.1006	3.2128	3.3230	3.4315	3.5384	3.6435
0.20 (389.7)	v,m³/kg	0.2543	0.2628	0.2826	0.3019	0.3207	0.3391	0.3574	0.3754	0.3934
	h,kJ/kg	999.42	1019.24	1068.32	1119.10	1171.62	1225.89	1281.91	1339.64	1399.05
	s,kJ/(kg·K)	2.7147	2.7649	2.8839	3.0000	3.1135	3.2249	3.3342	3.4416	3.5472
0.40 (412.1)	v,m³/kg	0.1294		0.1352	0.1460	0.1562	0.1661	0.1757	0.1852	0.1944
	h,kJ/kg	1031.17		1058.10	1110.86	1164.86	1220.26	1277.15	1335.57	1395.52
	s,kJ/(kg·K)	2.7050		2.7694	2.8900	3.0068	3.1204	3.2314	3.3401	3.4467
0.60 (426.9)	v,m³/kg	0.08636			0.09382	0.1013	0.1084	0.1151	0.1217	0.1281
	h,kJ/kg	1051.01			1102.09	1157.78	1214.43	1272.26	1331.41	1391.94
	s,kJ/(kg·K)	2.7022			2.8188	2.9392	3.0554	3.1683	3.2783	3.3859
0.80 (438.3)	v,m³/kg	0.06443			0.06756	0.07373	0.07942	0.08480	0.08995	0.09495
	h,kJ/kg	1065.48			1092.64	1150.32	1208.37	1267.23	1327.16	1388.29
	s,kJ/(kg·K)	2.7013			2.7625	2.8872	3.0063	3.1212	3.2327	3.3413
1.0 (447.7)	v,m³/kg	0.05108			0.05162	0.05709	0.06201	0.06657	0.07089	0.07503
	h,kJ/kg	1076.81			1082.35	1142.42	1202.05	1262.04	1322.81	1384.58
	s,kJ/(kg·K)	2.7010			2.7134	2.8433	2.9656	3.0827	3.1958	3.3056
2.0 (481.0)	v,m³/kg	0.02370					0.02663	0.02982	0.03259	0.03511
	h,kJ/kg	1110.00					1165.08	1233.15	1299.28	1364.89
	s,kJ/(kg·K)	2.6985					2.8108	2.9437	3.0668	3.1834
4.0 (521.4)	v,m³/kg	0.00893						0.00971	0.01283	0.01487
	h,kJ/kg	1116.55						1137.62	1237.75	1317.95
	s,kJ/(kg·K)	2.6531						2.6934	2.8800	3.0227

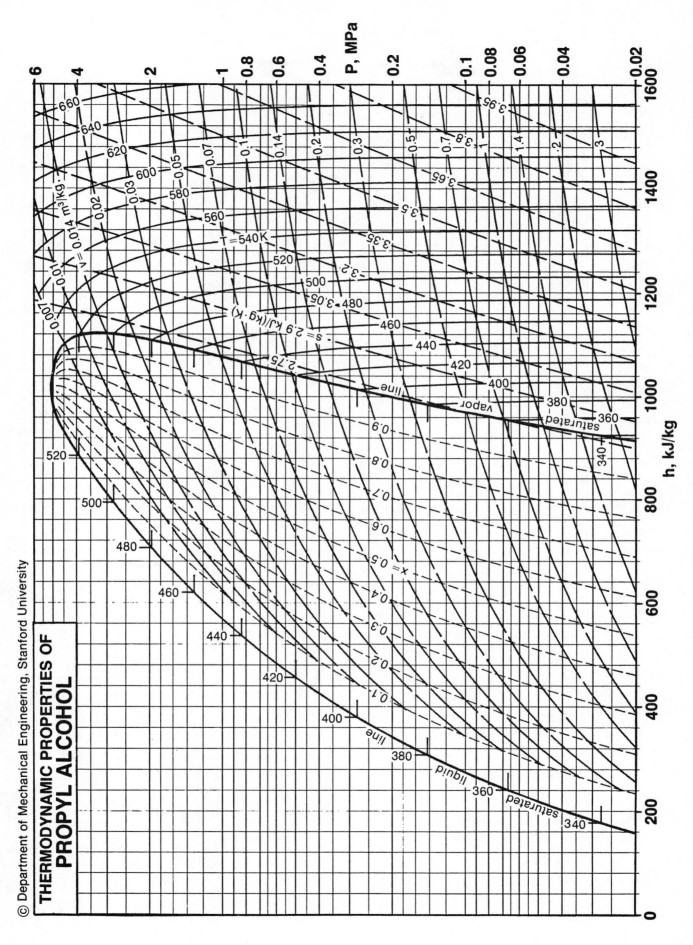

© Department of Mechanical Engineering, Stanford University

THERMODYNAMIC PROPERTIES OF
PROPYL ALCOHOL

P, MPa

h, kJ/kg

67

PROPERTIES OF SATURATED PROPYLENE

T K	P MPa	v_f	v_g	h_f	h_fg	h_g	s_f	s_fg	s_g
		volume, m³/kg		enthalpy, kJ/kg			entropy, kJ/(kg·K)		
200	0.02685	0.001558	1.454	0.0	469.31	469.31	0.0	2.3466	2.3466
210	0.04738	0.001587	0.8595	23.30	457.27	480.57	0.1135	2.1775	2.2910
220	0.07868	0.001618	0.5373	46.14	445.63	491.77	0.2196	2.0256	2.2452
225.41	0.101325	0.001636	0.4250	58.37	439.41	497.78	0.2743	1.9494	2.2237
230	0.1242	0.001652	0.3517	68.69	434.14	502.83	0.3195	1.8875	2.2070
240	0.1879	0.001688	0.2391	91.23	422.45	513.68	0.4150	1.7602	2.1752
250	0.2740	0.001727	0.1679	114.05	410.20	524.25	0.5075	1.6408	2.1483
260	0.3870	0.001769	0.1210	137.34	397.11	534.45	0.5980	1.5274	2.1254
270	0.5318	0.001815	0.08916	161.20	383.00	544.20	0.6871	1.4185	2.1056
280	0.7135	0.001866	0.06692	185.70	367.68	553.38	0.7750	1.3131	2.0881
290	0.9374	0.001923	0.05097	210.88	350.99	561.87	0.8618	1.2104	2.0722
300	1.209	0.001987	0.03927	236.86	332.65	569.51	0.9481	1.1089	2.0570
310	1.534	0.002061	0.03050	263.87	312.18	576.05	1.0345	1.0071	2.0416
320	1.919	0.002148	0.02378	292.24	288.92	581.16	1.1220	0.9029	2.0249
330	2.371	0.002255	0.01854	322.35	261.96	584.31	1.2116	0.7938	2.0054
340	2.897	0.002394	0.01433	354.74	229.76	584.50	1.3046	0.6758	1.9804
350	3.508	0.002598	0.01080	390.79	188.68	579.47	1.4047	0.5391	1.9438
360	4.219	0.003006	0.007451	437.27	123.26	560.53	1.5299	0.3424	1.8723
364.90	4.613	0.004405	0.004405	503.72	0.0	503.72	1.7092	0.0	1.7092

PROPERTIES OF GASEOUS PROPYLENE

P,MPa (T_sat,K)		sat	260	300	340	380	420	460	500	540
0.070 (217.6)	v,m³/kg	0.5988	0.7229	0.8385	0.9533	1.068	1.181	1.295	1.409	1.522
	h,kJ/kg	489.09	545.62	604.29	668.62	738.90	815.18	897.33	985.06	1078.00
	s,kJ/(kg·K)	2.2554	2.4924	2.7021	2.9032	3.0984	3.2892	3.4759	3.6587	3.8375
0.101325 (225.4)	v,m³/kg	0.4250	0.4960	0.5767	0.6566	0.7359	0.8150	0.8937	0.9724	1.051
	h,kJ/kg	497.78	544.60	603.51	668.01	738.40	814.77	896.98	984.75	1077.73
	s,kJ/(kg·K)	2.2237	2.4167	2.6273	2.8289	3.0245	3.2154	3.4023	3.5852	3.7640
0.20 (241.6)	v,m³/kg	0.2256	0.2456	0.2880	0.3295	0.3703	0.4109	0.4512	0.4913	0.5314
	h,kJ/kg	515.39	541.28	601.00	666.04	736.81	813.45	895.87	983.80	1076.91
	s,kJ/(kg·K)	2.1706	2.2738	2.4873	2.6906	2.8872	3.0789	3.2662	3.4495	3.6285
0.40 (261.0)	v,m³/kg	0.1172		0.1396	0.1614	0.1826	0.2034	0.2240	0.2444	0.2646
	h,kJ/kg	535.45		595.69	661.96	733.55	810.77	893.61	981.87	1075.23
	s,kJ/(kg·K)	2.1233		2.3383	2.5454	2.7444	2.9375	3.1258	3.3097	3.4893
0.70 (279.3)	v,m³/kg	0.06819		0.07576	0.08933	0.1021	0.1145	0.1266	0.1385	0.1503
	h,kJ/kg	552.78		587.03	655.54	728.51	806.67	890.19	978.96	1072.72
	s,kJ/(kg·K)	2.0893		2.2075	2.4218	2.6246	2.8200	3.0099	3.1949	3.3752
1.0 (292.5)	v,m³/kg	0.04774		0.04991	0.06039	0.06989	0.07891	0.08764	0.09619	0.1046
	h,kJ/kg	563.85		577.25	648.73	723.31	802.50	886.73	976.03	1070.20
	s,kJ/(kg·K)	2.0684		2.1136	2.3372	2.5445	2.7425	2.9340	3.1201	3.3012
2.0 (321.9)	v,m³/kg	0.02269			0.02608	0.03212	0.03734	0.04219	0.04681	0.05129
	h,kJ/kg	581.93			621.71	704.43	787.93	874.92	966.15	1061.76
	s,kJ/(kg·K)	2.0215			2.1417	2.3718	2.5807	2.7784	2.9686	3.1525
3.0 (341.8)	v,m³/kg	0.01366				0.01929	0.02343	0.02703	0.03036	0.03353
	h,kJ/kg	584.09				682.20	772.17	862.63	956.09	1053.28
	s,kJ/(kg·K)	1.9750				2.2479	2.4730	2.6787	2.8735	3.0604
4.0 (357.1)	v,m³/kg	0.00847				0.01256	0.01641	0.01944	0.02215	0.02467
	h,kJ/kg	568.95				654.01	754.88	849.80	945.84	1044.76
	s,kJ/(kg·K)	1.9007				2.1325	2.3852	2.6011	2.8013	2.9915
7.0	v,m³/kg					0.00314	0.00716	0.00970	0.01164	0.01334
	h,kJ/kg					490.13	689.17	807.70	914.06	1019.08
	s,kJ/(kg·K)					1.6498	2.1504	2.4205	2.6422	2.8443
10.	v,m³/kg					0.00263	0.00399	0.00596	0.00756	0.00891
	h,kJ/kg					463.63	618.60	762.41	881.75	993.83
	s,kJ/(kg·K)					1.5578	1.9449	2.2726	2.5216	2.7372

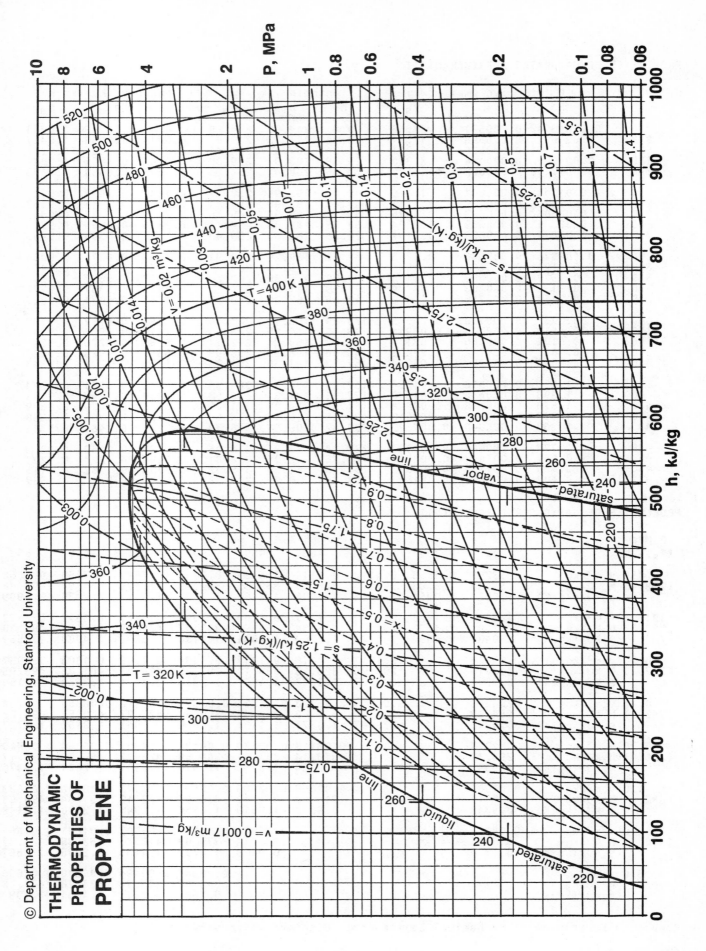

© Department of Mechanical Engineering, Stanford University

THERMODYNAMIC PROPERTIES OF PROPYLENE

P, MPa

h, kJ/kg

69

PROPERTIES OF SATURATED REFRIGERANT 11

T	P	volume, m³/kg		enthalpy, kJ/kg			entropy, kJ/(kg·K)		
K	MPa	v_f	v_g	h_f	h_{fg}	h_g	s_f	s_{fg}	s_g
200	0.0004374	0.000591	27.66	0.0	214.90	214.90	0.0	1.0745	1.0745
210	0.001012	0.000598	12.54	8.48	211.13	219.61	0.0414	1.0053	1.0467
220	0.002142	0.000606	6.201	16.94	207.47	224.41	0.0807	0.9431	1.0238
230	0.004203	0.000614	3.300	25.39	203.91	229.30	0.1183	0.8866	1.0049
240	0.007721	0.000622	1.870	33.85	200.41	234.26	0.1543	0.8350	0.9893
250	0.01340	0.000631	1.119	42.33	196.94	239.27	0.1889	0.7877	0.9766
260	0.02215	0.000639	0.7011	50.83	193.48	244.31	0.2222	0.7441	0.9663
270	0.03505	0.000649	0.4576	59.37	189.99	249.36	0.2544	0.7037	0.9581
280	0.05341	0.000659	0.3094	67.95	186.46	254.41	0.2856	0.6659	0.9515
290	0.07871	0.000669	0.2157	76.58	182.85	259.43	0.3158	0.6305	0.9463
296.97	0.101325	0.000676	0.1705	82.62	180.29	262.91	0.3363	0.6071	0.9434
300	0.1126	0.000680	0.1545	85.26	179.16	264.42	0.3451	0.5972	0.9423
310	0.1570	0.000691	0.1133	94.00	175.36	269.36	0.3737	0.5657	0.9394
320	0.2138	0.000703	0.08474	102.79	171.44	274.23	0.4015	0.5357	0.9372
330	0.2852	0.000716	0.06456	111.65	167.36	279.01	0.4286	0.5071	0.9357
340	0.3735	0.000730	0.04995	120.59	163.11	283.70	0.4551	0.4797	0.9348
350	0.4810	0.000744	0.03918	129.62	158.65	288.27	0.4810	0.4533	0.9343
360	0.6102	0.000760	0.03109	138.77	153.94	292.71	0.5065	0.4276	0.9341
370	0.7638	0.000778	0.02492	148.06	148.93	296.99	0.5317	0.4025	0.9342
380	0.9446	0.000797	0.02014	157.53	143.55	301.08	0.5565	0.3778	0.9343
390	1.155	0.000818	0.01639	167.23	137.71	304.94	0.5813	0.3531	0.9344
400	1.399	0.000842	0.01340	177.21	131.31	308.52	0.6060	0.3283	0.9343
410	1.679	0.000870	0.01098	187.56	124.20	311.76	0.6310	0.3029	0.9339
420	1.999	0.000902	0.009010	198.38	116.17	314.55	0.6564	0.2766	0.9330
430	2.363	0.000940	0.007372	209.82	106.91	316.73	0.6825	0.2486	0.9311
440	2.774	0.000988	0.005987	222.14	95.91	318.05	0.7099	0.2180	0.9279
450	3.237	0.001054	0.004782	235.76	82.25	318.01	0.7394	0.1828	0.9222
460	3.756	0.001157	0.003672	251.73	63.59	315.32	0.7733	0.1382	0.9115
471.15	4.409	0.001806	0.001806	288.78	0.0	288.78	0.8507	0.0	0.8507

PROPERTIES OF GASEOUS REFRIGERANT 11

P,MPa (T_{sat},K)		sat	300	350	400	T,K 450	500	550	600	650
0.050 (278.4)	v,m³/kg	0.3290	0.3566	0.4192	0.4810	0.5423	0.6033	0.6642	0.7250	0.7858
	h,kJ/kg	253.59	265.93	295.68	326.90	359.35	392.79	427.04	461.97	497.48
	s,kJ/(kg·K)	0.9524	0.9951	1.0868	1.1701	1.2465	1.3170	1.3823	1.4430	1.4999
0.101325 (297.0)	v,m³/kg	0.1705	0.1725	0.2046	0.2357	0.2664	0.2968	0.3270	0.3572	0.3872
	h,kJ/kg	262.91	264.70	294.87	326.34	358.93	392.47	426.79	461.76	497.30
	s,kJ/(kg·K)	0.9434	0.9494	1.0424	1.1264	1.2031	1.2738	1.3392	1.4000	1.4569
0.20 (317.8)	v,m³/kg	0.09024		0.1013	0.1178	0.1337	0.1494	0.1649	0.1803	0.1957
	h,kJ/kg	273.15		293.26	325.23	358.12	391.85	426.29	461.35	496.95
	s,kJ/(kg·K)	0.9376		0.9979	1.0832	1.1607	1.2318	1.2974	1.3584	1.4154
0.40 (342.6)	v,m³/kg	0.04678		0.04819	0.05720	0.06563	0.07375	0.08170	0.08955	0.09734
	h,kJ/kg	284.93		289.79	322.90	356.44	390.57	425.27	460.51	496.25
	s,kJ/(kg·K)	0.9346		0.9487	1.0371	1.1161	1.1880	1.2542	1.3155	1.3727
0.70 (366.0)	v,m³/kg	0.02717			0.03113	0.03639	0.04130	0.04603	0.05064	0.05519
	h,kJ/kg	295.32			319.14	353.81	388.59	423.72	459.23	495.17
	s,kJ/(kg·K)	0.9341			0.9964	1.0780	1.1513	1.2183	1.2801	1.3376
1.0 (382.8)	v,m³/kg	0.01901			0.02059	0.02465	0.02830	0.03175	0.03508	0.03833
	h,kJ/kg	302.17			314.98	351.02	386.54	422.12	457.94	494.08
	s,kJ/(kg·K)	0.9343			0.9670	1.0519	1.1268	1.1946	1.2570	1.3148
2.0 (420.0)	v,m³/kg	0.00901				0.01076	0.01307	0.01507	0.01691	0.01867
	h,kJ/kg	314.55				340.14	379.07	416.48	453.45	490.37
	s,kJ/(kg·K)	0.9330				0.9918	1.0739	1.1453	1.2096	1.2687
5.0	v,m³/kg						0.00341	0.00494	0.00600	0.00690
	h,kJ/kg						343.97	395.74	438.28	478.38
	s,kJ/(kg·K)						0.9621	1.0611	1.1351	1.1994

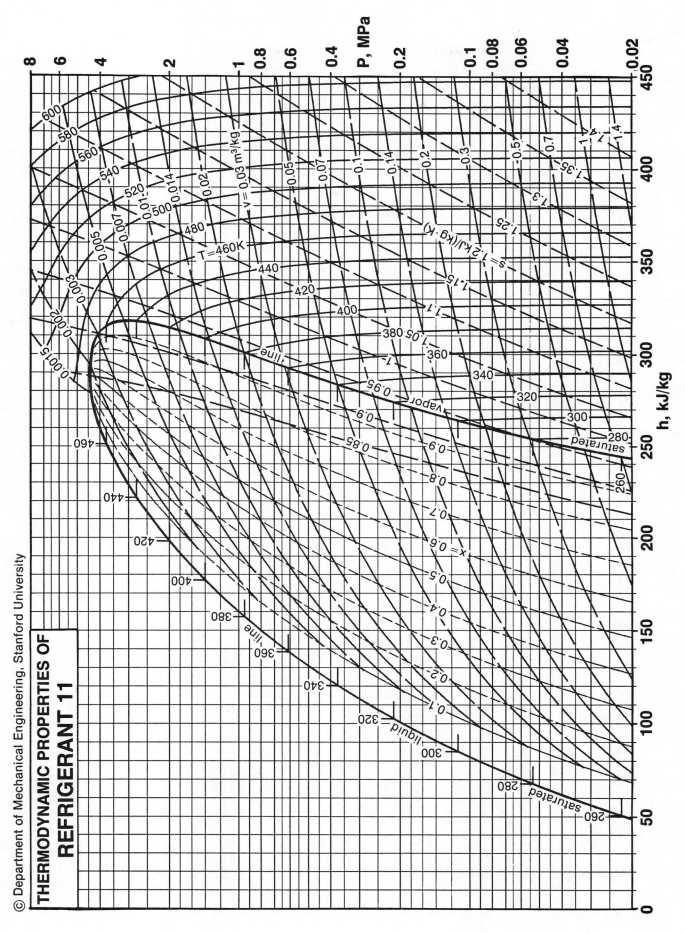

© Department of Mechanical Engineering, Stanford University

THERMODYNAMIC PROPERTIES OF REFRIGERANT 11

P, MPa

h, kJ/kg

71

PROPERTIES OF SATURATED REFRIGERANT 12

T	P	volume, m³/kg		enthalpy, kJ/kg			entropy, kJ/(kg·K)		
K	MPa	v_f	v_g	h_f	h_{fg}	h_g	s_f	s_{fg}	s_g
200	0.009957	0.000623	1.369	0.0	183.02	183.02	0.0	0.9151	0.9151
204	0.01294	0.000627	1.072	3.44	181.43	184.87	0.0170	0.8894	0.9064
208	0.01663	0.000631	0.8492	6.90	179.83	186.73	0.0338	0.8646	0.8984
212	0.02114	0.000636	0.6795	10.36	178.24	188.60	0.0503	0.8407	0.8910
216	0.02658	0.000640	0.5490	13.83	176.63	190.46	0.0665	0.8177	0.8842
220	0.03311	0.000644	0.4476	17.31	175.02	192.33	0.0824	0.7955	0.8779
224	0.04087	0.000649	0.3680	20.80	173.39	194.19	0.0981	0.7741	0.8722
228	0.05002	0.000653	0.3050	24.31	171.74	196.05	0.1136	0.7533	0.8669
232	0.06073	0.000658	0.2546	27.83	170.07	197.90	0.1289	0.7331	0.8620
236	0.07318	0.000663	0.2141	31.36	168.39	199.75	0.1439	0.7136	0.8575
240	0.08754	0.000668	0.1811	34.90	166.70	201.60	0.1588	0.6945	0.8533
243.38	0.101325	0.000672	0.1580	37.91	165.23	203.14	0.1712	0.6789	0.8501
244	0.1040	0.000673	0.1542	38.46	164.97	203.43	0.1734	0.6761	0.8495
248	0.1228	0.000678	0.1320	42.03	163.22	205.25	0.1879	0.6581	0.8460
252	0.1442	0.000684	0.1136	45.62	161.44	207.06	0.2022	0.6406	0.8428
256	0.1683	0.000689	0.09827	49.22	159.64	208.86	0.2163	0.6236	0.8399
260	0.1954	0.000695	0.08539	52.85	157.79	210.64	0.2303	0.6069	0.8372
264	0.2257	0.000701	0.07453	56.49	155.91	212.40	0.2441	0.5906	0.8347
266	0.2421	0.000704	0.06974	58.32	154.96	213.28	0.2510	0.5825	0.8335
268	0.2595	0.000708	0.06531	60.15	154.00	214.15	0.2578	0.5746	0.8324
270	0.2777	0.000711	0.06123	61.99	153.03	215.02	0.2646	0.5668	0.8314
272	0.2969	0.000714	0.05746	63.83	152.05	215.88	0.2713	0.5590	0.8303
274	0.3171	0.000717	0.05396	65.68	151.06	216.74	0.2780	0.5513	0.8293
276	0.3384	0.000721	0.05073	67.53	150.06	217.59	0.2847	0.5437	0.8284
278	0.3606	0.000724	0.04772	69.39	149.04	218.43	0.2914	0.5361	0.8275
280	0.3840	0.000728	0.04494	71.26	148.01	219.27	0.2980	0.5286	0.8266
282	0.4085	0.000731	0.04234	73.13	146.98	220.11	0.3046	0.5212	0.8258
284	0.4341	0.000735	0.03993	75.01	145.92	220.93	0.3112	0.5138	0.8250
286	0.4609	0.000739	0.03768	76.90	144.85	221.75	0.3177	0.5065	0.8242
288	0.4890	0.000742	0.03558	78.79	143.78	222.57	0.3243	0.4992	0.8235
290	0.5183	0.000746	0.03362	80.70	142.67	223.37	0.3308	0.4920	0.8228
292	0.5488	0.000750	0.03179	82.61	141.56	224.17	0.3373	0.4848	0.8221
294	0.5807	0.000754	0.03008	84.53	140.43	224.96	0.3437	0.4777	0.8214
296	0.6140	0.000758	0.02848	86.46	139.28	225.74	0.3502	0.4706	0.8208
298	0.6487	0.000762	0.02697	88.39	138.13	226.52	0.3566	0.4635	0.8201
300	0.6847	0.000767	0.02557	90.34	136.94	227.28	0.3630	0.4565	0.8195
302	0.7223	0.000771	0.02424	92.30	135.73	228.03	0.3695	0.4494	0.8189
304	0.7614	0.000776	0.02300	94.27	134.51	228.78	0.3758	0.4425	0.8183
306	0.8020	0.000780	0.02183	96.25	133.26	229.51	0.3822	0.4356	0.8178
308	0.8441	0.000785	0.02073	98.24	132.00	230.24	0.3886	0.4286	0.8172
310	0.8879	0.000790	0.01969	100.24	130.71	230.95	0.3950	0.4216	0.8166
312	0.9334	0.000795	0.01872	102.26	129.39	231.65	0.4014	0.4147	0.8161
316	1.029	0.000805	0.01692	106.33	126.68	233.01	0.4141	0.4009	0.8150
320	1.132	0.000817	0.01532	110.47	123.84	234.31	0.4268	0.3870	0.8138
324	1.243	0.000828	0.01388	114.67	120.88	235.55	0.4396	0.3731	0.8127
328	1.361	0.000841	0.01259	118.95	117.77	236.72	0.4524	0.3591	0.8115
332	1.488	0.000854	0.01143	123.31	114.50	237.81	0.4653	0.3449	0.8102
336	1.622	0.000868	0.01038	127.76	111.05	238.81	0.4783	0.3305	0.8088
340	1.766	0.000884	0.009421	132.32	107.39	239.71	0.4914	0.3158	0.8072
344	1.918	0.000901	0.008550	136.99	103.49	240.48	0.5047	0.3008	0.8055
348	2.080	0.000919	0.007754	141.80	99.31	241.11	0.5181	0.2854	0.8035
352	2.253	0.000940	0.007023	146.77	94.81	241.58	0.5319	0.2693	0.8012
356	2.435	0.000963	0.006349	151.91	89.94	241.85	0.5459	0.2526	0.7985
360	2.628	0.000989	0.005724	157.27	84.59	241.86	0.5604	0.2349	0.7953
364	2.832	0.001019	0.005139	162.89	78.67	241.56	0.5753	0.2161	0.7914
368	3.048	0.001054	0.004586	168.83	72.00	240.83	0.5909	0.1957	0.7866
372	3.275	0.001098	0.004055	175.20	64.31	239.51	0.6075	0.1729	0.7804
376	3.515	0.001156	0.003532	182.19	55.08	237.27	0.6255	0.1464	0.7719
380	3.769	0.001241	0.002985	190.24	43.04	233.28	0.6460	0.1132	0.7592
385.17	4.116	0.001700	0.001700	209.51	0.0	209.51	0.6950	0.0	0.6950

PROPERTIES OF SATURATED REFRIGERANT 12

P MPa	T K	volume, m³/kg v_f	v_g	enthalpy, kJ/kg h_f	h_{fg}	h_g	entropy, kJ/(kg·K) s_f	s_{fg}	s_g
0.020	211.06	0.000635	0.7153	9.54	178.62	188.16	0.0464	0.8463	0.8927
0.022	212.69	0.000636	0.6547	10.95	177.97	188.92	0.0531	0.8367	0.8898
0.024	214.19	0.000638	0.6038	12.26	177.36	189.62	0.0592	0.8280	0.8872
0.026	215.60	0.000639	0.5605	13.48	176.80	190.28	0.0649	0.8199	0.8848
0.028	216.93	0.000641	0.5232	14.64	176.25	190.89	0.0702	0.8125	0.8827
0.030	218.18	0.000642	0.4907	15.72	175.76	191.48	0.0752	0.8055	0.8807
0.035	221.04	0.000645	0.4251	18.21	174.60	192.81	0.0865	0.7899	0.8764
0.040	223.58	0.000648	0.3755	20.44	173.55	193.99	0.0965	0.7762	0.8727
0.045	225.88	0.000651	0.3366	22.45	172.62	195.07	0.1054	0.7642	0.8696
0.050	227.99	0.000653	0.3051	24.30	171.74	196.04	0.1136	0.7533	0.8669
0.055	229.94	0.000656	0.2793	26.01	170.94	196.95	0.1210	0.7434	0.8644
0.060	231.75	0.000658	0.2575	27.60	170.19	197.79	0.1279	0.7344	0.8623
0.070	235.03	0.000662	0.2231	30.50	168.81	199.31	0.1403	0.7182	0.8585
0.080	237.97	0.000665	0.1970	33.10	167.56	200.66	0.1513	0.7041	0.8554
0.090	240.63	0.000669	0.1765	35.46	166.43	201.89	0.1611	0.6916	0.8527
0.101325	243.38	0.000672	0.1580	37.91	165.23	203.14	0.1712	0.6789	0.8501
0.11	245.33	0.000675	0.1464	39.64	164.39	204.03	0.1783	0.6700	0.8483
0.12	247.43	0.000678	0.1349	41.52	163.47	204.99	0.1858	0.6607	0.8465
0.13	249.40	0.000680	0.1252	43.28	162.60	205.88	0.1929	0.6520	0.8449
0.14	251.25	0.000683	0.1168	44.95	161.77	206.72	0.1995	0.6439	0.8434
0.15	253.01	0.000685	0.1095	46.53	160.98	207.51	0.2058	0.6363	0.8421
0.16	254.67	0.000688	0.1030	48.03	160.23	208.26	0.2117	0.6291	0.8408
0.17	256.26	0.000690	0.09734	49.46	159.51	208.97	0.2173	0.6224	0.8397
0.18	257.78	0.000692	0.09225	50.84	158.81	209.65	0.2226	0.6161	0.8387
0.19	259.24	0.000694	0.08768	52.16	158.14	210.30	0.2277	0.6100	0.8377
0.20	260.64	0.000696	0.08354	53.43	157.49	210.92	0.2325	0.6043	0.8368
0.22	263.28	0.000700	0.07636	55.83	156.26	212.09	0.2416	0.5935	0.8351
0.24	265.74	0.000704	0.07033	58.08	155.09	213.17	0.2501	0.5836	0.8337
0.26	268.06	0.000708	0.06519	60.20	153.98	214.18	0.2580	0.5744	0.8324
0.28	270.24	0.000711	0.06076	62.21	152.91	215.12	0.2654	0.5658	0.8312
0.30	272.31	0.000714	0.05690	64.12	151.89	216.01	0.2724	0.5578	0.8302
0.33	275.22	0.000719	0.05196	66.81	150.45	217.26	0.2821	0.5467	0.8288
0.37	278.81	0.000725	0.04657	70.15	148.63	218.78	0.2941	0.5330	0.8271
0.40	281.32	0.000730	0.04321	72.49	147.33	219.82	0.3024	0.5237	0.8261
0.43	283.68	0.000734	0.04030	74.71	146.09	220.80	0.3102	0.5149	0.8251
0.47	286.66	0.000740	0.03698	77.52	144.50	222.02	0.3199	0.5041	0.8240
0.50	288.76	0.000744	0.03482	79.52	143.35	222.87	0.3268	0.4964	0.8232
0.55	292.07	0.000750	0.03173	82.68	141.52	224.20	0.3375	0.4845	0.8220
0.60	295.17	0.000757	0.02913	85.65	139.77	225.42	0.3475	0.4735	0.8210
0.70	300.82	0.000769	0.02501	91.14	136.45	227.59	0.3657	0.4536	0.8193
0.80	305.91	0.000780	0.02188	96.15	133.33	229.48	0.3819	0.4359	0.8178
0.90	310.54	0.000791	0.01942	100.78	130.36	231.14	0.3967	0.4198	0.8165
1.0	314.81	0.000802	0.01744	105.11	127.50	232.61	0.4103	0.4050	0.8153
1.1	318.77	0.000813	0.01579	109.19	124.73	233.92	0.4229	0.3913	0.8142
1.2	322.48	0.000824	0.01441	113.06	122.03	235.09	0.4347	0.3784	0.8131
1.3	325.96	0.000834	0.01323	116.76	119.38	236.14	0.4459	0.3662	0.8121
1.4	329.26	0.000845	0.01221	120.31	116.76	237.07	0.4565	0.3546	0.8111
1.5	332.38	0.000855	0.01132	123.73	114.18	237.91	0.4665	0.3436	0.8101
1.6	335.36	0.000866	0.01054	127.04	111.62	238.66	0.4762	0.3328	0.8090
1.7	338.20	0.000877	0.009840	130.25	109.07	239.32	0.4855	0.3225	0.8080
1.8	340.92	0.000888	0.009213	133.38	106.52	239.90	0.4944	0.3125	0.8069
1.9	343.53	0.000899	0.008648	136.44	103.96	240.40	0.5031	0.3026	0.8057
2.0	346.04	0.000910	0.008135	139.43	101.39	240.82	0.5115	0.2930	0.8045
2.2	350.80	0.000933	0.007236	145.26	96.20	241.46	0.5277	0.2743	0.8020
2.4	355.25	0.000958	0.006471	150.94	90.87	241.81	0.5433	0.2558	0.7991
2.6	359.44	0.000985	0.005809	156.50	85.38	241.88	0.5583	0.2375	0.7958
2.8	363.39	0.001014	0.005226	162.01	79.62	241.63	0.5730	0.2191	0.7921
3.0	367.14	0.001046	0.004703	167.51	73.52	241.03	0.5875	0.2002	0.7877
3.5	375.75	0.001151	0.003565	181.73	55.71	237.44	0.6243	0.1482	0.7725
4.116	385.17	0.001700	0.001700	209.51	0.0	209.51	0.6950	0.0	0.6950

PROPERTIES OF GASEOUS REFRIGERANT 12

P,MPa (T$_{sat}$,K)		sat	230	240	250	260	270	280	290	300
0.020	v,m³/kg	0.7153	0.7826	0.8178	0.8530	0.8880	0.9229	0.9577	0.9925	1.027
(211.1)	h,kJ/kg	188.16	198.05	203.44	208.94	214.55	220.27	226.10	232.02	238.04
	s,kJ/(kg·K)	0.8927	0.9376	0.9605	0.9830	1.0050	1.0265	1.0477	1.0685	1.0889
0.030	v,m³/kg	0.4907	0.5190	0.5428	0.5665	0.5900	0.6135	0.6369	0.6602	0.6835
(218.2)	h,kJ/kg	191.48	197.75	203.17	208.71	214.34	220.08	225.93	231.87	237.90
	s,kJ/(kg·K)	0.8807	0.9087	0.9318	0.9544	0.9765	0.9982	1.0194	1.0402	1.0607
0.040	v,m³/kg	0.3755	0.3872	0.4053	0.4232	0.4411	0.4588	0.4765	0.4941	0.5116
(223.6)	h,kJ/kg	193.99	197.45	202.91	208.47	214.13	219.89	225.75	231.71	237.76
	s,kJ/(kg·K)	0.8727	0.8880	0.9112	0.9339	0.9561	0.9779	0.9992	1.0201	1.0406
0.050	v,m³/kg	0.3051	0.3081	0.3228	0.3373	0.3517	0.3660	0.3802	0.3944	0.4085
(228.0)	h,kJ/kg	196.04	197.14	202.63	208.23	213.92	219.70	225.58	231.56	237.62
	s,kJ/(kg·K)	0.8669	0.8716	0.8950	0.9179	0.9402	0.9620	0.9834	1.0044	1.0249
0.070	v,m³/kg	0.2231		0.2284	0.2390	0.2495	0.2599	0.2702	0.2804	0.2906
(235.0)	h,kJ/kg	199.31		202.09	207.74	213.49	219.32	225.24	231.24	237.34
	s,kJ/(kg·K)	0.8585		0.8702	0.8933	0.9158	0.9378	0.9594	0.9804	1.0011
0.101325	v,m³/kg	0.1580			0.1630	0.1705	0.1779	0.1852	0.1924	0.1995
(243.4)	h,kJ/kg	203.14			206.97	212.80	218.70	224.69	230.75	236.89
	s,kJ/(kg·K)	0.8501			0.8656	0.8885	0.9108	0.9325	0.9538	0.9746
0.14	v,m³/kg	0.1168				0.1217	0.1272	0.1326	0.1380	0.1433
(251.3)	h,kJ/kg	206.72				211.93	217.93	224.00	230.13	236.33
	s,kJ/(kg·K)	0.8434				0.8638	0.8864	0.9085	0.9300	0.9510
0.20	v,m³/kg	0.08354					0.08734	0.09131	0.09520	0.09903
(260.6)	h,kJ/kg	210.92					216.70	222.90	229.14	235.44
	s,kJ/(kg·K)	0.8368					0.8585	0.8811	0.9030	0.9244
0.30	v,m³/kg	0.05690						0.05910	0.06187	0.06457
(272.3)	h,kJ/kg	216.01						220.98	227.44	233.91
	s,kJ/(kg·K)	0.8302						0.8482	0.8708	0.8928

P, MPa (T$_{sat}$,K)		310	320	330	340	350	360	370	380	400
0.020	v,m³/kg	1.062	1.097	1.131	1.166	1.200	1.235	1.269	1.304	1.373
(211.1)	h,kJ/kg	244.16	250.37	256.66	263.05	269.51	276.06	282.69	289.38	302.99
	s,kJ/(kg·K)	1.1090	1.1287	1.1481	1.1671	1.1859	1.2043	1.2225	1.2403	1.2752
0.030	v,m³/kg	0.7067	0.7299	0.7531	0.7762	0.7993	0.8224	0.8455	0.8686	0.9146
(218.2)	h,kJ/kg	244.03	250.25	256.56	262.95	269.42	275.98	282.61	289.31	302.93
	s,kJ/(kg·K)	1.0808	1.1005	1.1200	1.1390	1.1578	1.1763	1.1944	1.2123	1.2472
0.040	v,m³/kg	0.5291	0.5466	0.5640	0.5814	0.5988	0.6162	0.6335	0.6509	0.6855
(223.6)	h,kJ/kg	243.90	250.13	256.45	262.85	269.33	275.89	282.53	289.24	302.86
	s,kJ/(kg·K)	1.0607	1.0805	1.0999	1.1191	1.1378	1.1563	1.1745	1.1924	1.2273
0.050	v,m³/kg	0.4226	0.4366	0.4506	0.4646	0.4785	0.4924	0.5063	0.5202	0.5480
(228.0)	h,kJ/kg	243.77	250.02	256.34	262.75	269.24	275.80	282.45	289.16	302.80
	s,kJ/(kg·K)	1.0451	1.0649	1.0844	1.1035	1.1223	1.1408	1.1590	1.1769	1.2119
0.070	v,m³/kg	0.3008	0.3109	0.3209	0.3310	0.3410	0.3510	0.3610	0.3710	0.3908
(235.0)	h,kJ/kg	243.52	249.78	256.12	262.55	269.05	275.63	282.29	289.01	302.66
	s,kJ/(kg·K)	1.0214	1.0413	1.0608	1.0800	1.0988	1.1173	1.1356	1.1535	1.1885
0.101325	v,m³/kg	0.2066	0.2137	0.2207	0.2277	0.2347	0.2417	0.2486	0.2556	0.2694
(243.4)	h,kJ/kg	243.11	249.41	255.78	262.24	268.76	275.36	282.03	288.77	302.46
	s,kJ/(kg·K)	0.9950	1.0150	1.0346	1.0539	1.0728	1.0914	1.1097	1.1276	1.1627
0.14	v,m³/kg	0.1485	0.1537	0.1589	0.1640	0.1691	0.1742	0.1793	0.1843	0.1944
(251.3)	h,kJ/kg	242.60	248.94	255.36	261.84	268.40	275.03	281.72	288.48	302.20
	s,kJ/(kg·K)	0.9716	0.9917	1.0115	1.0308	1.0498	1.0685	1.0868	1.1049	1.1400
0.20	v,m³/kg	0.1028	0.1065	0.1102	0.1139	0.1175	0.1212	0.1248	0.1283	0.1355
(260.6)	h,kJ/kg	241.80	248.21	254.69	261.23	267.83	274.50	281.23	288.02	301.79
	s,kJ/(kg·K)	0.9452	0.9656	0.9855	1.0050	1.0242	1.0429	1.0614	1.0795	1.1148
0.30	v,m³/kg	0.06722	0.06982	0.07238	0.07491	0.07741	0.07989	0.08235	0.08480	0.08964
(272.3)	h,kJ/kg	240.42	246.96	253.55	260.18	266.87	273.61	280.40	287.25	301.12
	s,kJ/(kg·K)	0.9141	0.9349	0.9551	0.9750	0.9943	1.0133	1.0319	1.0502	1.0858

PROPERTIES OF GASEOUS REFRIGERANT 12

P, MPa (T_sat,K)		420	440	460	480	500	520	540	560	580
0.020 (211.1)	v,m³/kg	1.442	1.511	1.580	1.649	1.718	1.786	1.855	1.924	1.993
	h,kJ/kg	316.87	331.00	345.35	359.92	374.69	389.64	404.76	420.05	435.49
	s,kJ/(kg·K)	1.3091	1.3419	1.3738	1.4048	1.4350	1.4643	1.4928	1.5206	1.5477
0.030 (218.2)	v,m³/kg	0.9607	1.007	1.053	1.099	1.145	1.191	1.237	1.282	1.328
	h,kJ/kg	316.81	330.94	345.30	359.88	374.65	389.60	404.73	420.01	435.46
	s,kJ/(kg·K)	1.2811	1.3140	1.3459	1.3769	1.4070	1.4364	1.4649	1.4927	1.5198
0.040 (223.6)	v,m³/kg	0.7201	0.7546	0.7892	0.8237	0.8582	0.8927	0.9271	0.9616	0.9961
	h,kJ/kg	316.75	330.89	345.25	359.83	374.60	389.56	404.69	419.98	435.42
	s,kJ/(kg·K)	1.2612	1.2941	1.3260	1.3570	1.3872	1.4165	1.4451	1.4729	1.5000
0.050 (228.0)	v,m³/kg	0.5757	0.6034	0.6310	0.6587	0.6863	0.7139	0.7415	0.7691	0.7967
	h,kJ/kg	316.69	330.84	345.21	359.79	374.56	389.52	404.65	419.95	435.39
	s,kJ/(kg·K)	1.2458	1.2787	1.3106	1.3416	1.3718	1.4011	1.4297	1.4575	1.4846
0.070 (235.0)	v,m³/kg	0.4107	0.4305	0.4503	0.4701	0.4899	0.5096	0.5294	0.5491	0.5688
	h,kJ/kg	316.58	330.73	345.11	359.70	374.48	389.45	404.58	419.88	435.33
	s,kJ/(kg·K)	1.2225	1.2554	1.2873	1.3184	1.3485	1.3779	1.4065	1.4343	1.4614
0.101325 (243.4)	v,m³/kg	0.2832	0.2969	0.3107	0.3244	0.3381	0.3518	0.3654	0.3791	0.3927
	h,kJ/kg	316.39	330.56	344.96	359.56	374.35	389.32	404.47	419.77	435.23
	s,kJ/(kg·K)	1.1967	1.2297	1.2617	1.2927	1.3229	1.3523	1.3809	1.4087	1.4358
0.14 (251.3)	v,m³/kg	0.2045	0.2145	0.2244	0.2344	0.2444	0.2543	0.2642	0.2741	0.2840
	h,kJ/kg	316.16	330.35	344.77	359.38	374.19	389.18	404.33	419.64	435.11
	s,kJ/(kg·K)	1.1741	1.2071	1.2392	1.2703	1.3005	1.3299	1.3585	1.3863	1.4134
0.20 (260.6)	v,m³/kg	0.1426	0.1496	0.1567	0.1637	0.1707	0.1777	0.1847	0.1916	0.1986
	h,kJ/kg	315.80	330.03	344.47	359.11	373.94	388.94	404.11	419.44	434.92
	s,kJ/(kg·K)	1.1490	1.1821	1.2142	1.2453	1.2756	1.3050	1.3336	1.3615	1.3887
0.30 (272.3)	v,m³/kg	0.09445	0.09922	0.1040	0.1087	0.1134	0.1181	0.1228	0.1275	0.1321
	h,kJ/kg	315.20	329.48	343.98	358.66	373.52	388.56	403.75	419.10	434.60
	s,kJ/(kg·K)	1.1201	1.1533	1.1855	1.2168	1.2471	1.2766	1.3053	1.3332	1.3604

P,MPa (T_sat,K)		sat	300	310	320	330	340	350	360	370
0.40 (281.3)	v,m³/kg	0.04321	0.04730	0.04939	0.05144	0.05343	0.05540	0.05733	0.05924	0.06114
	h,kJ/kg	219.82	232.32	238.99	245.67	252.37	259.11	265.88	272.70	279.56
	s,kJ/(kg·K)	0.8261	0.8691	0.8910	0.9122	0.9328	0.9529	0.9725	0.9917	1.0105
0.50 (288.8)	v,m³/kg	0.03482	0.03690	0.03867	0.04038	0.04205	0.04368	0.04527	0.04685	0.04840
	h,kJ/kg	222.87	230.64	237.49	244.33	251.16	258.01	264.88	271.77	278.70
	s,kJ/(kg·K)	0.8232	0.8496	0.8721	0.8938	0.9148	0.9352	0.9551	0.9746	0.9935
0.70 (300.8)	v,m³/kg	0.02501		0.02632	0.02768	0.02898	0.03024	0.03146	0.03266	0.03382
	h,kJ/kg	227.59		234.29	241.49	248.62	255.71	262.78	269.85	276.93
	s,kJ/(kg·K)	0.8193		0.8412	0.8641	0.8860	0.9072	0.9277	0.9476	0.9670
1.0 (314.8)	v,m³/kg	0.01744			0.01802	0.01909	0.02009	0.02105	0.02197	0.02286
	h,kJ/kg	232.61			236.70	244.41	251.97	259.42	266.80	274.14
	s,kJ/(kg·K)	0.8153			0.8282	0.8519	0.8745	0.8961	0.9169	0.9370
1.4 (329.3)	v,m³/kg	0.01221				0.01229	0.01318	0.01400	0.01476	0.01549
	h,kJ/kg	237.07				237.72	246.22	254.38	262.31	270.10
	s,kJ/(kg·K)	0.8111				0.8131	0.8384	0.8621	0.8844	0.9058
2.0 (346.0)	v,m³/kg	0.00813						0.00846	0.00919	0.00984
	h,kJ/kg	240.82						244.81	254.23	263.07
	s,kJ/(kg·K)	0.8045						0.8160	0.8425	0.8667
2.5 (357.4)	v,m³/kg	0.00613							0.00635	0.00707
	h,kJ/kg	241.88							245.02	255.74
	s,kJ/(kg·K)	0.7975							0.8062	0.8356
3.0 (367.1)	v,m³/kg	0.00470								0.00497
	h,kJ/kg	241.03								245.34
	s,kJ/(kg·K)	0.7877								0.7994
4.0 (383.5)	v,m³/kg	0.00239								
	h,kJ/kg	225.75								
	s,kJ/(kg·K)	0.7379								

PROPERTIES OF GASEOUS REFRIGERANT 12

P, MPa (T_sat,K)		380	390	400	410	420	430	440	450	460
0.40 (281.3)	v,m³/kg	0.06301	0.06487	0.06672	0.06855	0.07038	0.07220	0.07401	0.07581	0.07761
	h,kJ/kg	286.47	293.42	300.43	307.48	314.58	321.74	328.94	336.18	343.48
	s,kJ/(kg·K)	1.0290	1.0470	1.0648	1.0822	1.0993	1.1161	1.1327	1.1490	1.1650
0.50 (288.8)	v,m³/kg	0.04993	0.05145	0.05296	0.05445	0.05593	0.05741	0.05888	0.06034	0.06179
	h,kJ/kg	285.67	292.68	299.73	306.83	313.97	321.15	328.38	335.66	342.98
	s,kJ/(kg·K)	1.0121	1.0303	1.0482	1.0657	1.0829	1.0998	1.1164	1.1328	1.1489
0.70 (300.8)	v,m³/kg	0.03497	0.03610	0.03722	0.03832	0.03942	0.04050	0.04158	0.04265	0.04372
	h,kJ/kg	284.03	291.16	298.31	305.49	312.71	319.97	327.26	334.59	341.96
	s,kJ/(kg·K)	0.9859	1.0044	1.0225	1.0403	1.0577	1.0747	1.0915	1.1080	1.1242
1.0 (314.8)	v,m³/kg	0.02372	0.02457	0.02540	0.02622	0.02702	0.02782	0.02860	0.02938	0.03015
	h,kJ/kg	281.46	288.78	296.10	303.43	310.77	318.14	325.54	332.96	340.41
	s,kJ/(kg·K)	0.9565	0.9755	0.9940	1.0121	1.0298	1.0472	1.0642	1.0809	1.0972
1.4 (329.3)	v,m³/kg	0.01618	0.01685	0.01749	0.01812	0.01874	0.01935	0.01994	0.02053	0.02111
	h,kJ/kg	277.79	285.41	292.99	300.54	308.08	315.62	323.16	330.72	338.29
	s,kJ/(kg·K)	0.9263	0.9461	0.9653	0.9839	1.0021	1.0198	1.0372	1.0541	1.0708
2.0 (346.0)	v,m³/kg	0.01044	0.01099	0.01151	0.01202	0.01250	0.01297	0.01343	0.01387	0.01431
	h,kJ/kg	271.55	279.80	287.89	295.87	303.77	311.61	319.42	327.21	334.98
	s,kJ/(kg·K)	0.8894	0.9108	0.9313	0.9510	0.9700	0.9885	1.0064	1.0239	1.0410
2.5 (357.4)	v,m³/kg	0.00766	0.00819	0.00868	0.00913	0.00956	0.00998	0.01037	0.01076	0.01113
	h,kJ/kg	265.38	274.44	283.14	291.59	299.87	308.03	316.11	324.12	332.10
	s,kJ/(kg·K)	0.8614	0.8849	0.9069	0.9278	0.9477	0.9669	0.9855	1.0035	1.0210
3.0 (367.1)	v,m³/kg	0.00570	0.00626	0.00674	0.00718	0.00759	0.00797	0.00833	0.00867	0.00901
	h,kJ/kg	257.66	268.13	277.75	286.86	295.64	304.20	312.60	320.88	329.09
	s,kJ/(kg·K)	0.8323	0.8595	0.8839	0.9063	0.9275	0.9477	0.9670	0.9856	1.0036
4.0 (383.5)	v,m³/kg		0.00349	0.00416	0.00465	0.00505	0.00541	0.00575	0.00605	0.00634
	h,kJ/kg		248.64	263.62	275.37	285.83	295.57	304.88	313.87	322.66
	s,kJ/(kg·K)		0.7972	0.8351	0.8642	0.8894	0.9123	0.9337	0.9539	0.9732

P, MPa (T_sat,K)		470	480	500	520	540	560	580	600	620
0.40 (281.3)	v,m³/kg	0.07940	0.08119	0.08476	0.08831	0.09185	0.09538	0.09891	0.1024	0.1059
	h,kJ/kg	350.82	358.20	373.10	388.17	403.39	418.76	434.28	449.93	465.72
	s,kJ/(kg·K)	1.1808	1.1963	1.2267	1.2563	1.2850	1.3130	1.3402	1.3667	1.3926
0.50 (288.8)	v,m³/kg	0.06324	0.06469	0.06757	0.07043	0.07329	0.07613	0.07897	0.08180	0.08463
	h,kJ/kg	350.34	357.74	372.68	387.77	403.02	418.42	433.96	449.63	465.44
	s,kJ/(kg·K)	1.1647	1.1803	1.2108	1.2404	1.2692	1.2972	1.3244	1.3510	1.3769
0.70 (300.8)	v,m³/kg	0.04478	0.04583	0.04792	0.05001	0.05208	0.05414	0.05619	0.05823	0.06027
	h,kJ/kg	349.37	356.82	371.83	386.99	402.29	417.74	433.32	449.03	464.87
	s,kJ/(kg·K)	1.1401	1.1558	1.1864	1.2162	1.2450	1.2731	1.3005	1.3271	1.3531
1.0 (314.8)	v,m³/kg	0.03092	0.03168	0.03319	0.03468	0.03617	0.03764	0.03910	0.04056	0.04201
	h,kJ/kg	347.89	355.41	370.54	385.80	401.19	416.71	432.35	448.12	464.01
	s,kJ/(kg·K)	1.1133	1.1292	1.1600	1.1900	1.2190	1.2472	1.2747	1.3014	1.3275
1.4 (329.3)	v,m³/kg	0.02168	0.02225	0.02337	0.02447	0.02556	0.02664	0.02771	0.02878	0.02984
	h,kJ/kg	345.88	353.49	368.79	384.19	399.70	415.32	431.06	446.91	462.87
	s,kJ/(kg·K)	1.0871	1.1031	1.1343	1.1645	1.1938	1.2222	1.2498	1.2767	1.3029
2.0 (346.0)	v,m³/kg	0.01474	0.01517	0.01600	0.01681	0.01761	0.01840	0.01918	0.01995	0.02071
	h,kJ/kg	342.75	350.52	366.10	381.73	397.43	413.22	429.10	445.08	461.16
	s,kJ/(kg·K)	1.0577	1.0741	1.1059	1.1365	1.1662	1.1949	1.2227	1.2498	1.2762
2.5 (357.4)	v,m³/kg	0.01150	0.01186	0.01256	0.01324	0.01390	0.01455	0.01520	0.01583	0.01646
	h,kJ/kg	340.04	347.97	363.80	379.64	395.51	411.45	427.46	443.55	459.72
	s,kJ/(kg·K)	1.0381	1.0548	1.0871	1.1182	1.1481	1.1771	1.2052	1.2325	1.2590
3.0 (367.1)	v,m³/kg	0.00933	0.00965	0.01026	0.01086	0.01143	0.01199	0.01254	0.01309	0.01362
	h,kJ/kg	337.23	345.33	361.44	377.51	393.57	409.66	425.81	442.01	458.29
	s,kJ/(kg·K)	1.0211	1.0382	1.0711	1.1026	1.1329	1.1622	1.1905	1.2179	1.2446
4.0 (383.5)	v,m³/kg	0.00662	0.00689	0.00740	0.00788	0.00835	0.00880	0.00924	0.00967	0.01009
	h,kJ/kg	331.28	339.79	356.57	373.15	389.62	406.05	422.48	438.93	455.42
	s,kJ/(kg·K)	0.9918	1.0097	1.0439	1.0764	1.1075	1.1374	1.1662	1.1941	1.2212

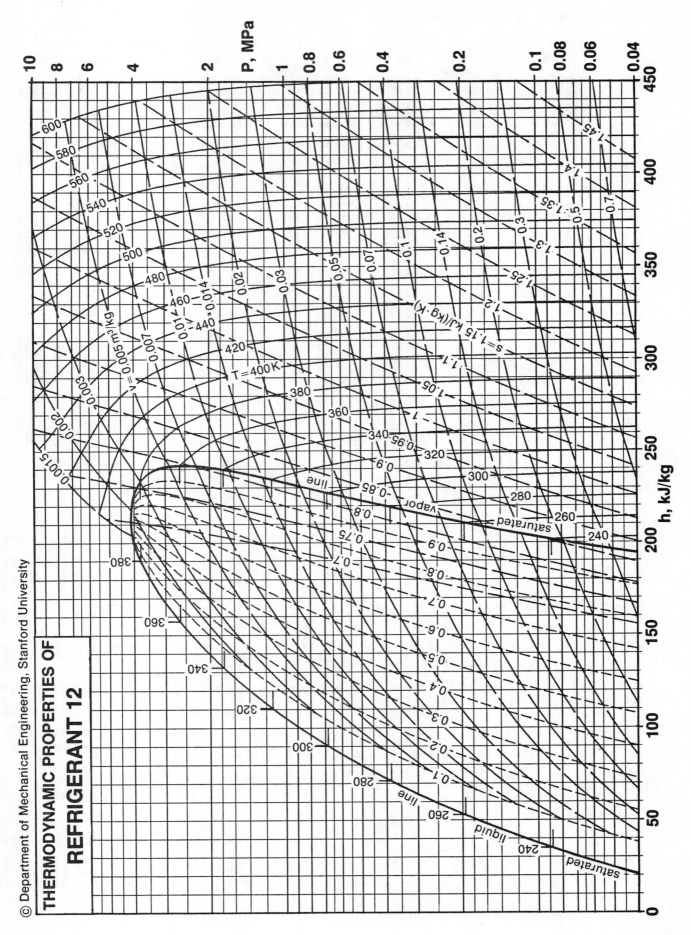

© Department of Mechanical Engineering, Stanford University

THERMODYNAMIC PROPERTIES OF REFRIGERANT 12

P, MPa

h, kJ/kg

PROPERTIES OF SATURATED REFRIGERANT 13

T K	P MPa	volume, m³/kg vf	vg	enthalpy, kJ/kg hf	hfg	hg	entropy, kJ/(kg·K) sf	sfg	sg
150	0.005238	0.000598	2.268	0.0	166.90	166.90	0.0	1.1127	1.1127
155	0.008225	0.000604	1.490	3.90	165.09	168.99	0.0255	1.0652	1.0907
160	0.01251	0.000611	1.008	7.85	163.24	171.09	0.0506	1.0203	1.0709
165	0.01849	0.000617	0.7012	11.87	161.32	173.19	0.0753	0.9778	1.0531
170	0.02663	0.000624	0.4997	15.96	159.34	175.30	0.0997	0.9373	1.0370
175	0.03746	0.000631	0.3640	20.11	157.29	177.40	0.1238	0.8987	1.0225
180	0.05158	0.000639	0.2704	24.35	155.13	179.48	0.1476	0.8618	1.0094
185	0.06964	0.000646	0.2044	28.67	152.87	181.54	0.1712	0.8263	0.9975
190	0.09238	0.000654	0.1571	33.07	150.51	183.58	0.1946	0.7921	0.9867
191.70	0.101325	0.000657	0.1441	34.59	149.67	184.26	0.2025	0.7808	0.9833
195	0.1205	0.000663	0.1225	37.55	148.03	185.58	0.2177	0.7592	0.9769
200	0.1550	0.000672	0.09677	42.11	145.43	187.54	0.2407	0.7272	0.9679
205	0.1965	0.000681	0.07736	46.75	142.70	189.45	0.2635	0.6961	0.9596
210	0.2461	0.000690	0.06252	51.46	139.85	191.31	0.2861	0.6659	0.9520
215	0.3045	0.000700	0.05101	56.26	136.85	193.11	0.3084	0.6366	0.9450
220	0.3729	0.000711	0.04200	61.12	133.73	194.85	0.3306	0.6078	0.9384
225	0.4521	0.000722	0.03485	66.07	130.44	196.51	0.3525	0.5798	0.9323
230	0.5431	0.000734	0.02912	71.08	127.01	198.09	0.3743	0.5522	0.9265
235	0.6470	0.000747	0.02449	76.17	123.40	199.57	0.3959	0.5251	0.9210
240	0.7647	0.000761	0.02071	81.34	119.62	200.96	0.4173	0.4984	0.9157
245	0.8972	0.000776	0.01759	86.59	115.65	202.24	0.4385	0.4720	0.9105
250	1.046	0.000792	0.01501	91.92	111.46	203.38	0.4595	0.4459	0.9054
255	1.211	0.000810	0.01285	97.35	107.04	204.39	0.4805	0.4198	0.9003
260	1.395	0.000829	0.01103	102.88	102.35	205.23	0.5014	0.3937	0.8951
265	1.598	0.000851	0.009477	108.53	97.34	205.87	0.5223	0.3673	0.8896
270	1.821	0.000876	0.008148	114.34	91.94	206.28	0.5433	0.3405	0.8838
275	2.066	0.000905	0.006998	120.33	86.07	206.40	0.5645	0.3129	0.8774
280	2.335	0.000940	0.005990	126.58	79.56	206.14	0.5861	0.2841	0.8702
285	2.630	0.000982	0.005094	133.20	72.15	205.35	0.6085	0.2532	0.8617
290	2.952	0.001038	0.004278	140.40	63.37	203.77	0.6324	0.2186	0.8510
295	3.306	0.001120	0.003496	148.70	52.05	200.75	0.6595	0.1765	0.8360
302.00	3.870	0.001731	0.001731	177.26	0.0	177.26	0.7524	0.0	0.7524

PROPERTIES OF GASEOUS REFRIGERANT 13

P,MPa (Tsat,K)		sat	250	300	350	400	450	500	550	600
0.050 (179.5)	v,m³/kg	0.2783	0.3946	0.4754	0.5557	0.6358	0.7157	0.7955	0.8753	0.9551
	h,kJ/kg	179.27	217.31	248.13	281.82	318.04	356.41	396.55	438.07	480.58
	s,kJ/(kg·K)	1.0107	1.1886	1.3008	1.4046	1.5012	1.5915	1.6761	1.7552	1.8292
0.101325 (191.7)	v,m³/kg	0.1441	0.1930	0.2335	0.2735	0.3132	0.3528	0.3924	0.4318	0.4713
	h,kJ/kg	184.26	216.71	247.74	281.55	317.83	356.25	396.42	437.96	480.49
	s,kJ/(kg·K)	0.9833	1.1307	1.2436	1.3478	1.4446	1.5350	1.6197	1.6988	1.7728
0.20 (205.4)	v,m³/kg	0.07608	0.09606	0.1172	0.1379	0.1582	0.1784	0.1986	0.2187	0.2388
	h,kJ/kg	189.60	215.54	246.98	281.01	317.43	355.93	396.16	437.75	480.31
	s,kJ/(kg·K)	0.9590	1.0732	1.1877	1.2925	1.3897	1.4804	1.5651	1.6444	1.7184
0.40 (221.8)	v,m³/kg	0.03924	0.04621	0.05750	0.06820	0.07863	0.08891	0.09911	0.1093	0.1194
	h,kJ/kg	195.45	213.05	245.41	279.92	316.61	355.29	395.64	437.32	479.95
	s,kJ/(kg·K)	0.9362	1.0108	1.1287	1.2350	1.3330	1.4240	1.5090	1.5885	1.6627
0.70 (237.3)	v,m³/kg	0.02263	0.02470	0.03187	0.03834	0.04451	0.05054	0.05647	0.06236	0.06820
	h,kJ/kg	200.23	208.93	242.96	278.24	315.38	354.33	394.87	436.68	479.42
	s,kJ/(kg·K)	0.9185	0.9542	1.0782	1.1870	1.2861	1.3778	1.4632	1.5429	1.6172
1.0 (248.5)	v,m³/kg	0.01573	0.01593	0.02159	0.02639	0.03086	0.03518	0.03942	0.04359	0.04773
	h,kJ/kg	203.06	204.18	240.38	276.53	314.12	353.36	394.09	436.04	478.89
	s,kJ/(kg·K)	0.9069	0.9114	1.0435	1.1549	1.2553	1.3477	1.4335	1.5134	1.5880
2.0 (273.7)	v,m³/kg	0.00728		0.00943	0.01241	0.01493	0.01727	0.01952	0.02171	0.02386
	h,kJ/kg	206.40		230.48	270.49	309.84	350.10	391.49	433.92	477.13
	s,kJ/(kg·K)	0.8792		0.9633	1.0868	1.1919	1.2867	1.3739	1.4547	1.5299
3.0 (290.7)	v,m³/kg	0.00417		0.00506	0.00770	0.00961	0.01130	0.01289	0.01441	0.01589
	h,kJ/kg	203.45		216.59	263.83	305.39	346.78	388.89	431.81	475.38
	s,kJ/(kg·K)	0.8492		0.8937	1.0399	1.1509	1.2484	1.3371	1.4189	1.4948

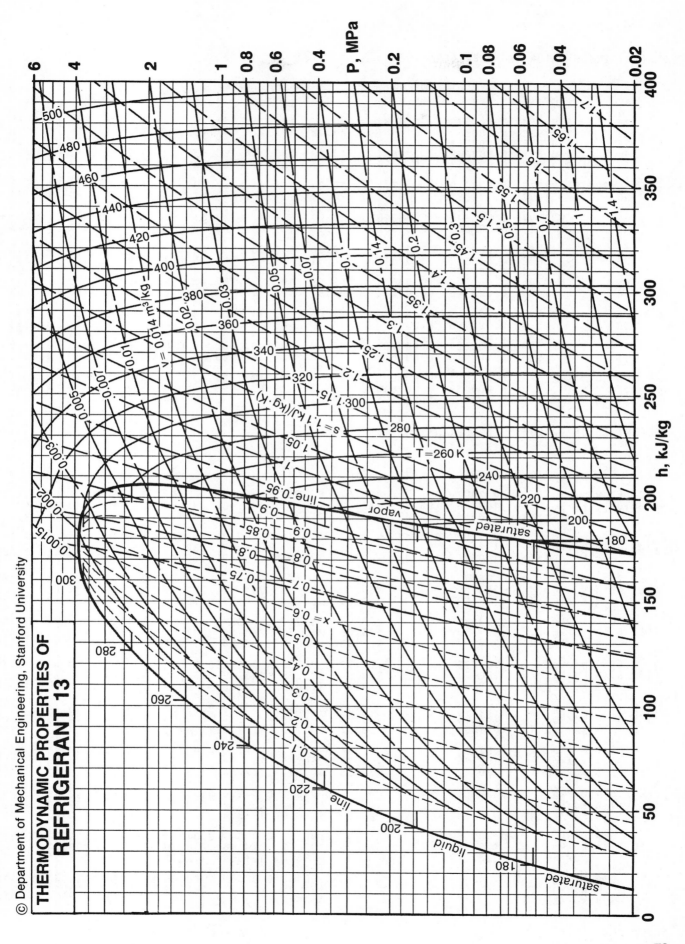

© Department of Mechanical Engineering, Stanford University

THERMODYNAMIC PROPERTIES OF
REFRIGERANT 13

P, MPa

h, kJ/kg

79

PROPERTIES OF SATURATED REFRIGERANT 14

T K	P MPa	volume, m³/kg v_f	v_g	enthalpy, kJ/kg h_f	h_fg	h_g	entropy, kJ/(kg·K) s_f	s_fg	s_g
125	0.01854	0.000575	0.6284	0.0	144.76	144.76	0.0	1.1581	1.1581
130	0.02984	0.000583	0.4037	4.28	142.42	146.70	0.0335	1.0956	1.1291
135	0.04616	0.000592	0.2690	8.68	139.92	148.60	0.0667	1.0364	1.1031
140	0.06897	0.000602	0.1851	13.22	137.23	150.45	0.0996	0.9802	1.0798
145	0.09987	0.000612	0.1310	17.88	134.34	152.22	0.1322	0.9264	1.0586
145.20	0.101325	0.000612	0.1292	18.08	134.21	152.29	0.1335	0.9243	1.0578
150	0.1407	0.000622	0.09497	22.67	131.24	153.91	0.1645	0.8749	1.0394
155	0.1933	0.000634	0.07038	27.59	127.92	155.51	0.1965	0.8253	1.0218
160	0.2597	0.000646	0.05316	32.61	124.40	157.01	0.2281	0.7775	1.0056
165	0.3420	0.000659	0.04082	37.74	120.65	158.39	0.2594	0.7311	0.9905
170	0.4425	0.000673	0.03181	42.98	116.66	159.64	0.2902	0.6863	0.9765
175	0.5632	0.000689	0.02510	48.31	112.44	160.75	0.3206	0.6425	0.9631
180	0.7064	0.000705	0.02002	53.73	107.97	161.70	0.3506	0.5998	0.9504
185	0.8745	0.000724	0.01611	59.25	103.22	162.47	0.3802	0.5579	0.9381
190	1.070	0.000745	0.01306	64.87	98.16	163.03	0.4094	0.5166	0.9260
195	1.295	0.000768	0.01064	70.60	92.74	163.34	0.4383	0.4756	0.9139
200	1.553	0.000796	0.008694	76.49	86.87	163.36	0.4671	0.4343	0.9014
205	1.846	0.000828	0.007104	82.59	80.39	162.98	0.4961	0.3921	0.8882
210	2.179	0.000867	0.005781	89.00	73.06	162.06	0.5256	0.3479	0.8735
215	2.556	0.000918	0.004650	95.95	64.36	160.31	0.5567	0.2994	0.8561
220	2.984	0.000992	0.003638	103.97	53.12	157.09	0.5917	0.2414	0.8331
225	3.473	0.001132	0.002610	115.03	34.87	149.90	0.6391	0.1549	0.7940
227.50	3.745	0.001598	0.001598	132.41	0.0	132.41	0.7142	0.0	0.7142

PROPERTIES OF GASEOUS REFRIGERANT 14

P,MPa (T_sat,K)		sat	150	200	250	300	350	400	500	600
0.050 (136.0)	v,m³/kg	0.2497	0.2778	0.3752	0.4708	0.5659	0.6607	0.7554	0.9447	1.134
	h,kJ/kg	148.96	155.76	182.10	212.01	245.46	282.26	322.16	410.08	506.54
	s,kJ/(kg·K)	1.0984	1.1460	1.2971	1.4303	1.5520	1.6654	1.7718	1.9676	2.1433
0.101325 (145.2)	v,m³/kg	0.1292	0.1342	0.1837	0.2315	0.2787	0.3257	0.3726	0.4661	0.5596
	h,kJ/kg	152.29	154.73	181.61	211.73	245.27	282.12	322.06	410.02	506.49
	s,kJ/(kg·K)	1.0578	1.0743	1.2286	1.3627	1.4849	1.5983	1.7049	1.9008	2.0765
0.20 (155.6)	v,m³/kg	0.06813		0.09172	0.1165	0.1407	0.1647	0.1886	0.2361	0.2836
	h,kJ/kg	155.69		180.65	211.19	244.92	281.87	321.86	409.89	506.41
	s,kJ/(kg·K)	1.0199		1.1609	1.2969	1.4197	1.5335	1.6403	1.8363	2.0121
0.30 (162.6)	v,m³/kg	0.04630		0.06020	0.07717	0.09351	0.1096	0.1256	0.1574	0.1891
	h,kJ/kg	157.74		179.65	210.63	244.55	281.61	321.66	409.76	506.32
	s,kJ/(kg·K)	0.9977		1.1190	1.2570	1.3806	1.4947	1.6015	1.7977	1.9736
0.50 (172.5)	v,m³/kg	0.02822		0.03493	0.04566	0.05572	0.06553	0.07522	0.09443	0.1135
	h,kJ/kg	160.21		177.57	209.50	243.82	281.08	321.26	409.50	506.15
	s,kJ/(kg·K)	0.9697		1.0631	1.2055	1.3305	1.4452	1.5525	1.7490	1.9250
0.70 (179.8)	v,m³/kg	0.02020		0.02405	0.03215	0.03952	0.04664	0.05363	0.06744	0.08114
	h,kJ/kg	161.66		175.35	208.34	243.09	280.56	320.86	409.25	505.98
	s,kJ/(kg·K)	0.9509		1.0232	1.1703	1.2969	1.4123	1.5199	1.7167	1.8929
1.0 (188.3)	v,m³/kg	0.01402		0.01581	0.02201	0.02738	0.03247	0.03744	0.04720	0.05685
	h,kJ/kg	162.86		171.71	206.55	241.97	279.77	320.26	408.86	505.72
	s,kJ/(kg·K)	0.9302		0.9758	1.1314	1.2604	1.3769	1.4849	1.6822	1.8586
2.0 (207.4)	v,m³/kg	0.00644			0.01012	0.01320	0.01594	0.01855	0.02360	0.02852
	h,kJ/kg	162.62			200.07	238.12	277.10	318.26	407.60	504.89
	s,kJ/(kg·K)	0.8814			1.0466	1.1853	1.3054	1.4153	1.6143	1.7915
3.0 (220.2)	v,m³/kg	0.00360			0.00608	0.00847	0.01044	0.01227	0.01573	0.01908
	h,kJ/kg	156.92			192.52	234.08	274.39	316.26	406.37	504.09
	s,kJ/(kg·K)	0.8321			0.9850	1.1368	1.2611	1.3728	1.5736	1.7515
5.0	v,m³/kg				0.00265	0.00469	0.00606	0.00726	0.00946	0.01154
	h,kJ/kg				171.29	225.43	268.89	312.29	403.97	502.54
	s,kJ/(kg·K)				0.8672	1.0663	1.2004	1.3162	1.5205	1.7001

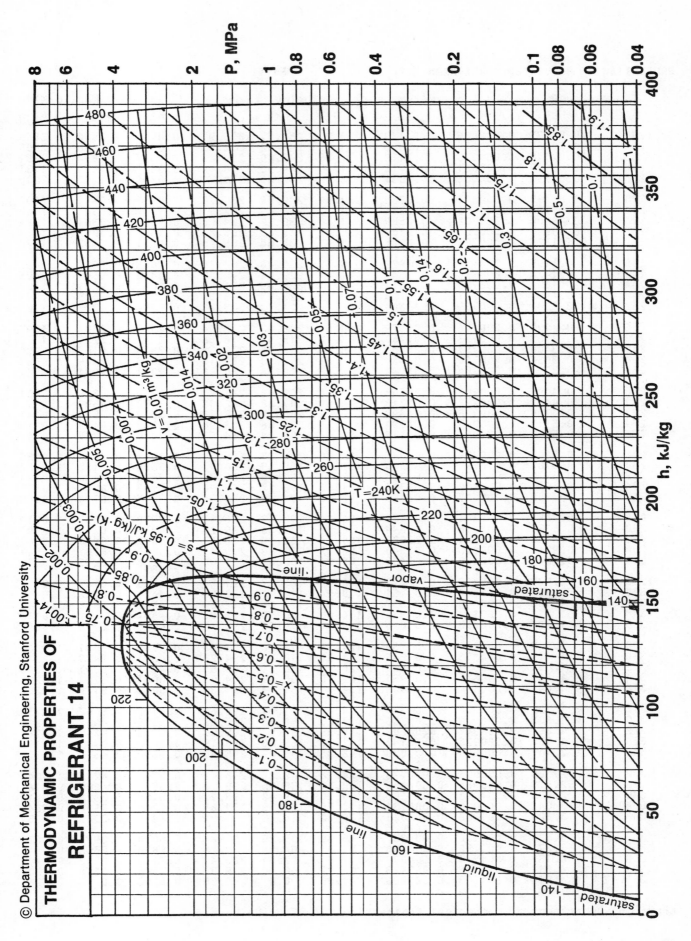

© Department of Mechanical Engineering, Stanford University

THERMODYNAMIC PROPERTIES OF REFRIGERANT 14

P, MPa

h, kJ/kg

PROPERTIES OF SATURATED REFRIGERANT 22

T K	P MPa	volume, m³/kg		enthalpy, kJ/kg			entropy, kJ/(kg·K)		
		v_f	v_g	h_f	h_{fg}	h_g	s_f	s_{fg}	s_g
200	0.01673	0.000666	1.139	0.0	250.97	250.97	0.0	1.2548	1.2548
204	0.02165	0.000671	0.8955	3.93	249.00	252.93	0.0194	1.2206	1.2400
208	0.02770	0.000676	0.7118	7.89	247.00	254.89	0.0387	1.1874	1.2261
212	0.03507	0.000681	0.5715	11.89	244.95	256.84	0.0577	1.1554	1.2131
216	0.04396	0.000686	0.4631	15.93	242.85	258.78	0.0765	1.1243	1.2008
220	0.05460	0.000691	0.3785	20.01	240.69	260.70	0.0952	1.0941	1.1893
224	0.06721	0.000696	0.3118	24.12	238.49	262.61	0.1137	1.0647	1.1784
228	0.08206	0.000702	0.2589	28.28	236.22	264.50	0.1320	1.0361	1.1681
232	0.09941	0.000708	0.2164	32.48	233.88	266.36	0.1502	1.0082	1.1584
232.41	0.101325	0.000708	0.2126	32.91	233.64	266.55	0.1521	1.0053	1.1574
236	0.1195	0.000714	0.1822	36.72	231.48	268.20	0.1683	0.9809	1.1492
240	0.1428	0.000720	0.1543	41.01	229.01	270.02	0.1863	0.9542	1.1405
244	0.1694	0.000726	0.1314	45.35	226.45	271.80	0.2041	0.9281	1.1322
248	0.1997	0.000732	0.1125	49.72	223.83	273.55	0.2218	0.9025	1.1243
252	0.2341	0.000739	0.09688	54.14	221.13	275.27	0.2394	0.8775	1.1169
256	0.2728	0.000746	0.08379	58.61	218.33	276.94	0.2569	0.8528	1.1097
260	0.3163	0.000753	0.07280	63.12	215.46	278.58	0.2742	0.8287	1.1029
262	0.3400	0.000757	0.06796	65.40	213.98	279.38	0.2829	0.8167	1.0996
264	0.3650	0.000760	0.06351	67.68	212.50	280.18	0.2915	0.8049	1.0964
266	0.3913	0.000764	0.05941	69.98	210.98	280.96	0.3001	0.7931	1.0932
268	0.4191	0.000768	0.05563	72.28	209.45	281.73	0.3086	0.7815	1.0901
270	0.4483	0.000772	0.05213	74.60	207.88	282.48	0.3172	0.7699	1.0871
272	0.4790	0.000776	0.04890	76.94	206.29	283.23	0.3257	0.7584	1.0841
274	0.5113	0.000780	0.04591	79.28	204.68	283.96	0.3342	0.7470	1.0812
276	0.5453	0.000784	0.04313	81.63	203.04	284.67	0.3426	0.7357	1.0783
278	0.5809	0.000789	0.04055	84.00	201.38	285.38	0.3511	0.7244	1.0755
280	0.6182	0.000793	0.03816	86.38	199.69	286.07	0.3595	0.7132	1.0727
282	0.6572	0.000797	0.03593	88.78	197.96	286.74	0.3679	0.7020	1.0699
284	0.6981	0.000802	0.03386	91.18	196.22	287.40	0.3763	0.6909	1.0672
286	0.7408	0.000807	0.03193	93.60	194.44	288.04	0.3847	0.6798	1.0645
288	0.7855	0.000811	0.03013	96.04	192.63	288.67	0.3930	0.6689	1.0619
290	0.8321	0.000816	0.02844	98.48	190.80	289.28	0.4014	0.6579	1.0593
292	0.8808	0.000821	0.02687	100.94	188.93	289.87	0.4097	0.6470	1.0567
294	0.9315	0.000826	0.02540	103.42	187.03	290.45	0.4180	0.6361	1.0541
296	0.9843	0.000832	0.02402	105.91	185.09	291.00	0.4263	0.6253	1.0516
298	1.039	0.000837	0.02272	108.42	183.12	291.54	0.4346	0.6145	1.0491
300	1.097	0.000843	0.02151	110.94	181.11	292.05	0.4428	0.6038	1.0466
302	1.156	0.000849	0.02037	113.48	179.06	292.54	0.4511	0.5930	1.0441
304	1.218	0.000854	0.01930	116.03	176.99	293.02	0.4594	0.5822	1.0416
306	1.283	0.000860	0.01829	118.61	174.85	293.46	0.4676	0.5715	1.0391
308	1.349	0.000867	0.01734	121.20	172.68	293.88	0.4759	0.5607	1.0366
310	1.419	0.000873	0.01645	123.81	170.47	294.28	0.4841	0.5499	1.0340
312	1.491	0.000880	0.01560	126.44	168.21	294.65	0.4924	0.5391	1.0315
314	1.565	0.000887	0.01481	129.10	165.89	294.99	0.5007	0.5283	1.0290
316	1.642	0.000894	0.01405	131.77	163.53	295.30	0.5089	0.5175	1.0264
318	1.722	0.000901	0.01334	134.47	161.11	295.58	0.5172	0.5067	1.0239
320	1.805	0.000909	0.01266	137.20	158.62	295.82	0.5255	0.4957	1.0212
322	1.891	0.000917	0.01202	139.95	156.08	296.03	0.5339	0.4847	1.0186
324	1.980	0.000925	0.01142	142.73	153.46	296.19	0.5422	0.4737	1.0159
328	2.167	0.000943	0.01029	148.38	148.02	296.40	0.5590	0.4513	1.0103
332	2.366	0.000963	0.009278	154.18	142.24	296.42	0.5760	0.4284	1.0044
336	2.579	0.000984	0.008353	160.14	136.06	296.20	0.5932	0.4050	0.9982
340	2.806	0.001008	0.007508	166.30	129.42	295.72	0.6108	0.3806	0.9914
344	3.048	0.001036	0.006731	172.70	122.19	294.89	0.6288	0.3552	0.9840
348	3.305	0.001068	0.006011	179.42	114.23	293.65	0.6474	0.3283	0.9757
352	3.580	0.001106	0.005337	186.55	105.29	291.84	0.6670	0.2991	0.9661
356	3.871	0.001152	0.004696	194.27	94.98	289.25	0.6878	0.2668	0.9546
360	4.182	0.001214	0.004070	202.93	82.51	285.44	0.7110	0.2292	0.9402
364	4.514	0.001305	0.003423	213.32	66.05	279.37	0.7385	0.1815	0.9200
369.17	4.978	0.001906	0.001906	246.26	0.0	246.26	0.8263	0.0	0.8263

PROPERTIES OF SATURATED REFRIGERANT 22

P MPa	T K	volume, m³/kg		enthalpy, kJ/kg			entropy, kJ/(kg·K)		
		v_f	v_g	h_f	h_{fg}	h_g	s_f	s_{fg}	s_g
0.018	201.12	0.000667	1.063	1.10	250.42	251.52	0.0055	1.2451	1.2506
0.020	202.75	0.000669	0.9639	2.70	249.62	252.32	0.0134	1.2311	1.2445
0.022	204.26	0.000671	0.8820	4.18	248.88	253.06	0.0207	1.2184	1.2391
0.024	205.65	0.000673	0.8134	5.56	248.18	253.74	0.0274	1.2068	1.2342
0.026	206.96	0.000674	0.7550	6.85	247.53	254.38	0.0337	1.1960	1.2297
0.028	208.18	0.000676	0.7047	8.07	246.91	254.98	0.0395	1.1860	1.2255
0.030	209.33	0.000677	0.6608	9.22	246.32	255.54	0.0450	1.1767	1.2217
0.035	211.97	0.000681	0.5725	11.86	244.96	256.82	0.0575	1.1557	1.2132
0.040	214.31	0.000684	0.5056	14.21	243.75	257.96	0.0686	1.1373	1.2059
0.045	216.42	0.000686	0.4531	16.36	242.62	258.98	0.0785	1.1211	1.1996
0.050	218.36	0.000689	0.4108	18.32	241.59	259.91	0.0875	1.1064	1.1939
0.055	220.14	0.000691	0.3759	20.15	240.62	260.77	0.0958	1.0931	1.1889
0.060	221.80	0.000693	0.3466	21.85	239.71	261.56	0.1035	1.0808	1.1843
0.070	224.80	0.000698	0.3002	24.95	238.04	262.99	0.1174	1.0589	1.1763
0.080	227.48	0.000701	0.2651	27.74	236.51	264.25	0.1297	1.0397	1.1694
0.090	229.91	0.000705	0.2375	30.28	235.11	265.39	0.1407	1.0227	1.1634
0.101325	232.41	0.000708	0.2126	32.91	233.64	266.55	0.1521	1.0053	1.1574
0.11	234.18	0.000711	0.1969	34.79	232.58	267.37	0.1601	0.9932	1.1533
0.12	236.08	0.000714	0.1815	36.82	231.42	268.24	0.1687	0.9803	1.1490
0.13	237.87	0.000716	0.1684	38.73	230.33	269.06	0.1767	0.9683	1.1450
0.14	239.55	0.000719	0.1571	40.53	229.29	269.82	0.1843	0.9571	1.1414
0.15	241.14	0.000721	0.1473	42.25	228.28	270.53	0.1914	0.9466	1.1380
0.16	242.65	0.000724	0.1386	43.88	227.32	271.20	0.1981	0.9368	1.1349
0.17	244.09	0.000726	0.1309	45.45	226.39	271.84	0.2045	0.9275	1.1320
0.18	245.46	0.000728	0.1241	46.94	225.50	272.44	0.2106	0.9187	1.1293
0.19	246.78	0.000730	0.1179	48.38	224.64	273.02	0.2164	0.9103	1.1267
0.20	248.04	0.000732	0.1124	49.77	223.80	273.57	0.2220	0.9023	1.1243
0.22	250.42	0.000736	0.1027	52.40	222.19	274.59	0.2325	0.8873	1.1198
0.24	252.65	0.000740	0.09461	54.87	220.67	275.54	0.2422	0.8735	1.1157
0.26	254.73	0.000744	0.08770	57.19	219.23	276.42	0.2513	0.8606	1.1119
0.28	256.69	0.000747	0.08175	59.39	217.84	277.23	0.2599	0.8486	1.1085
0.30	258.55	0.000750	0.07657	61.49	216.50	277.99	0.2680	0.8373	1.1053
0.35	262.82	0.000758	0.06611	66.33	213.38	279.71	0.2864	0.8119	1.0983
0.40	266.64	0.000765	0.05817	70.71	210.49	281.20	0.3028	0.7894	1.0922
0.45	270.11	0.000772	0.05194	74.74	207.78	282.52	0.3176	0.7693	1.0869
0.50	273.31	0.000779	0.04691	78.47	205.24	283.71	0.3312	0.7510	1.0822
0.55	276.27	0.000785	0.04277	81.96	202.81	284.77	0.3438	0.7341	1.0779
0.60	279.04	0.000791	0.03929	85.24	200.50	285.74	0.3555	0.7185	1.0740
0.70	284.09	0.000802	0.03377	91.29	196.14	287.43	0.3767	0.6904	1.0671
0.80	288.63	0.000813	0.02958	96.81	192.05	288.86	0.3957	0.6654	1.0611
0.90	292.77	0.000823	0.02629	101.89	188.21	290.10	0.4129	0.6428	1.0557
1.0	296.58	0.000833	0.02364	106.63	184.53	291.16	0.4287	0.6222	1.0509
1.1	300.11	0.000843	0.02144	111.08	181.00	292.08	0.4433	0.6031	1.0464
1.2	303.42	0.000853	0.01960	115.29	177.59	292.88	0.4570	0.5853	1.0423
1.3	306.53	0.000862	0.01803	119.29	174.29	293.58	0.4698	0.5686	1.0384
1.4	309.47	0.000871	0.01668	123.11	171.07	294.18	0.4820	0.5527	1.0347
1.5	312.26	0.000881	0.01550	126.78	167.92	294.70	0.4935	0.5377	1.0312
1.6	314.91	0.000890	0.01446	130.31	164.82	295.13	0.5044	0.5234	1.0278
1.7	317.45	0.000899	0.01353	133.72	161.78	295.50	0.5149	0.5097	1.0246
1.8	319.87	0.000909	0.01271	137.02	158.79	295.81	0.5250	0.4964	1.0214
1.9	322.20	0.000918	0.01196	140.23	155.82	296.05	0.5347	0.4836	1.0183
2.0	324.44	0.000927	0.01129	143.35	152.88	296.23	0.5441	0.4712	1.0153
2.2	328.69	0.000946	0.01011	149.37	147.05	296.42	0.5619	0.4474	1.0093
2.4	332.65	0.000966	0.009121	155.14	141.26	296.40	0.5788	0.4247	1.0035
2.6	336.38	0.000986	0.008270	160.71	135.46	296.17	0.5949	0.4027	0.9976
2.8	339.90	0.001008	0.007529	166.13	129.60	295.73	0.6103	0.3813	0.9916
3.0	343.23	0.001030	0.006876	171.44	123.64	295.08	0.6253	0.3602	0.9855
3.5	350.87	0.001094	0.005524	184.47	107.95	292.42	0.6613	0.3077	0.9690
4.0	357.69	0.001176	0.004432	197.78	90.05	287.83	0.6972	0.2518	0.9490
4.978	369.17	0.001906	0.001906	246.26	0.0	246.26	0.8263	0.0	0.8263

PROPERTIES OF GASEOUS REFRIGERANT 22

P,MPa (T_sat,K)		sat	220	230	240	250	260	270	280	290
0.020 (202.8)	v,m³/kg	0.9639	1.049	1.098	1.147	1.195	1.244	1.293	1.341	1.390
	h,kJ/kg	252.32	261.78	267.43	273.19	279.07	285.06	291.16	297.39	303.72
	s,kJ/(kg·K)	1.2445	1.2893	1.3144	1.3389	1.3629	1.3864	1.4095	1.4321	1.4543
0.030 (209.3)	v,m³/kg	0.6608	0.6962	0.7292	0.7620	0.7948	0.8274	0.8600	0.8925	0.9250
	h,kJ/kg	255.54	261.47	267.15	272.94	278.84	284.85	290.98	297.22	303.57
	s,kJ/(kg·K)	1.2217	1.2493	1.2746	1.2992	1.3233	1.3469	1.3700	1.3927	1.4150
0.040 (214.3)	v,m³/kg	0.5056	0.5199	0.5449	0.5697	0.5945	0.6191	0.6437	0.6682	0.6926
	h,kJ/kg	257.96	261.16	266.87	272.69	278.61	284.65	290.79	297.05	303.41
	s,kJ/(kg·K)	1.2059	1.2207	1.2460	1.2708	1.2950	1.3186	1.3418	1.3646	1.3869
0.050 (218.4)	v,m³/kg	0.4108	0.4141	0.4343	0.4543	0.4743	0.4941	0.5139	0.5336	0.5532
	h,kJ/kg	259.91	260.85	266.59	272.44	278.39	284.44	290.61	296.88	303.26
	s,kJ/(kg·K)	1.1939	1.1982	1.2237	1.2486	1.2729	1.2966	1.3199	1.3427	1.3651
0.070 (224.8)	v,m³/kg	0.3002		0.3079	0.3224	0.3369	0.3512	0.3655	0.3797	0.3938
	h,kJ/kg	262.99		266.02	271.93	277.93	284.03	290.23	296.53	302.94
	s,kJ/(kg·K)	1.1763		1.1896	1.2147	1.2392	1.2631	1.2865	1.3095	1.3320
0.101325 (232.4)	v,m³/kg	0.2126		0.2205	0.2307	0.2408	0.2508	0.2608	0.2707
	h,kJ/kg	266.55			271.11	277.20	283.37	289.63	295.99	302.45
	s,kJ/(kg·K)	1.1574			1.1767	1.2015	1.2258	1.2494	1.2725	1.2952
0.14 (239.6)	v,m³/kg	0.1571		0.1575	0.1651	0.1726	0.1800	0.1874	0.1946
	h,kJ/kg	269.82			270.09	276.28	282.55	288.89	295.32	301.84
	s,kJ/(kg·K)	1.1414			1.1425	1.1678	1.1924	1.2163	1.2397	1.2626
0.20 (248.0)	v,m³/kg	0.1124				0.1135	0.1189	0.1243	0.1296	0.1349
	h,kJ/kg	273.57				274.82	281.24	287.71	294.25	300.87
	s,kJ/(kg·K)	1.1243				1.1293	1.1544	1.1789	1.2027	1.2259
0.30 (258.6)	v,m³/kg	0.07657					0.07713	0.08094	0.08467	0.08833
	h,kJ/kg	277.99					278.96	285.68	292.42	299.21
	s,kJ/(kg·K)	1.1053					1.1091	1.1344	1.1589	1.1828

P, MPa (T_sat,K)		300	310	320	330	340	350	360	370	380
0.020 (202.8)	v,m³/kg	1.438	1.487	1.535	1.583	1.631	1.680	1.728	1.776	1.824
	h,kJ/kg	310.17	316.73	323.40	330.18	337.07	344.06	351.16	358.37	365.67
	s,kJ/(kg·K)	1.4762	1.4977	1.5189	1.5397	1.5603	1.5806	1.6006	1.6203	1.6398
0.030 (209.3)	v,m³/kg	0.9574	0.9897	1.022	1.054	1.087	1.119	1.151	1.183	1.216
	h,kJ/kg	310.03	316.60	323.28	330.07	336.97	343.97	351.07	358.28	365.59
	s,kJ/(kg·K)	1.4369	1.4584	1.4796	1.5005	1.5211	1.5414	1.5614	1.5812	1.6007
0.040 (214.3)	v,m³/kg	0.7170	0.7414	0.7657	0.7900	0.8142	0.8385	0.8627	0.8869	0.9111
	h,kJ/kg	309.89	316.47	323.16	329.96	336.86	343.87	350.99	358.20	365.52
	s,kJ/(kg·K)	1.4089	1.4305	1.4517	1.4726	1.4932	1.5135	1.5336	1.5533	1.5729
0.050 (218.4)	v,m³/kg	0.5728	0.5923	0.6118	0.6313	0.6508	0.6702	0.6896	0.7090	0.7284
	h,kJ/kg	309.74	316.34	323.04	329.85	336.76	343.78	350.90	358.12	365.44
	s,kJ/(kg·K)	1.3871	1.4087	1.4300	1.4509	1.4716	1.4919	1.5119	1.5317	1.5513
0.070 (224.8)	v,m³/kg	0.4080	0.4220	0.4360	0.4500	0.4640	0.4779	0.4918	0.5057	0.5196
	h,kJ/kg	309.46	316.08	322.80	329.62	336.55	343.58	350.72	357.95	365.28
	s,kJ/(kg·K)	1.3540	1.3757	1.3971	1.4181	1.4388	1.4592	1.4792	1.4991	1.5186
0.101325 (232.4)	v,m³/kg	0.2805	0.2904	0.3001	0.3099	0.3196	0.3293	0.3390	0.3486	0.3583
	h,kJ/kg	309.01	315.66	322.42	329.27	336.23	343.28	350.43	357.69	365.04
	s,kJ/(kg·K)	1.3174	1.3392	1.3607	1.3818	1.4025	1.4230	1.4431	1.4630	1.4826
0.14 (239.6)	v,m³/kg	0.2019	0.2091	0.2162	0.2234	0.2305	0.2375	0.2446	0.2516	0.2587
	h,kJ/kg	308.45	315.15	321.94	328.83	335.82	342.91	350.09	357.36	364.73
	s,kJ/(kg·K)	1.2850	1.3070	1.3285	1.3497	1.3706	1.3911	1.4114	1.4313	1.4509
0.20 (248.0)	v,m³/kg	0.1400	0.1452	0.1503	0.1554	0.1604	0.1654	0.1704	0.1754	0.1804
	h,kJ/kg	307.56	314.34	321.20	328.15	335.19	342.32	349.54	356.85	364.26
	s,kJ/(kg·K)	1.2486	1.2708	1.2926	1.3140	1.3350	1.3556	1.3760	1.3960	1.4158
0.30 (258.6)	v,m³/kg	0.09192	0.09547	0.09898	0.1025	0.1059	0.1093	0.1127	0.1161	0.1195
	h,kJ/kg	306.06	312.96	319.94	326.99	334.12	341.33	348.62	356.00	363.46
	s,kJ/(kg·K)	1.2060	1.2286	1.2508	1.2725	1.2938	1.3146	1.3352	1.3554	1.3753

PROPERTIES OF GASEOUS REFRIGERANT 22

P, MPa (T_{sat},K)		T,K 400	420	440	460	480	500	520	540	560
0.020 (202.8)	v,m³/kg	1.921	2.017	2.114	2.210	2.306	2.402	2.499	2.595	2.691
	h,kJ/kg	380.58	395.89	411.56	427.61	444.00	460.73	477.78	495.15	512.80
	s,kJ/(kg·K)	1.6780	1.7154	1.7518	1.7875	1.8223	1.8565	1.8899	1.9227	1.9548
0.030 (209.3)	v,m³/kg	1.280	1.344	1.409	1.473	1.537	1.601	1.665	1.730	1.794
	h,kJ/kg	380.52	395.82	411.51	427.56	443.95	460.69	477.74	495.11	512.77
	s,kJ/(kg·K)	1.6389	1.6763	1.7127	1.7484	1.7833	1.8174	1.8509	1.8837	1.9158
0.040 (214.3)	v,m³/kg	0.9594	1.008	1.056	1.104	1.152	1.201	1.249	1.297	1.345
	h,kJ/kg	380.45	395.76	411.45	427.51	443.91	460.64	477.70	495.07	512.74
	s,kJ/(kg·K)	1.6111	1.6485	1.6850	1.7207	1.7556	1.7897	1.8232	1.8560	1.8881
0.050 (218.4)	v,m³/kg	0.7671	0.8058	0.8445	0.8831	0.9217	0.9603	0.9989	1.037	1.076
	h,kJ/kg	380.38	395.70	411.40	427.46	443.86	460.60	477.67	495.04	512.70
	s,kJ/(kg·K)	1.5896	1.6269	1.6635	1.6991	1.7340	1.7682	1.8017	1.8345	1.8666
0.070 (224.8)	v,m³/kg	0.5474	0.5751	0.6027	0.6304	0.6580	0.6856	0.7132	0.7407	0.7683
	h,kJ/kg	380.24	395.58	411.29	427.36	443.77	460.52	477.59	494.97	512.64
	s,kJ/(kg·K)	1.5570	1.5944	1.6309	1.6666	1.7016	1.7357	1.7692	1.8020	1.8341
0.101325 (232.4)	v,m³/kg	0.3775	0.3967	0.4159	0.4350	0.4542	0.4733	0.4924	0.5114	0.5305
	h,kJ/kg	380.02	395.38	411.11	427.20	443.63	460.39	477.47	494.85	512.53
	s,kJ/(kg·K)	1.5210	1.5585	1.5951	1.6308	1.6658	1.7000	1.7335	1.7663	1.7984
0.14 (239.6)	v,m³/kg	0.2727	0.2866	0.3006	0.3145	0.3283	0.3422	0.3560	0.3699	0.3837
	h,kJ/kg	379.75	395.15	410.90	427.00	443.45	460.23	477.32	494.72	512.40
	s,kJ/(kg·K)	1.4895	1.5270	1.5637	1.5994	1.6344	1.6687	1.7022	1.7350	1.7672
0.20 (248.0)	v,m³/kg	0.1902	0.2001	0.2099	0.2197	0.2294	0.2392	0.2489	0.2586	0.2683
	h,kJ/kg	379.33	394.77	410.57	426.70	443.18	459.97	477.09	494.50	512.20
	s,kJ/(kg·K)	1.4544	1.4921	1.5288	1.5647	1.5997	1.6340	1.6676	1.7004	1.7326
0.30 (258.6)	v,m³/kg	0.1261	0.1328	0.1394	0.1460	0.1525	0.1591	0.1656	0.1721	0.1786
	h,kJ/kg	378.63	394.15	410.01	426.20	442.72	459.55	476.70	494.14	511.87
	s,kJ/(kg·K)	1.4142	1.4521	1.4889	1.5249	1.5601	1.5944	1.6281	1.6610	1.6932

P,MPa (T_{sat},K)		T,K sat	290	300	310	320	330	340	350	360
0.40 (266.6)	v,m³/kg	0.05817	0.06502	0.06783	0.07059	0.07331	0.07599	0.07864	0.08126	0.08386
	h,kJ/kg	281.20	297.50	304.51	311.56	318.66	325.81	333.03	340.33	347.69
	s,kJ/(kg·K)	1.0922	1.1508	1.1746	1.1977	1.2202	1.2422	1.2638	1.2849	1.3057
0.50 (273.3)	v,m³/kg	0.04691	0.05100	0.05335	0.05564	0.05789	0.06010	0.06227	0.06442	0.06654
	h,kJ/kg	283.71	295.73	302.91	310.11	317.34	324.61	331.93	339.31	346.75
	s,kJ/(kg·K)	1.0822	1.1249	1.1492	1.1728	1.1958	1.2182	1.2400	1.2614	1.2823
0.70 (284.1)	v,m³/kg	0.03377	0.03490	0.03674	0.03851	0.04023	0.04190	0.04354	0.04515	0.04673
	h,kJ/kg	287.43	291.96	299.56	307.09	314.61	322.12	329.66	337.22	344.82
	s,kJ/(kg·K)	1.0671	1.0829	1.1086	1.1333	1.1572	1.1803	1.2028	1.2247	1.2461
1.0 (296.6)	v,m³/kg	0.02364		0.02414	0.02556	0.02691	0.02820	0.02945	0.03066	0.03184
	h,kJ/kg	291.16		294.01	302.19	310.23	318.18	326.07	333.94	341.81
	s,kJ/(kg·K)	1.0509		1.0604	1.0873	1.1128	1.1372	1.1608	1.1836	1.2058
1.4 (309.5)	v,m³/kg	0.01668			0.01674	0.01790	0.01897	0.01998	0.02095	0.02188
	h,kJ/kg	294.18			294.67	303.69	312.40	320.90	329.28	337.57
	s,kJ/(kg·K)	1.0347			1.0363	1.0649	1.0917	1.1171	1.1414	1.1648
2.0 (324.4)	v,m³/kg	0.01129					0.01184	0.01274	0.01356	0.01433
	h,kJ/kg	296.23					302.06	311.99	321.43	330.56
	s,kJ/(kg·K)	1.0153					1.0331	1.0628	1.0901	1.1158
2.5 (334.5)	v,m³/kg	0.00868						0.00919	0.01001	0.01073
	h,kJ/kg	296.31						302.81	313.75	323.93
	s,kJ/(kg·K)	1.0005						1.0198	1.0515	1.0802
3.0 (343.2)	v,m³/kg	0.00688							0.00749	0.00825
	h,kJ/kg	295.08							304.30	316.23
	s,kJ/(kg·K)	0.9855							1.0121	1.0457
4.0 (357.7)	v,m³/kg	0.00443								0.00472
	h,kJ/kg	287.84								293.22
	s,kJ/(kg·K)	0.9490								0.9640

PROPERTIES OF GASEOUS REFRIGERANT 22

P, MPa (T_sat,K)		370	380	390	400	410	420	430	440	450
0.40 (266.6)	v,m³/kg	0.08644	0.08900	0.09155	0.09409	0.09662	0.09913	0.1016	0.1041	0.1066
	h,kJ/kg	355.13	362.65	370.25	377.92	385.68	393.52	401.44	409.44	417.53
	s,kJ/(kg·K)	1.3261	1.3461	1.3658	1.3853	1.4044	1.4233	1.4420	1.4604	1.4785
0.50 (273.3)	v,m³/kg	0.06864	0.07073	0.07280	0.07485	0.07690	0.07894	0.08096	0.08298	0.08499
	h,kJ/kg	354.25	361.83	369.48	377.21	385.01	392.89	400.84	408.88	416.99
	s,kJ/(kg·K)	1.3029	1.3231	1.3430	1.3626	1.3818	1.4008	1.4195	1.4380	1.4562
0.70 (284.1)	v,m³/kg	0.04829	0.04983	0.05135	0.05286	0.05436	0.05585	0.05733	0.05880	0.06027
	h,kJ/kg	352.47	360.17	367.93	375.76	383.65	391.61	399.64	407.74	415.91
	s,kJ/(kg·K)	1.2671	1.2876	1.3078	1.3276	1.3471	1.3663	1.3852	1.4038	1.4222
1.0 (296.6)	v,m³/kg	0.03300	0.03414	0.03526	0.03636	0.03745	0.03853	0.03960	0.04066	0.04172
	h,kJ/kg	349.69	357.60	365.54	373.53	381.56	389.65	397.79	406.00	414.26
	s,kJ/(kg·K)	1.2274	1.2485	1.2691	1.2893	1.3092	1.3286	1.3478	1.3667	1.3852
1.4 (309.5)	v,m³/kg	0.02278	0.02365	0.02451	0.02535	0.02617	0.02698	0.02778	0.02857	0.02935
	h,kJ/kg	345.81	354.02	362.23	370.45	378.69	386.97	395.27	403.62	412.02
	s,kJ/(kg·K)	1.1873	1.2092	1.2306	1.2514	1.2717	1.2917	1.3112	1.3304	1.3493
2.0 (324.4)	v,m³/kg	0.01505	0.01575	0.01641	0.01706	0.01769	0.01830	0.01890	0.01949	0.02007
	h,kJ/kg	339.48	348.27	356.96	365.59	374.19	382.77	391.36	399.95	408.57
	s,kJ/(kg·K)	1.1403	1.1637	1.1863	1.2082	1.2294	1.2501	1.2703	1.2900	1.3094
2.5 (334.5)	v,m³/kg	0.01140	0.01202	0.01261	0.01317	0.01371	0.01424	0.01475	0.01525	0.01573
	h,kJ/kg	333.64	343.04	352.23	361.28	370.22	379.11	387.95	396.78	405.59
	s,kJ/(kg·K)	1.1068	1.1319	1.1558	1.1787	1.2008	1.2222	1.2430	1.2633	1.2831
3.0 (343.2)	v,m³/kg	0.00890	0.00950	0.01004	0.01056	0.01105	0.01152	0.01197	0.01241	0.01284
	h,kJ/kg	327.08	337.30	347.13	356.68	366.04	375.27	384.41	393.49	402.53
	s,kJ/(kg·K)	1.0755	1.1027	1.1282	1.1524	1.1756	1.1978	1.2193	1.2402	1.2605
4.0 (357.7)	v,m³/kg	0.00559	0.00623	0.00677	0.00725	0.00769	0.00810	0.00849	0.00886	0.00922
	h,kJ/kg	310.25	323.59	335.43	346.43	356.90	367.01	376.87	386.55	396.11
	s,kJ/(kg·K)	1.0107	1.0463	1.0771	1.1049	1.1308	1.1551	1.1783	1.2006	1.2221

P, MPa (T_sat,K)		460	480	500	520	540	560	580	600	620
0.40 (266.6)	v,m³/kg	0.1091	0.1141	0.1190	0.1239	0.1288	0.1337	0.1386	0.1435	0.1484
	h,kJ/kg	425.69	442.26	459.13	476.31	493.78	511.54	529.56	547.85	566.38
	s,kJ/(kg·K)	1.4965	1.5317	1.5662	1.5999	1.6328	1.6651	1.6967	1.7277	1.7581
0.50 (273.3)	v,m³/kg	0.08700	0.09099	0.09497	0.09893	0.1029	0.1068	0.1107	0.1147	0.1186
	h,kJ/kg	425.18	441.79	458.71	475.92	493.42	511.20	529.25	547.55	566.10
	s,kJ/(kg·K)	1.4742	1.5096	1.5441	1.5779	1.6109	1.6432	1.6749	1.7059	1.7363
0.70 (284.1)	v,m³/kg	0.06172	0.06462	0.06750	0.07036	0.07321	0.07605	0.07889	0.08171	0.08453
	h,kJ/kg	424.15	440.86	457.86	475.14	492.70	510.53	528.62	546.97	565.55
	s,kJ/(kg·K)	1.4403	1.4758	1.5105	1.5444	1.5775	1.6100	1.6417	1.6728	1.7033
1.0 (296.6)	v,m³/kg	0.04277	0.04484	0.04690	0.04894	0.05097	0.05299	0.05499	0.05700	0.05899
	h,kJ/kg	422.59	439.45	456.57	473.96	491.61	509.52	527.68	546.09	564.72
	s,kJ/(kg·K)	1.4035	1.4394	1.4744	1.5085	1.5418	1.5743	1.6062	1.6374	1.6679
1.4 (309.5)	v,m³/kg	0.03012	0.03166	0.03317	0.03466	0.03614	0.03761	0.03907	0.04052	0.04197
	h,kJ/kg	420.47	437.54	454.83	472.37	490.15	508.16	526.42	544.91	563.62
	s,kJ/(kg·K)	1.3679	1.4042	1.4395	1.4739	1.5074	1.5402	1.5722	1.6035	1.6342
2.0 (324.4)	v,m³/kg	0.02064	0.02177	0.02287	0.02395	0.02502	0.02608	0.02713	0.02817	0.02921
	h,kJ/kg	417.21	434.61	452.19	469.95	487.93	506.12	524.52	543.14	561.97
	s,kJ/(kg·K)	1.3284	1.3654	1.4013	1.4361	1.4700	1.5031	1.5354	1.5670	1.5978
2.5 (334.5)	v,m³/kg	0.01621	0.01715	0.01807	0.01896	0.01984	0.02071	0.02157	0.02241	0.02326
	h,kJ/kg	414.42	432.12	449.94	467.92	486.06	504.40	522.93	541.66	560.59
	s,kJ/(kg·K)	1.3025	1.3401	1.3765	1.4118	1.4460	1.4793	1.5119	1.5436	1.5746
3.0 (343.2)	v,m³/kg	0.01326	0.01408	0.01486	0.01563	0.01639	0.01713	0.01786	0.01858	0.01930
	h,kJ/kg	411.55	429.58	447.66	465.85	484.18	502.67	521.34	540.18	559.21
	s,kJ/(kg·K)	1.2803	1.3187	1.3556	1.3913	1.4258	1.4595	1.4922	1.5242	1.5554
4.0 (357.7)	v,m³/kg	0.00957	0.01023	0.01087	0.01148	0.01208	0.01266	0.01323	0.01380	0.01435
	h,kJ/kg	405.58	424.34	443.00	461.66	480.38	499.20	518.14	537.22	556.46
	s,kJ/(kg·K)	1.2429	1.2828	1.3209	1.3575	1.3928	1.4270	1.4603	1.4926	1.5242

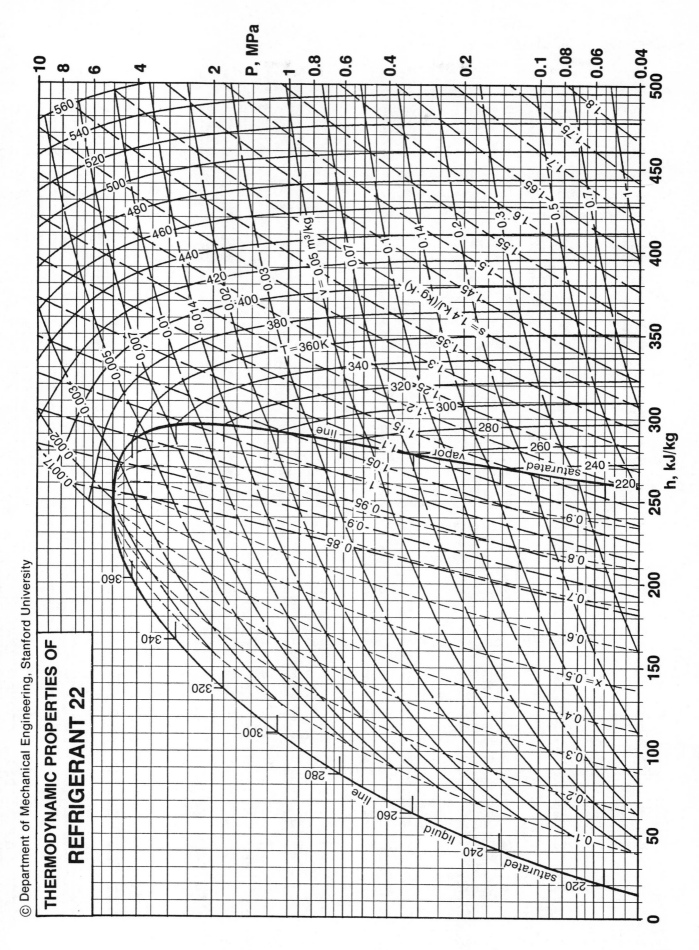

© Department of Mechanical Engineering, Stanford University

THERMODYNAMIC PROPERTIES OF
REFRIGERANT 22

P, MPa

h, kJ/kg

PROPERTIES OF SATURATED REFRIGERANT 23

T K	P MPa	volume, m³/kg v_f	v_g	enthalpy, kJ/kg h_f	h_{fg}	h_g	entropy, kJ/(kg·K) s_f	s_{fg}	s_g
150	0.004367	0.000643	4.058	0.0	269.59	269.59	0.0	1.7973	1.7973
155	0.007111	0.000648	2.569	6.67	265.40	272.07	0.0437	1.7123	1.7560
160	0.01117	0.000654	1.684	13.02	261.49	274.51	0.0841	1.6343	1.7184
165	0.01698	0.000659	1.138	19.13	257.78	276.91	0.1217	1.5623	1.6840
170	0.02510	0.000665	0.7900	25.07	254.20	279.27	0.1571	1.4952	1.6523
175	0.03616	0.000672	0.5616	30.91	250.65	281.56	0.1909	1.4323	1.6232
180	0.05090	0.000678	0.4079	36.69	247.09	283.78	0.2234	1.3727	1.5961
185	0.07016	0.000686	0.3020	42.47	243.45	285.92	0.2550	1.3159	1.5709
190	0.09490	0.000693	0.2275	48.28	239.69	287.97	0.2859	1.2615	1.5474
191.13	0.101325	0.000695	0.2139	49.60	238.82	288.42	0.2928	1.2495	1.5423
195	0.1261	0.000701	0.1741	54.16	235.77	289.93	0.3163	1.2091	1.5254
200	0.1650	0.000710	0.1351	60.13	231.65	291.78	0.3464	1.1583	1.5047
205	0.2128	0.000719	0.1062	66.20	227.33	293.53	0.3762	1.1090	1.4852
210	0.2706	0.000729	0.08443	72.40	222.77	295.17	0.4059	1.0608	1.4667
215	0.3400	0.000740	0.06786	78.72	217.96	296.68	0.4354	1.0138	1.4492
220	0.4221	0.000751	0.05506	85.17	212.90	298.07	0.4648	0.9677	1.4325
225	0.5186	0.000763	0.04507	91.75	207.59	299.34	0.4940	0.9226	1.4166
230	0.6309	0.000777	0.03719	98.44	202.03	300.47	0.5231	0.8783	1.4014
235	0.7604	0.000791	0.03090	105.25	196.20	301.45	0.5519	0.8349	1.3868
240	0.9087	0.000807	0.02583	112.15	190.13	302.28	0.5805	0.7922	1.3727
245	1.078	0.000824	0.02171	119.16	183.78	302.94	0.6088	0.7501	1.3589
250	1.268	0.000844	0.01833	126.27	177.13	303.40	0.6369	0.7085	1.3454
255	1.483	0.000865	0.01552	133.49	170.15	303.64	0.6647	0.6673	1.3320
260	1.724	0.000889	0.01318	140.84	162.78	303.62	0.6925	0.6261	1.3186
265	1.994	0.000917	0.01120	148.38	154.89	303.27	0.7203	0.5845	1.3048
270	2.293	0.000948	0.009519	156.18	146.33	302.51	0.7484	0.5420	1.2904
275	2.627	0.000986	0.008064	164.37	136.84	301.21	0.7773	0.4975	1.2748
280	2.998	0.001031	0.006791	173.20	125.94	299.14	0.8077	0.4498	1.2575
285	3.409	0.001089	0.005654	183.04	112.91	295.95	0.8410	0.3962	1.2372
290	3.867	0.001168	0.004602	194.69	96.16	290.85	0.8797	0.3316	1.2113
295	4.377	0.001298	0.003547	210.19	71.39	281.58	0.9305	0.2420	1.1725
299.07	4.836	0.001905	0.001905	245.68	0.0	245.68	1.0475	0.0	1.0475

PROPERTIES OF GASEOUS REFRIGERANT 23

P,MPa (T_{sat},K)		sat	250	300	350	T,K 400	450	500	550	600
0.070 (185.0)	v,m³/kg	0.3027	0.4199	0.5064	0.5920	0.6773	0.7625	0.8476	0.9326	1.018
	h,kJ/kg	285.90	328.01	363.46	402.37	444.76	490.35	538.57	588.63	639.50
	s,kJ/(kg·K)	1.5711	1.7658	1.8949	2.0147	2.1278	2.2351	2.3367	2.4321	2.5206
0.101325 (191.1)	v,m³/kg	0.2139	0.2887	0.3490	0.4085	0.4676	0.5265	0.5853	0.6441	0.7029
	h,kJ/kg	288.42	327.48	363.17	402.18	444.62	490.24	538.48	588.55	639.43
	s,kJ/(kg·K)	1.5423	1.7203	1.8503	1.9704	2.0837	2.1911	2.2927	2.3881	2.4766
0.20 (203.8)	v,m³/kg	0.1126	0.1441	0.1756	0.2061	0.2363	0.2663	0.2962	0.3261	0.3560
	h,kJ/kg	293.11	325.78	362.25	401.59	444.19	489.90	538.20	588.32	639.23
	s,kJ/(kg·K)	1.4899	1.6345	1.7673	1.8885	2.0021	2.1097	2.2115	2.3070	2.3956
0.40 (218.7)	v,m³/kg	0.05801	0.06981	0.08649	0.1022	0.1175	0.1327	0.1478	0.1629	0.1779
	h,kJ/kg	297.73	322.20	360.34	400.37	443.31	489.21	537.64	587.84	638.82
	s,kJ/(kg·K)	1.4367	1.5413	1.6803	1.8037	1.9182	2.0263	2.1283	2.2240	2.3127
0.70 (232.8)	v,m³/kg	0.03355	0.03782	0.04828	0.05765	0.06664	0.07547	0.08420	0.09288	0.1015
	h,kJ/kg	301.03	316.41	357.40	398.52	441.99	488.17	536.79	587.13	638.21
	s,kJ/(kg·K)	1.3933	1.4571	1.6067	1.7334	1.8494	1.9581	2.0605	2.1565	2.2453
1.0 (242.8)	v,m³/kg	0.02343	0.02487	0.03297	0.03983	0.04629	0.05257	0.05876	0.06490	0.07100
	h,kJ/kg	302.67	309.97	354.33	396.64	440.64	487.13	535.93	586.41	637.60
	s,kJ/(kg·K)	1.3650	1.3946	1.5567	1.6871	1.8046	1.9140	2.0168	2.1130	2.2021
2.0 (265.1)	v,m³/kg	0.01116		0.01499	0.01901	0.02254	0.02587	0.02909	0.03226	0.03539
	h,kJ/kg	303.26		343.04	390.06	436.06	483.62	533.09	584.04	635.59
	s,kJ/(kg·K)	1.3044		1.4459	1.5910	1.7138	1.8258	1.9300	2.0271	2.1168
4.0 (291.4)	v,m³/kg	0.00432		0.00544	0.00855	0.01067	0.01254	0.01429	0.01598	0.01762
	h,kJ/kg	288.93		310.40	375.30	426.41	476.43	527.38	579.34	631.64
	s,kJ/(kg·K)	1.2027		1.2754	1.4769	1.6134	1.7313	1.8386	1.9376	2.0287

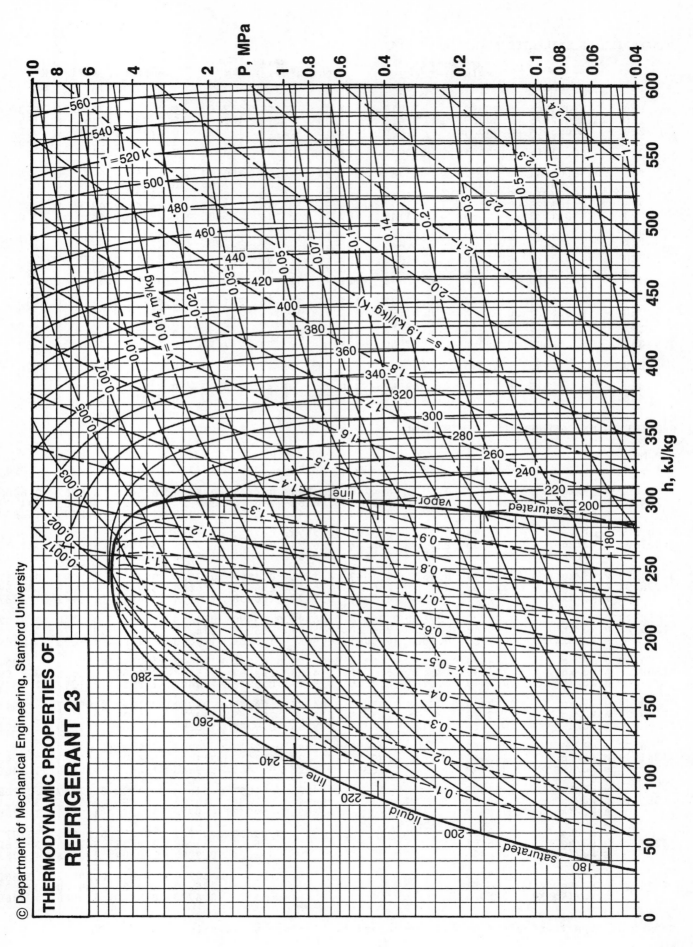

© Department of Mechanical Engineering, Stanford University

THERMODYNAMIC PROPERTIES OF
REFRIGERANT 23

P, MPa

h, kJ/kg

89

PROPERTIES OF SATURATED REFRIGERANT 114

T K	P MPa	volume, m³/kg v_f	v_g	enthalpy, kJ/kg h_f	h_fg	h_g	entropy, kJ/(kg·K) s_f	s_fg	s_g
200	0.001385	0.000583	7.017	0.0	157.07	157.07	0.0	0.7853	0.7853
210	0.002975	0.000591	3.426	7.96	154.73	162.69	0.0388	0.7368	0.7756
220	0.005904	0.000600	1.805	16.12	152.34	168.46	0.0768	0.6924	0.7692
230	0.01095	0.000609	1.015	24.48	149.87	174.35	0.1139	0.6516	0.7655
240	0.01915	0.000618	0.6031	33.08	147.27	180.35	0.1505	0.6136	0.7641
250	0.03181	0.000628	0.3761	41.90	144.54	186.44	0.1865	0.5781	0.7646
260	0.05052	0.000639	0.2445	50.98	141.62	192.60	0.2220	0.5447	0.7667
270	0.07714	0.000650	0.1648	60.32	138.49	198.81	0.2572	0.5129	0.7701
276.93	0.101325	0.000658	0.1277	66.94	136.19	203.13	0.2814	0.4918	0.7732
280	0.1138	0.000662	0.1146	69.91	135.14	205.05	0.2920	0.4826	0.7746
290	0.1627	0.000675	0.08182	79.75	131.54	211.29	0.3264	0.4536	0.7800
300	0.2264	0.000689	0.05982	89.84	127.66	217.50	0.3605	0.4255	0.7860
310	0.3075	0.000705	0.04463	100.16	123.51	223.67	0.3941	0.3984	0.7925
320	0.4088	0.000721	0.03387	110.71	119.06	229.77	0.4274	0.3720	0.7994
330	0.5330	0.000740	0.02608	121.47	114.28	235.75	0.4602	0.3463	0.8065
340	0.6831	0.000761	0.02033	132.44	109.16	241.60	0.4926	0.3211	0.8137
350	0.8622	0.000784	0.01599	143.61	103.64	247.25	0.5246	0.2961	0.8207
360	1.074	0.000811	0.01266	155.00	97.65	252.65	0.5562	0.2713	0.8275
370	1.321	0.000843	0.01006	166.63	91.07	257.70	0.5875	0.2461	0.8336
380	1.609	0.000881	0.007986	178.56	83.71	262.27	0.6187	0.2202	0.8389
390	1.943	0.000930	0.006293	190.94	75.17	266.11	0.6500	0.1928	0.8428
400	2.331	0.000998	0.004860	204.11	64.61	268.72	0.6824	0.1615	0.8439
410	2.785	0.001112	0.003557	219.22	49.44	268.66	0.7185	0.1206	0.8391
418.86	3.268	0.001719	0.001719	249.17	0.0	249.17	0.7891	0.0	0.7891

PROPERTIES OF GASEOUS REFRIGERANT 114

P,MPa (T_sat,K)		sat	325	350	375	T,K 400	425	450	475	500
0.040 (254.8)	v,m³/kg	0.3039	0.3916	0.4226	0.4534	0.4842	0.5149	0.5456	0.5762	0.6068
	h,kJ/kg	189.42	238.31	257.15	276.64	296.70	317.27	338.27	359.63	381.29
	s,kJ/(kg·K)	0.7655	0.9345	0.9903	1.0441	1.0959	1.1458	1.1938	1.2400	1.2844
0.070 (267.6)	v,m³/kg	0.1804	0.2222	0.2401	0.2579	0.2757	0.2933	0.3110	0.3286	0.3462
	h,kJ/kg	197.34	237.96	256.85	276.38	296.47	317.06	338.08	359.47	381.14
	s,kJ/(kg·K)	0.7692	0.9065	0.9625	1.0164	1.0683	1.1182	1.1662	1.2125	1.2570
0.101325 (276.9)	v,m³/kg	0.1277	0.1523	0.1649	0.1773	0.1897	0.2020	0.2143	0.2265	0.2387
	h,kJ/kg	203.13	237.59	256.53	276.10	296.22	316.84	337.89	359.29	380.99
	s,kJ/(kg·K)	0.7732	0.8878	0.9439	0.9979	1.0498	1.0998	1.1479	1.1942	1.2387
0.20 (296.2)	v,m³/kg	0.06730	0.07521	0.08188	0.08844	0.09490	0.1013	0.1077	0.1140	0.1202
	h,kJ/kg	215.12	236.38	255.50	275.21	295.44	316.15	337.28	358.74	380.49
	s,kJ/(kg·K)	0.7836	0.8521	0.9088	0.9632	1.0154	1.0656	1.1139	1.1603	1.2049
0.30 (309.2)	v,m³/kg	0.04570	0.04876	0.05344	0.05799	0.06244	0.06682	0.07115	0.07544	0.07969
	h,kJ/kg	223.16	235.10	254.42	274.28	294.63	315.44	336.65	358.18	379.99
	s,kJ/(kg·K)	0.7920	0.8297	0.8869	0.9417	0.9942	1.0447	1.0932	1.1397	1.1845
0.40 (319.2)	v,m³/kg	0.03459	0.03548	0.03919	0.04275	0.04620	0.04958	0.05290	0.05617	0.05941
	h,kJ/kg	229.29	233.75	253.29	273.32	293.81	314.72	336.01	357.61	379.48
	s,kJ/(kg·K)	0.7989	0.8127	0.8706	0.9259	0.9788	1.0295	1.0782	1.1249	1.1697
0.70 (341.0)	v,m³/kg	0.01983		0.02072	0.02307	0.02527	0.02737	0.02941	0.03139	0.03334
	h,kJ/kg	242.18		249.56	270.23	291.19	312.46	334.03	355.86	377.92
	s,kJ/(kg·K)	0.8144		0.8357	0.8928	0.9469	0.9985	1.0478	1.0950	1.1402
1.0 (356.7)	v,m³/kg	0.01367		0.01508	0.01683	0.01845	0.01999	0.02147	0.02290	
	h,kJ/kg	250.89		266.74	288.34	310.06	331.96	354.05	376.31	
	s,kJ/(kg·K)	0.8253		0.8686	0.9243	0.9770	1.0271	1.0749	1.1205	
2.0 (391.6)	v,m³/kg	0.00606			0.00660	0.00787	0.00892	0.00985	0.01071	
	h,kJ/kg	266.61			275.68	300.48	324.16	347.46	370.62	
	s,kJ/(kg·K)	0.8432			0.8661	0.9263	0.9804	1.0308	1.0783	
3.0 (414.2)	v,m³/kg	0.00298				0.00396	0.00510	0.00592	0.00662	
	h,kJ/kg	266.58				285.41	314.26	339.80	364.31	
	s,kJ/(kg·K)	0.8324				0.8773	0.9434	0.9986	1.0489	

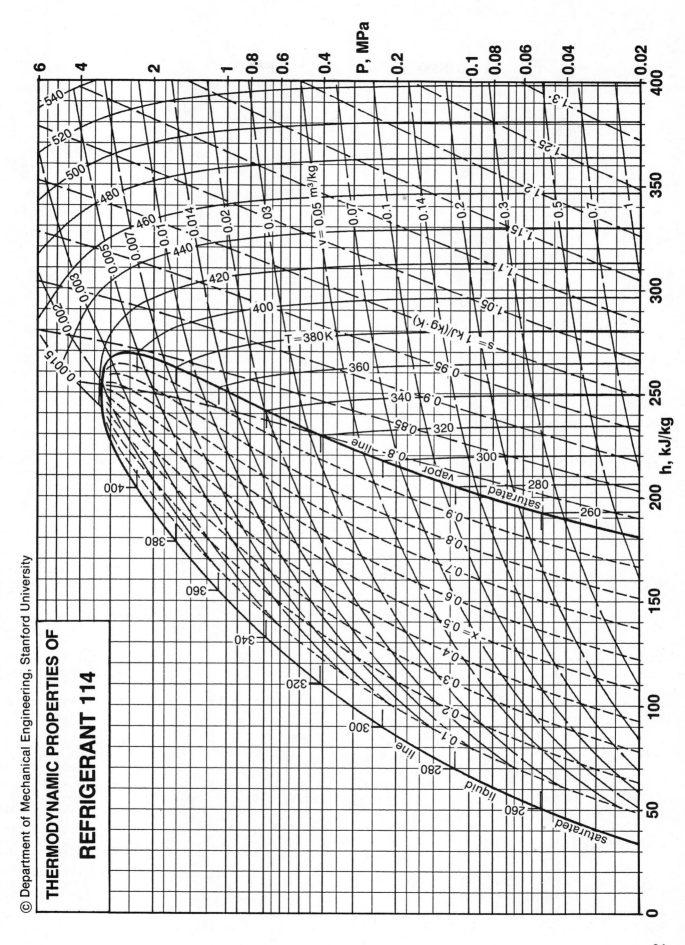

© Department of Mechanical Engineering, Stanford University

**THERMODYNAMIC PROPERTIES OF
REFRIGERANT 114**

PROPERTIES OF SATURATED REFRIGERANT C-318

T K	P MPa	volume, m³/kg v_f	v_g	enthalpy, kJ/kg h_f	h_{fg}	h_g	entropy, kJ/(kg·K) s_f	s_{fg}	s_g
250	0.04660	0.000599	0.2165	0.0	121.86	121.86	0.0	0.4874	0.4874
255	0.05905	0.000605	0.1733	4.75	120.40	125.15	0.0188	0.4722	0.4910
260	0.07406	0.000611	0.1400	9.59	118.87	128.46	0.0375	0.4572	0.4947
265	0.09197	0.000617	0.1141	14.52	117.25	131.77	0.0563	0.4424	0.4987
267.31	0.101325	0.000620	0.1041	16.83	116.47	133.30	0.0649	0.4358	0.5007
270	0.1132	0.000623	0.09376	19.55	115.54	135.09	0.0750	0.4279	0.5029
275	0.1380	0.000630	0.07762	24.67	113.73	138.40	0.0938	0.4135	0.5073
280	0.1670	0.000637	0.06471	29.89	111.83	141.72	0.1125	0.3994	0.5119
285	0.2005	0.000645	0.05430	35.20	109.83	145.03	0.1312	0.3854	0.5166
290	0.2390	0.000653	0.04583	40.60	107.73	148.33	0.1499	0.3715	0.5214
295	0.2829	0.000661	0.03890	46.09	105.53	151.62	0.1686	0.3577	0.5263
300	0.3327	0.000670	0.03319	51.68	103.22	154.90	0.1873	0.3440	0.5313
305	0.3889	0.000679	0.02845	57.35	100.80	158.15	0.2059	0.3305	0.5364
310	0.4519	0.000689	0.02449	63.12	98.26	161.38	0.2245	0.3170	0.5415
315	0.5222	0.000700	0.02116	68.97	95.61	164.58	0.2431	0.3035	0.5466
320	0.6004	0.000711	0.01835	74.92	92.83	167.75	0.2616	0.2901	0.5517
325	0.6869	0.000723	0.01595	80.95	89.92	170.87	0.2801	0.2767	0.5568
330	0.7822	0.000736	0.01391	87.07	86.87	173.94	0.2986	0.2633	0.5619
335	0.8869	0.000751	0.01215	93.28	83.67	176.95	0.3171	0.2497	0.5668
340	1.001	0.000767	0.01063	99.58	80.30	179.88	0.3355	0.2362	0.5717
345	1.127	0.000784	0.009309	105.99	76.74	182.73	0.3539	0.2224	0.5763
350	1.263	0.000803	0.008151	112.50	72.96	185.46	0.3723	0.2085	0.5808
355	1.410	0.000825	0.007131	119.13	68.92	188.05	0.3908	0.1941	0.5849
360	1.571	0.000851	0.006225	125.91	64.55	190.46	0.4094	0.1793	0.5887
365	1.744	0.000881	0.005412	132.86	59.76	192.62	0.4281	0.1638	0.5919
370	1.932	0.000917	0.004672	140.05	54.37	194.42	0.4473	0.1469	0.5942
375	2.136	0.000964	0.003985	147.61	48.09	195.70	0.4670	0.1283	0.5953
380	2.358	0.001029	0.003321	155.80	40.25	196.05	0.4882	0.1059	0.5941
388.48	2.783	0.001613	0.001613	181.64	0.0	181.64	0.5539	0.0	0.5539

PROPERTIES OF GASEOUS REFRIGERANT C-318

P,MPa (T_{sat},K)		sat	300	340	380	420	460	500	540	580
0.101325 (267.3)	v,m³/kg	0.1041	0.1191	0.1367	0.1538	0.1707	0.1874	0.2041	0.2207	0.2373
	h,kJ/kg	133.30	158.70	191.79	227.02	264.26	303.34	344.08	386.32	429.88
	s,kJ/(kg·K)	0.5007	0.5903	0.6937	0.7916	0.8848	0.9736	1.0585	1.1398	1.2176
0.20 (284.9)	v,m³/kg	0.05443	0.05825	0.06780	0.07686	0.08567	0.09434	0.1029	0.1114	0.1199
	h,kJ/kg	144.98	157.16	190.75	226.26	263.68	302.87	343.70	385.99	429.60
	s,kJ/(kg·K)	0.5165	0.5582	0.6632	0.7619	0.8555	0.9446	1.0297	1.1110	1.1889
0.30 (296.8)	v,m³/kg	0.03674	0.03733	0.04419	0.05052	0.05657	0.06247	0.06828	0.07404	0.07975
	h,kJ/kg	152.79	155.48	189.64	225.47	263.07	302.39	343.30	385.66	429.31
	s,kJ/(kg·K)	0.5281	0.5371	0.6440	0.7435	0.8376	0.9270	1.0122	1.0937	1.1717
0.40 (305.9)	v,m³/kg	0.02766		0.03236	0.03733	0.04201	0.04653	0.05096	0.05533	0.05966
	h,kJ/kg	158.75		188.49	224.66	262.47	301.91	342.91	385.32	429.02
	s,kJ/(kg·K)	0.5373		0.6295	0.7300	0.8246	0.9143	0.9997	1.0813	1.1593
0.60 (320.0)	v,m³/kg	0.01836		0.02045	0.02412	0.02744	0.03059	0.03364	0.03663	0.03958
	h,kJ/kg	167.73		186.00	222.97	261.21	300.93	342.10	384.65	428.44
	s,kJ/(kg·K)	0.5517		0.6071	0.7099	0.8055	0.8958	0.9816	1.0635	1.1417
0.80 (330.9)	v,m³/kg	0.01358		0.01440	0.01748	0.02015	0.02262	0.02499	0.02728	0.02954
	h,kJ/kg	174.48		183.19	221.18	259.92	299.93	341.29	383.97	427.85
	s,kJ/(kg·K)	0.5628		0.5887	0.6944	0.7913	0.8822	0.9684	1.0505	1.1289
1.0 (339.9)	v,m³/kg	0.01065		0.01065	0.01347	0.01576	0.01783	0.01979	0.02168	0.02352
	h,kJ/kg	179.85		179.91	219.26	258.57	298.90	340.47	383.28	427.27
	s,kJ/(kg·K)	0.5716		0.5718	0.6812	0.7796	0.8713	0.9579	1.0403	1.1188
2.0 (371.7)	v,m³/kg	0.00443			0.00506	0.00691	0.00824	0.00940	0.01047	0.01149
	h,kJ/kg	194.93			206.04	250.90	293.40	336.18	379.78	424.32
	s,kJ/(kg·K)	0.5948			0.6243	0.7367	0.8333	0.9225	1.0064	1.0859

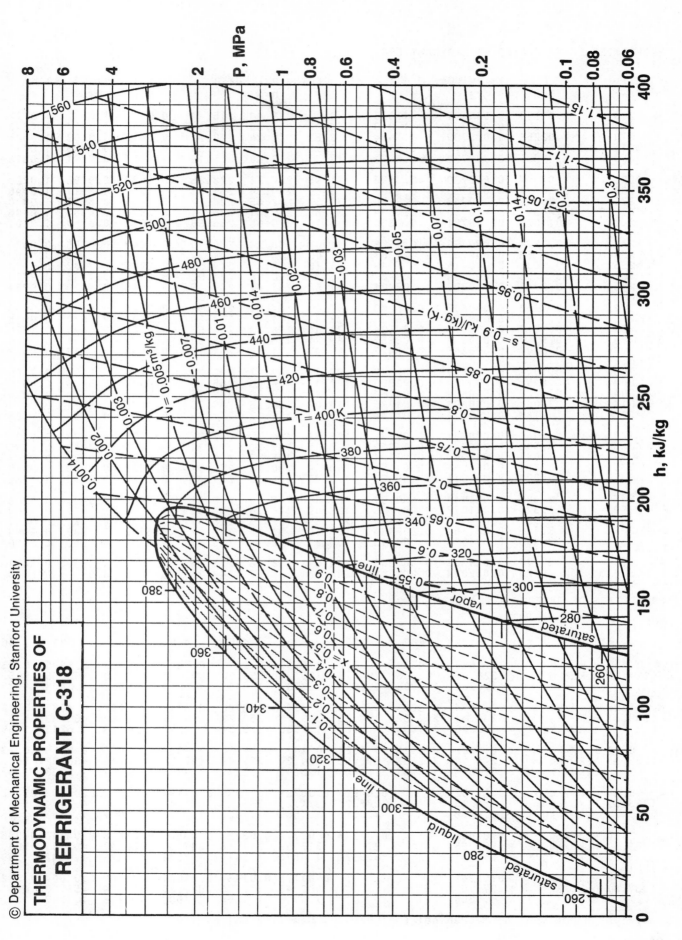

THERMODYNAMIC PROPERTIES OF
REFRIGERANT C-318

© Department of Mechanical Engineering, Stanford University

P, MPa

h, kJ/kg

PROPERTIES OF SATURATED REFRIGERANT 500

T K	P MPa	volume, m³/kg v_f	v_g	enthalpy, kJ/kg h_f	h_{fg}	h_g	entropy, kJ/(kg·K) s_f	s_{fg}	s_g
200	0.01219	0.000697	1.360	0.0	215.44	215.44	0.0	1.0772	1.0772
205	0.01672	0.000703	1.013	4.23	213.89	218.12	0.0209	1.0434	1.0643
210	0.02258	0.000709	0.7664	8.53	212.28	220.81	0.0416	1.0109	1.0525
215	0.03002	0.000716	0.5880	12.92	210.58	223.50	0.0622	0.9795	1.0417
220	0.03936	0.000722	0.4571	17.39	208.80	226.19	0.0827	0.9491	1.0318
225	0.05094	0.000729	0.3596	21.95	206.91	228.86	0.1032	0.9196	1.0228
230	0.06511	0.000736	0.2861	26.59	204.94	231.53	0.1235	0.8911	1.0146
235	0.08230	0.000743	0.2300	31.32	202.85	234.17	0.1438	0.8632	1.0070
239.64	0.101325	0.000750	0.1894	35.80	200.81	236.61	0.1626	0.8380	1.0006
240	0.1029	0.000751	0.1866	36.15	200.65	236.80	0.1641	0.8360	1.0001
245	0.1274	0.000759	0.1528	41.06	198.34	239.40	0.1843	0.8095	0.9938
250	0.1563	0.000767	0.1261	46.06	195.91	241.97	0.2044	0.7836	0.9880
255	0.1901	0.000775	0.1049	51.16	193.35	244.51	0.2245	0.7582	0.9827
260	0.2293	0.000784	0.08787	56.34	190.68	247.02	0.2445	0.7333	0.9778
265	0.2745	0.000793	0.07408	61.62	187.87	249.49	0.2645	0.7089	0.9734
270	0.3262	0.000802	0.06283	67.00	184.91	251.91	0.2844	0.6849	0.9693
275	0.3851	0.000812	0.05359	72.47	181.82	254.29	0.3043	0.6612	0.9655
280	0.4517	0.000823	0.04594	78.04	178.59	256.63	0.3242	0.6378	0.9620
285	0.5267	0.000834	0.03957	83.71	175.19	258.90	0.3440	0.6148	0.9588
290	0.6107	0.000845	0.03422	89.47	171.65	261.12	0.3638	0.5919	0.9557
295	0.7042	0.000857	0.02972	95.35	167.92	263.27	0.3836	0.5693	0.9529
300	0.8081	0.000870	0.02590	101.32	164.03	265.35	0.4034	0.5468	0.9502
305	0.9229	0.000884	0.02264	107.41	159.94	267.35	0.4232	0.5244	0.9476
310	1.049	0.000898	0.01985	113.61	155.65	269.26	0.4430	0.5021	0.9451
315	1.188	0.000914	0.01744	119.94	151.12	271.06	0.4629	0.4797	0.9426
320	1.340	0.000931	0.01535	126.39	146.36	272.75	0.4828	0.4573	0.9401
325	1.506	0.000949	0.01353	132.98	141.33	274.31	0.5027	0.4348	0.9375
330	1.686	0.000969	0.01194	139.73	135.97	275.70	0.5228	0.4120	0.9348
335	1.881	0.000991	0.01054	146.64	130.28	276.92	0.5430	0.3889	0.9319
340	2.093	0.001016	0.009303	153.75	124.15	277.90	0.5634	0.3652	0.9286
345	2.322	0.001044	0.008199	161.08	117.54	278.62	0.5841	0.3407	0.9248
350	2.570	0.001077	0.007208	168.69	110.30	278.99	0.6053	0.3151	0.9204
355	2.837	0.001115	0.006310	176.65	102.26	278.91	0.6270	0.2881	0.9151
360	3.125	0.001162	0.005485	185.10	93.12	278.22	0.6497	0.2587	0.9084
365	3.436	0.001223	0.004713	194.27	82.34	276.61	0.6740	0.2256	0.8996
370	3.772	0.001307	0.003963	204.67	68.78	273.45	0.7012	0.1859	0.8871
378.66	4.426	0.002014	0.002014	244.28	0.0	244.28	0.8040	0.0	0.8040

PROPERTIES OF GASEOUS REFRIGERANT 500

P,MPa (T_{sat},K)		sat	280	320	360	T,K 400	440	480	520	560
0.050 (224.6)	v,m³/kg	0.3659	0.4634	0.5320	0.5999	0.6675	0.7349	0.8023	0.8695	0.9367
	h,kJ/kg	228.67	265.68	294.76	325.77	358.60	393.13	429.20	466.65	505.32
	s,kJ/(kg·K)	1.0234	1.1705	1.2675	1.3587	1.4452	1.5274	1.6058	1.6808	1.7524
0.101325 (239.6)	v,m³/kg	0.1894	0.2259	0.2606	0.2946	0.3283	0.3618	0.3952	0.4285	0.4618
	h,kJ/kg	236.61	264.63	294.06	325.26	358.22	392.82	428.94	466.43	505.13
	s,kJ/(kg·K)	1.0006	1.1086	1.2067	1.2986	1.3854	1.4678	1.5463	1.6213	1.6930
0.20 (256.3)	v,m³/kg	0.1000	0.1116	0.1301	0.1478	0.1652	0.1824	0.1995	0.2165	0.2335
	h,kJ/kg	245.18	262.52	292.68	324.29	357.48	392.24	428.46	466.02	504.77
	s,kJ/(kg·K)	0.9814	1.0461	1.1467	1.2397	1.3271	1.4099	1.4887	1.5638	1.6356
0.50 (283.3)	v,m³/kg	0.04162		0.04957	0.05737	0.06476	0.07192	0.07897	0.08593	0.09285
	h,kJ/kg	258.13		288.24	321.21	355.19	390.42	426.96	464.74	503.66
	s,kJ/(kg·K)	0.9598		1.0598	1.1569	1.2463	1.3303	1.4097	1.4853	1.5574
1.0 (308.1)	v,m³/kg	0.02086		0.02246	0.02712	0.03122	0.03507	0.03878	0.04240	0.04597
	h,kJ/kg	268.55		279.75	315.69	351.18	387.31	424.42	462.59	501.80
	s,kJ/(kg·K)	0.9461		0.9818	1.0876	1.1811	1.2672	1.3479	1.4242	1.4969
2.0 (337.8)	v,m³/kg	0.00982		0.01172	0.01437	0.01661	0.01867	0.02064	0.02254	
	h,kJ/kg	277.51		302.45	342.36	380.70	419.14	458.20	498.04	
	s,kJ/(kg·K)	0.9300		1.0016	1.1068	1.1982	1.2818	1.3599	1.4337	

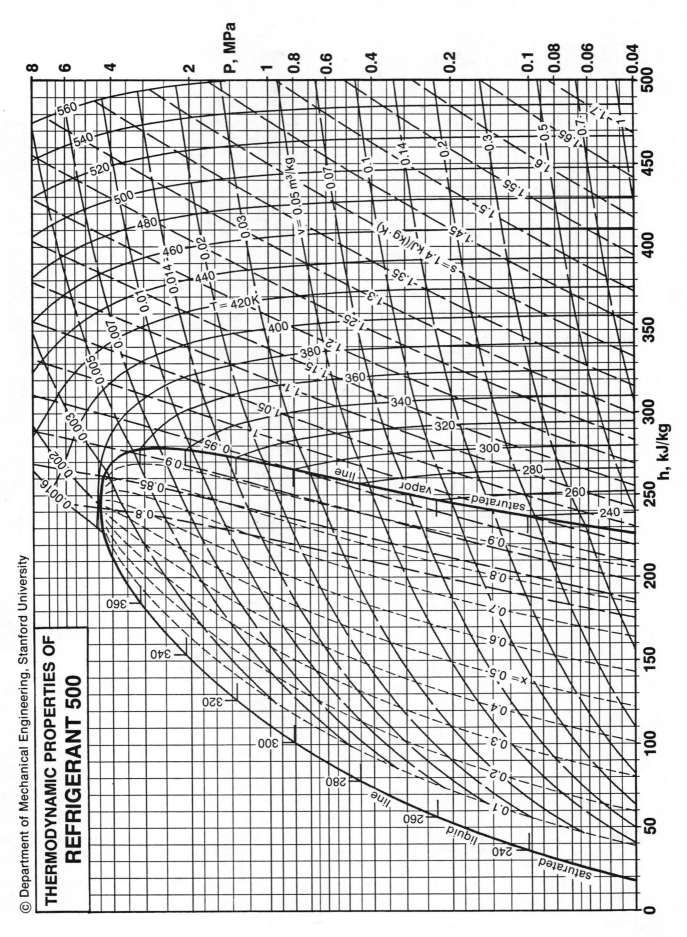

© Department of Mechanical Engineering, Stanford University

THERMODYNAMIC PROPERTIES OF
REFRIGERANT 500

P, MPa

h, kJ/kg

PROPERTIES OF SATURATED REFRIGERANT 502

T K	P MPa	volume, m³/kg vf	vg	enthalpy, kJ/kg hf	hfg	hg	entropy, kJ/(kg·K) sf	sfg	sg
200	0.02274	0.000638	0.6463	0.0	182.38	182.38	0.0	0.9119	0.9119
205	0.03077	0.000644	0.4880	4.05	180.87	184.92	0.0200	0.8823	0.9023
210	0.04098	0.000651	0.3739	8.21	179.26	187.47	0.0400	0.8536	0.8936
215	0.05378	0.000657	0.2903	12.49	177.51	190.00	0.0601	0.8256	0.8857
220	0.06964	0.000664	0.2282	16.89	175.64	192.53	0.0803	0.7983	0.8786
225	0.08904	0.000671	0.1815	21.41	173.64	195.05	0.1005	0.7717	0.8722
227.73	0.101325	0.000675	0.1608	23.94	172.47	196.41	0.1116	0.7574	0.8690
230	0.1125	0.000680	0.1458	26.06	171.48	197.54	0.1209	0.7456	0.8665
235	0.1406	0.000686	0.1183	30.82	169.20	200.02	0.1413	0.7200	0.8613
240	0.1739	0.000694	0.09688	35.70	166.76	202.46	0.1617	0.6949	0.8566
245	0.2131	0.000702	0.07998	40.70	164.17	204.87	0.1823	0.6700	0.8523
250	0.2587	0.000711	0.06653	45.82	161.43	207.25	0.2028	0.6457	0.8485
255	0.3114	0.000720	0.05574	51.05	158.53	209.58	0.2234	0.6216	0.8450
260	0.3719	0.000729	0.04700	56.40	155.46	211.86	0.2440	0.5979	0.8419
265	0.4408	0.000739	0.03987	61.85	152.24	214.09	0.2645	0.5745	0.8390
270	0.5189	0.000749	0.03401	67.40	148.86	216.26	0.2851	0.5513	0.8364
275	0.6068	0.000760	0.02915	73.06	145.30	218.36	0.3056	0.5284	0.8340
280	0.7053	0.000772	0.02510	78.81	141.58	220.39	0.3261	0.5056	0.8317
285	0.8149	0.000785	0.02169	84.66	137.68	222.34	0.3464	0.4832	0.8296
290	0.9366	0.000798	0.01882	90.59	133.62	224.21	0.3668	0.4607	0.8275
295	1.071	0.000812	0.01638	96.62	129.35	225.97	0.3870	0.4385	0.8255
300	1.219	0.000828	0.01429	102.73	124.88	227.61	0.4071	0.4163	0.8234
305	1.380	0.000845	0.01249	108.94	120.19	229.13	0.4272	0.3941	0.8213
310	1.557	0.000864	0.01093	115.23	115.27	230.50	0.4472	0.3718	0.8190
315	1.750	0.000885	0.009572	121.63	110.05	231.68	0.4671	0.3494	0.8165
320	1.960	0.000908	0.008381	128.14	104.52	232.66	0.4870	0.3266	0.8136
325	2.188	0.000935	0.007327	134.80	98.57	233.37	0.5070	0.3033	0.8103
330	2.435	0.000967	0.006387	141.64	92.09	233.73	0.5272	0.2791	0.8063
335	2.703	0.001005	0.005538	148.76	84.88	233.64	0.5478	0.2534	0.8012
340	2.995	0.001053	0.004756	156.30	76.59	232.89	0.5693	0.2252	0.7945
345	3.313	0.001117	0.004015	164.63	66.45	231.08	0.5926	0.1926	0.7852
350	3.661	0.001220	0.003262	174.72	52.40	227.12	0.6204	0.1497	0.7701
355.31	4.075	0.001784	0.001784	202.78	0.0	202.78	0.6982	0.0	0.6982

PROPERTIES OF GASEOUS REFRIGERANT 502

P,MPa (Tsat,K)		sat	300	325	350	T,K 375	400	425	450	475
0.050 (213.6)	v,m³/kg	0.3107	0.4435	0.4813	0.5190	0.5566	0.5941	0.6316	0.6690	0.7064
	h,kJ/kg	189.31	243.84	261.35	279.57	298.47	318.01	338.16	358.89	380.14
	s,kJ/(kg·K)	0.8878	1.1011	1.1572	1.2112	1.2633	1.3137	1.3626	1.4100	1.4559
0.101325 (227.7)	v,m³/kg	0.1608	0.2171	0.2361	0.2549	0.2736	0.2923	0.3109	0.3295	0.3480
	h,kJ/kg	196.41	243.26	260.87	279.17	298.13	317.72	337.90	358.65	379.94
	s,kJ/(kg·K)	0.8690	1.0472	1.1035	1.1577	1.2101	1.2606	1.3096	1.3570	1.4030
0.20 (243.4)	v,m³/kg	0.08490	0.1083	0.1182	0.1280	0.1376	0.1472	0.1568	0.1663	0.1758
	h,kJ/kg	204.11	242.13	259.94	278.39	297.46	317.14	337.40	358.21	379.54
	s,kJ/(kg·K)	0.8536	0.9938	1.0509	1.1055	1.1582	1.2090	1.2581	1.3057	1.3518
0.50 (268.8)	v,m³/kg	0.03526	0.04114	0.04552	0.04974	0.05384	0.05786	0.06183	0.06575	0.06965
	h,kJ/kg	215.76	238.45	256.97	275.94	295.39	315.36	335.85	356.84	378.31
	s,kJ/(kg·K)	0.8370	0.9168	0.9761	1.0323	1.0860	1.1376	1.1872	1.2352	1.2817
0.70 (279.7)	v,m³/kg	0.02528	0.02826	0.03163	0.03481	0.03786	0.04083	0.04373	0.04660	0.04943
	h,kJ/kg	220.29	235.78	254.88	274.23	293.97	314.15	334.80	355.92	377.49
	s,kJ/(kg·K)	0.8318	0.8853	0.9464	1.0038	1.0583	1.1103	1.1604	1.2087	1.2553
1.0 (292.4)	v,m³/kg	0.01759	0.01848	0.02116	0.02358	0.02586	0.02804	0.03016	0.03223	0.03427
	h,kJ/kg	225.07	231.33	251.52	271.56	291.77	312.29	333.20	354.51	376.25
	s,kJ/(kg·K)	0.8265	0.8476	0.9123	0.9717	1.0275	1.0804	1.1311	1.1798	1.2268
2.0 (320.9)	v,m³/kg	0.00818		0.00853	0.01032	0.01178	0.01309	0.01431	0.01546	0.01658
	h,kJ/kg	232.81		237.14	261.25	283.69	305.66	327.59	349.67	371.99
	s,kJ/(kg·K)	0.8131		0.8265	0.8980	0.9599	1.0167	1.0698	1.1203	1.1686

Copyright Department of Mechanical Engineering, Stanford University

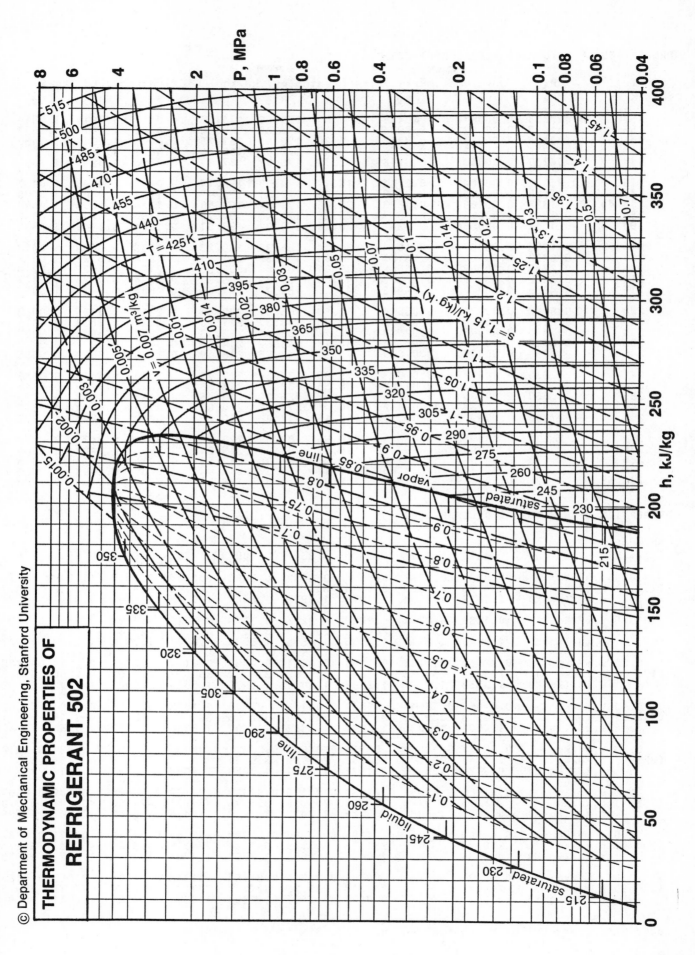

© Department of Mechanical Engineering, Stanford University

THERMODYNAMIC PROPERTIES OF
REFRIGERANT 502

97

PROPERTIES OF SATURATED REFRIGERANT 503

T K	P MPa	volume, m³/kg		enthalpy, kJ/kg			entropy, kJ/(kg·K)		
		v_f	v_g	h_f	h_fg	h_g	s_f	s_fg	s_g
150	0.009838	0.000617	1.445	0.0	178.66	178.66	0.0	1.1910	1.1910
155	0.01475	0.000622	0.9944	3.10	177.85	180.95	0.0203	1.1474	1.1677
160	0.02154	0.000627	0.7012	6.26	176.99	183.25	0.0403	1.1062	1.1465
165	0.03072	0.000633	0.5055	9.48	176.08	185.56	0.0602	1.0671	1.1273
170	0.04289	0.000639	0.3718	12.79	175.08	187.87	0.0798	1.0299	1.1097
175	0.05871	0.000646	0.2784	16.17	174.00	190.17	0.0994	0.9943	1.0937
180	0.07895	0.000653	0.2119	19.66	172.81	192.47	0.1190	0.9600	1.0790
184.44	0.101325	0.000659	0.1683	22.86	171.64	194.50	0.1364	0.9306	1.0670
185	0.1044	0.000660	0.1637	23.26	171.49	194.75	0.1386	0.9270	1.0656
190	0.1361	0.000668	0.1281	26.99	170.02	197.01	0.1584	0.8948	1.0532
195	0.1750	0.000677	0.1014	30.84	168.39	199.23	0.1783	0.8635	1.0418
200	0.2222	0.000687	0.08121	34.85	166.56	201.41	0.1984	0.8328	1.0312
205	0.2789	0.000697	0.06566	39.01	164.54	203.55	0.2187	0.8027	1.0214
210	0.3462	0.000708	0.05355	43.34	162.29	205.63	0.2394	0.7728	1.0122
215	0.4256	0.000720	0.04402	47.86	159.77	207.63	0.2604	0.7431	1.0035
220	0.5183	0.000733	0.03644	52.59	156.97	209.56	0.2818	0.7135	0.9953
225	0.6259	0.000747	0.03036	57.53	153.87	211.40	0.3037	0.6838	0.9875
230	0.7497	0.000762	0.02543	62.72	150.41	213.13	0.3260	0.6540	0.9800
235	0.8915	0.000779	0.02140	68.16	146.57	214.73	0.3490	0.6237	0.9727
240	1.053	0.000797	0.01809	73.90	142.29	216.19	0.3726	0.5929	0.9655
245	1.235	0.000817	0.01533	79.95	137.54	217.49	0.3970	0.5613	0.9583
250	1.440	0.000839	0.01303	86.36	132.22	218.58	0.4222	0.5289	0.9511
255	1.669	0.000864	0.01109	93.16	126.29	219.45	0.4483	0.4953	0.9436
260	1.925	0.000891	0.009442	100.41	119.62	220.03	0.4756	0.4601	0.9357
265	2.208	0.000922	0.008031	108.18	112.08	220.26	0.5042	0.4230	0.9272
270	2.520	0.000958	0.006810	116.55	103.50	220.05	0.5344	0.3833	0.9177
275	2.863	0.001000	0.005741	125.65	93.59	219.24	0.5666	0.3403	0.9069
280	3.238	0.001051	0.004788	135.70	81.86	217.56	0.6014	0.2924	0.8938
285	3.646	0.001120	0.003906	147.11	67.33	214.44	0.6402	0.2363	0.8765
292.59	4.326	0.001919	0.001919	188.07	0.0	188.07	0.7784	0.0	0.7784

PROPERTIES OF GASEOUS REFRIGERANT 503

P,MPa (T_sat,K)		sat	250	300	350	400	450	500	550	600
0.050 (172.4)	v,m³/kg	0.3228	0.4733	0.5694	0.6652	0.7609	0.8564	0.9519	1.047	1.143
	h,kJ/kg	188.98	232.59	265.04	300.73	339.38	380.63	424.00	468.92	514.74
	s,kJ/(kg·K)	1.1018	1.3094	1.4276	1.5375	1.6407	1.7378	1.8291	1.9147	1.9945
0.101325 (184.4)	v,m³/kg	0.1683	0.2321	0.2799	0.3275	0.3749	0.4221	0.4694	0.5165	0.5637
	h,kJ/kg	194.50	232.16	264.72	300.49	339.19	380.47	423.87	468.81	514.65
	s,kJ/(kg·K)	1.0670	1.2411	1.3596	1.4698	1.5730	1.6702	1.7616	1.8473	1.9271
0.20 (197.8)	v,m³/kg	0.08960	0.1161	0.1408	0.1651	0.1893	0.2134	0.2375	0.2614	0.2854
	h,kJ/kg	200.44	231.33	264.11	300.02	338.82	380.17	423.62	468.60	514.48
	s,kJ/(kg·K)	1.0358	1.1741	1.2935	1.4041	1.5076	1.6050	1.6965	1.7822	1.8621
0.40 (213.5)	v,m³/kg	0.04669	0.05649	0.06931	0.08179	0.09408	0.1063	0.1184	0.1305	0.1425
	h,kJ/kg	207.03	229.58	262.85	299.06	338.06	379.56	423.11	468.18	514.12
	s,kJ/(kg·K)	1.0061	1.1035	1.2247	1.3362	1.4403	1.5380	1.6297	1.7156	1.7956
0.70 (228.1)	v,m³/kg	0.02721	0.03087	0.03866	0.04606	0.05326	0.06035	0.06737	0.07434	0.08127
	h,kJ/kg	212.48	226.79	260.91	297.59	336.91	378.63	422.35	467.55	513.59
	s,kJ/(kg·K)	0.9829	1.0428	1.1671	1.2801	1.3850	1.4832	1.5753	1.6614	1.7416
1.0 (238.4)	v,m³/kg	0.01906	0.02054	0.02638	0.03176	0.03693	0.04199	0.04696	0.05189	0.05678
	h,kJ/kg	215.75	223.74	258.88	296.10	335.76	377.71	421.60	466.92	513.05
	s,kJ/(kg·K)	0.9678	1.0005	1.1285	1.2432	1.3490	1.4478	1.5402	1.6266	1.7069
2.0 (261.4)	v,m³/kg	0.00903		0.01196	0.01506	0.01788	0.02056	0.02316	0.02571	0.02822
	h,kJ/kg	220.13		251.38	290.89	331.81	374.59	419.06	464.82	511.30
	s,kJ/(kg·K)	0.9334		1.0450	1.1668	1.2760	1.3768	1.4704	1.5577	1.6385
3.0 (276.9)	v,m³/kg	0.00537		0.00701	0.00948	0.01154	0.01343	0.01524	0.01699	0.01871
	h,kJ/kg	218.73		242.17	285.25	327.74	371.44	416.54	462.75	509.57
	s,kJ/(kg·K)	0.9023		0.9838	1.1167	1.2301	1.3331	1.4281	1.5161	1.5976

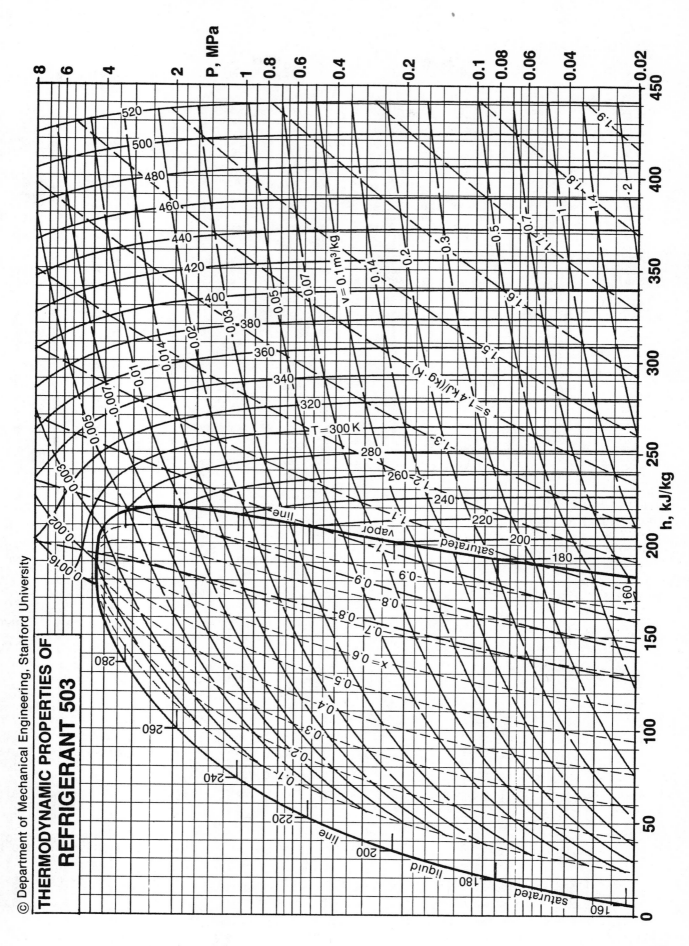

© Department of Mechanical Engineering, Stanford University

THERMODYNAMIC PROPERTIES OF REFRIGERANT 503

P, MPa

h, kJ/kg

99

PROPERTIES OF SATURATED RUBIDIUM

T K	P MPa	volume, m³/kg v_f	v_g	enthalpy, kJ/kg h_f	h_{fg}	h_g	entropy, kJ/(kg·K) s_f	s_{fg}	s_g
1000	0.1406	0.000850	0.6216	0.0	788.48	788.48	0.0	0.7885	0.7885
1020	0.1678	0.000856	0.5272	4.63	785.00	789.63	0.0046	0.7696	0.7742
1040	0.1992	0.000862	0.4498	9.73	780.98	790.71	0.0095	0.7509	0.7604
1060	0.2349	0.000869	0.3858	15.25	776.48	791.73	0.0147	0.7325	0.7472
1080	0.2754	0.000875	0.3328	21.15	771.56	792.71	0.0202	0.7144	0.7346
1100	0.3211	0.000882	0.2885	27.40	766.27	793.67	0.0259	0.6966	0.7225
1120	0.3724	0.000888	0.2514	33.96	760.65	794.61	0.0318	0.6791	0.7109
1140	0.4297	0.000895	0.2202	40.81	754.76	795.57	0.0378	0.6620	0.6998
1160	0.4933	0.000902	0.1937	47.92	748.63	796.55	0.0439	0.6454	0.6893
1180	0.5637	0.000909	0.1712	55.27	742.30	797.57	0.0501	0.6291	0.6792
1200	0.6412	0.000915	0.1519	62.85	735.79	798.64	0.0564	0.6132	0.6696
1220	0.7263	0.000922	0.1354	70.65	729.11	799.76	0.0628	0.5977	0.6605
1240	0.8191	0.000929	0.1211	78.67	722.27	800.94	0.0693	0.5825	0.6518
1260	0.9202	0.000936	0.1088	86.92	715.25	802.17	0.0758	0.5677	0.6435
1280	1.030	0.000943	0.09806	95.41	708.04	803.45	0.0824	0.5532	0.6356
1300	1.148	0.000951	0.08868	104.17	700.60	804.77	0.0891	0.5389	0.6280
1320	1.276	0.000958	0.08046	113.22	692.88	806.10	0.0959	0.5249	0.6208
1340	1.412	0.000965	0.07321	122.59	684.83	807.42	0.1029	0.5110	0.6139
1360	1.559	0.000973	0.06679	132.32	676.37	808.69	0.1100	0.4973	0.6073
1380	1.715	0.000981	0.06108	142.44	667.44	809.88	0.1173	0.4836	0.6009
1400	1.881	0.000989	0.05598	153.00	657.94	810.94	0.1247	0.4700	0.5947
1420	2.057	0.000997	0.05140	164.03	647.78	811.81	0.1324	0.4562	0.5886
1440	2.243	0.001005	0.04726	175.55	636.86	812.41	0.1404	0.4422	0.5826
1460	2.439	0.001014	0.04351	187.60	625.08	812.68	0.1485	0.4282	0.5767
1480	2.646	0.001022	0.04010	200.17	612.35	812.52	0.1569	0.4138	0.5707
1500	2.863	0.001031	0.03697	213.21	598.61	811.82	0.1655	0.3991	0.5646
1520	3.090	0.001041	0.03411	226.59	583.90	810.49	0.1742	0.3842	0.5584
1540	3.327	0.001050	0.03148	240.06	568.41	808.47	0.1829	0.3691	0.5520
1560	3.575	0.001060	0.02910	253.15	552.66	805.81	0.1912	0.3542	0.5454
1580	3.833	0.001070	0.02698	265.08	537.75	802.83	0.1986	0.3403	0.5389
1600	4.100	0.001081	0.02516	274.96	525.25	800.21	0.2046	0.3283	0.5329

PROPERTIES OF GASEOUS RUBIDIUM

P,MPa (T_{sat},K)		sat	1075	1150	1225	1300	1375	1450	1525	1600
0.101325 (964.9)	v,m³/kg	0.8421	0.9810	1.066	1.146	1.224	1.300	1.375	1.449	1.523
	h,kJ/kg	786.24	836.31	862.76	886.18	907.84	928.43	948.34	967.80	986.97
	s,kJ/(kg·K)	0.8150	0.8643	0.8881	0.9078	0.9250	0.9404	0.9545	0.9676	0.9798
0.20 (1040.)	v,m³/kg	0.4480	0.4725	0.5213	0.5660	0.6082	0.6487	0.6882	0.7270	0.7652
	h,kJ/kg	790.74	809.57	843.85	872.27	897.24	920.11	941.65	962.30	982.37
	s,kJ/(kg·K)	0.7601	0.7779	0.8088	0.8327	0.8525	0.8696	0.8849	0.8988	0.9116
0.30 (1091.)	v,m³/kg	0.3074		0.3354	0.3677	0.3977	0.4260	0.4533	0.4799	0.5059
	h,kJ/kg	793.24		825.05	858.37	886.63	911.78	934.94	956.79	977.74
	s,kJ/(kg·K)	0.7278		0.7563	0.7844	0.8068	0.8256	0.8420	0.8567	0.8701
0.40 (1130.)	v,m³/kg	0.2353		0.2428	0.2688	0.2925	0.3147	0.3359	0.3564	0.3764
	h,kJ/kg	795.09		806.79	844.73	876.18	903.55	928.31	951.33	973.17
	s,kJ/(kg·K)	0.7054		0.7156	0.7476	0.7726	0.7931	0.8106	0.8261	0.8401
0.70 (1214.)	v,m³/kg	0.1401			0.1425	0.1579	0.1721	0.1853	0.1978	0.2099
	h,kJ/kg	799.42			805.97	845.98	879.61	908.93	935.34	959.75
	s,kJ/(kg·K)	0.6631			0.6685	0.7003	0.7254	0.7462	0.7640	0.7796
1.0 (1275.)	v,m³/kg	0.1008				0.1046	0.1153	0.1253	0.1346	0.1435
	h,kJ/kg	803.11				817.87	856.90	890.38	919.95	946.78
	s,kJ/(kg·K)	0.6376				0.6491	0.6783	0.7020	0.7219	0.7391
2.0 (1414.)	v,m³/kg	0.05279						0.05570	0.06126	0.06639
	h,kJ/kg	811.56						832.91	872.04	906.21
	s,kJ/(kg·K)	0.5905						0.6054	0.6318	0.6536
4.0 (1593.)	v,m³/kg	0.02580								0.02630
	h,kJ/kg	801.07								808.39
	s,kJ/(kg·K)	0.5350								0.5396

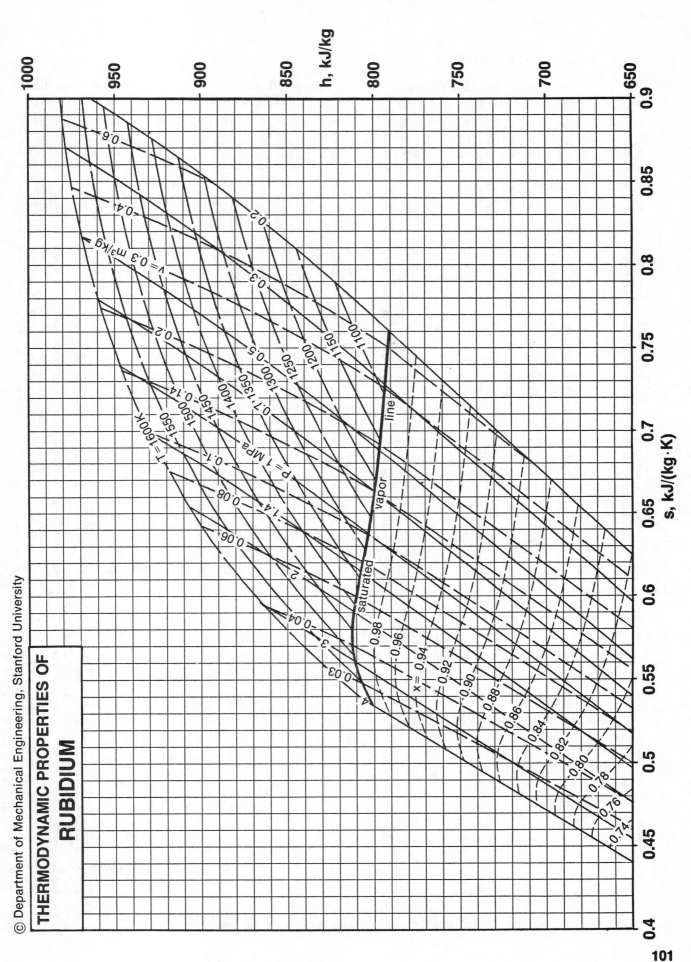

© Department of Mechanical Engineering, Stanford University

THERMODYNAMIC PROPERTIES OF
RUBIDIUM

PROPERTIES OF SATURATED SODIUM

T K	P MPa	volume, m³/kg		enthalpy, kJ/kg			entropy, kJ/(kg·K)		
		v_f	v_g	h_f	h_{fg}	h_g	s_f	s_{fg}	s_g
800	0.0009436	0.001211	298.0	0.0	4315.5	4315.5	0.0	5.3944	5.3944
825	0.001502	0.001220	192.3	32.8	4292.1	4324.9	0.0404	5.2025	5.2429
850	0.002325	0.001229	127.4	65.9	4267.5	4333.4	0.0799	5.0206	5.1005
875	0.003508	0.001238	86.52	99.2	4241.9	4341.1	0.1185	4.8479	4.9664
900	0.005170	0.001247	60.07	132.7	4215.5	4348.2	0.1563	4.6838	4.8401
925	0.007460	0.001257	42.57	166.4	4188.2	4354.6	0.1932	4.5278	4.7210
950	0.01055	0.001266	30.74	200.3	4160.2	4360.5	0.2293	4.3792	4.6085
975	0.01466	0.001276	22.58	234.2	4131.8	4366.0	0.2646	4.2377	4.5023
1000	0.02002	0.001286	16.86	268.2	4102.9	4371.1	0.2990	4.1029	4.4019
1025	0.02693	0.001296	12.78	302.2	4073.8	4376.0	0.3325	3.9745	4.3070
1050	0.03569	0.001306	9.815	336.2	4044.5	4380.7	0.3653	3.8519	4.2172
1075	0.04668	0.001317	7.638	370.1	4015.3	4385.4	0.3973	3.7351	4.1324
1100	0.06029	0.001327	6.015	404.1	3986.0	4390.1	0.4284	3.6237	4.0521
1125	0.07696	0.001338	4.791	437.9	3957.1	4395.0	0.4588	3.5174	3.9762
1150	0.09718	0.001349	3.855	471.6	3928.5	4400.1	0.4885	3.4160	3.9045
1154.60	0.101325	0.001351	3.708	477.9	3923.1	4401.0	0.4938	3.3979	3.8917
1175	0.1215	0.001360	3.133	505.3	3900.1	4405.4	0.5174	3.3193	3.8367
1200	0.1504	0.001372	2.570	538.9	3872.2	4411.1	0.5457	3.2268	3.7725
1225	0.1845	0.001383	2.126	572.5	3844.7	4417.2	0.5733	3.1386	3.7119
1250	0.2244	0.001395	1.773	606.0	3817.7	4423.7	0.6003	3.0542	3.6545
1275	0.2709	0.001407	1.490	639.5	3791.2	4430.7	0.6268	2.9735	3.6003
1300	0.3245	0.001419	1.261	673.0	3765.0	4438.0	0.6528	2.8962	3.5490
1325	0.3861	0.001431	1.075	706.6	3739.2	4445.8	0.6783	2.8221	3.5004
1350	0.4562	0.001443	0.9218	740.3	3713.7	4454.0	0.7035	2.7508	3.4543
1375	0.5358	0.001456	0.7953	774.2	3688.2	4462.4	0.7283	2.6823	3.4106
1400	0.6254	0.001469	0.6899	808.4	3662.8	4471.2	0.7528	2.6163	3.3691
1425	0.7260	0.001482	0.6017	842.9	3637.2	4480.1	0.7771	2.5525	3.3296
1450	0.8383	0.001496	0.5274	877.8	3611.4	4489.2	0.8013	2.4906	3.2919
1475	0.9631	0.001509	0.4643	913.1	3585.1	4498.2	0.8253	2.4305	3.2558
1500	1.101	0.001523	0.4106	949.1	3557.9	4507.0	0.8493	2.3720	3.2213
1525	1.253	0.001537	0.3645	985.7	3529.9	4515.6	0.8734	2.3147	3.1881
1550	1.420	0.001551	0.3249	1023.0	3500.7	4523.7	0.8975	2.2585	3.1560
1575	1.603	0.001566	0.2905	1061.3	3469.9	4531.2	0.9218	2.2032	3.1250
1600	1.802	0.001581	0.2606	1100.5	3437.4	4537.9	0.9463	2.1484	3.0947
1625	2.018	0.001596	0.2344	1140.9	3402.7	4543.6	0.9712	2.0939	3.0651
1650	2.252	0.001611	0.2114	1182.7	3365.1	4547.8	0.9964	2.0395	3.0359

PROPERTIES OF GASEOUS SODIUM

P,MPa (T_{sat},K)		sat	1175	1250	1325	1400	1475	1550	1625	1700
0.050 (1082.)	v,m³/kg	7.163	8.110	8.773	9.390	9.981	10.56	11.12	11.68	12.24
	h,kJ/kg	4386.6	4592.2	4709.2	4805.4	4890.4	4968.8	5043.3	5115.3	5185.8
	s,kJ/(kg·K)	4.1108	4.2936	4.3902	4.4651	4.5275	4.5820	4.6313	4.6767	4.7191
0.101325 (1155.)	v,m³/kg	3.708	3.821	4.200	4.539	4.854	5.154	5.444	5.728	6.008
	h,kJ/kg	4401.0	4455.2	4617.9	4742.6	4845.5	4935.8	5018.3	5095.9	5170.4
	s,kJ/(kg·K)	3.8917	3.9383	4.0727	4.1696	4.2453	4.3081	4.3627	4.4116	4.4564
0.20 (1235.)	v,m³/kg	1.973		2.015	2.213	2.392	2.559	2.716	2.868	3.015
	h,kJ/kg	4419.8		4458.9	4628.5	4762.6	4874.0	4971.2	5059.2	5141.2
	s,kJ/(kg·K)	3.6882		3.7196	3.8515	3.9501	4.0277	4.0920	4.1474	4.1968
0.40 (1330.)	v,m³/kg	1.040				1.135	1.229	1.317	1.400	1.479
	h,kJ/kg	4447.5				4610.5	4756.7	4880.0	4987.3	5083.5
	s,kJ/(kg·K)	3.4905				3.6101	3.7119	3.7935	3.8611	3.9190
0.70 (1419.)	v,m³/kg	0.6222					0.6655	0.7208	0.7728	0.8220
	h,kJ/kg	4477.9					4604.9	4755.7	4886.3	5001.1
	s,kJ/(kg·K)	3.3392					3.4270	3.5268	3.6091	3.6782
1.0 (1482.)	v,m³/kg	0.4486						0.4849	0.5235	0.5601
	h,kJ/kg	4500.6						4647.9	4794.4	4923.9
	s,kJ/(kg·K)	3.2461						3.3433	3.4356	3.5136

THERMODYNAMIC PROPERTIES OF SODIUM

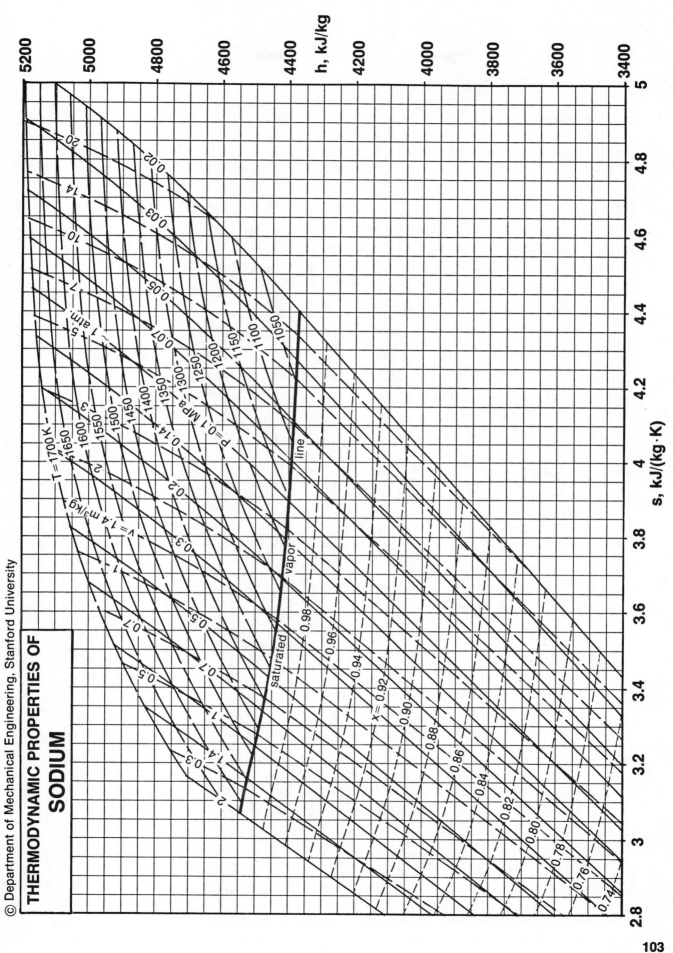

h, kJ/kg

s, kJ/(kg·K)

PROPERTIES OF SATURATED WATER

T	P	volume, m³/kg		enthalpy, kJ/kg			entropy, kJ/(kg·K)		
K	MPa	v_f	v_g	h_f	h_{fg}	h_g	s_f	s_{fg}	s_g
273.16	0.0006113	0.001000	206.1	0.0	2500.9	2500.9	0.0	9.1555	9.1555
275	0.0006980	0.001000	181.7	7.5	2496.8	2504.3	0.0274	9.0792	9.1066
280	0.0009912	0.001000	130.3	28.1	2485.4	2513.5	0.1015	8.8765	8.9780
285	0.001388	0.001001	94.67	48.8	2473.9	2522.7	0.1749	8.6803	8.8552
290	0.001919	0.001001	69.67	69.7	2462.2	2531.9	0.2475	8.4903	8.7378
295	0.002620	0.001002	51.90	90.7	2450.3	2541.0	0.3193	8.3061	8.6254
300	0.003536	0.001004	39.10	111.7	2438.4	2550.1	0.3900	8.1279	8.5179
305	0.004718	0.001005	29.78	132.8	2426.3	2559.1	0.4598	7.9551	8.4149
310	0.006230	0.001007	22.91	153.9	2414.3	2568.2	0.5285	7.7878	8.3163
315	0.008143	0.001009	17.80	175.1	2402.0	2577.1	0.5961	7.6255	8.2216
320	0.01054	0.001011	13.96	196.2	2389.8	2586.0	0.6626	7.4682	8.1308
325	0.01353	0.001013	11.04	217.3	2377.6	2594.9	0.7280	7.3156	8.0436
330	0.01721	0.001015	8.809	238.4	2365.3	2603.7	0.7924	7.1675	7.9599
335	0.02171	0.001018	7.083	259.4	2353.0	2612.4	0.8557	7.0236	7.8793
340	0.02718	0.001021	5.737	280.5	2340.5	2621.0	0.9180	6.8838	7.8018
345	0.03377	0.001024	4.680	301.5	2328.0	2629.5	0.9793	6.7479	7.7272
350	0.04166	0.001027	3.844	322.5	2315.4	2637.9	1.0397	6.6156	7.6553
355	0.05105	0.001030	3.178	343.4	2302.9	2646.3	1.0991	6.4869	7.5860
360	0.06215	0.001034	2.643	364.4	2290.1	2654.5	1.1577	6.3615	7.5192
365	0.07521	0.001037	2.211	385.3	2277.3	2662.6	1.2155	6.2391	7.4546
370	0.09047	0.001041	1.860	406.3	2264.3	2670.6	1.2725	6.1198	7.3923
375	0.1082	0.001045	1.573	427.3	2251.2	2678.5	1.3288	6.0032	7.3320
380	0.1288	0.001049	1.337	448.3	2237.9	2686.2	1.3843	5.8894	7.2737
385	0.1524	0.001053	1.142	469.3	2224.5	2693.8	1.4393	5.7779	7.2172
390	0.1795	0.001058	0.9800	490.4	2210.9	2701.3	1.4936	5.6688	7.1624
395	0.2104	0.001062	0.8445	511.5	2197.0	2708.5	1.5473	5.5621	7.1094
400	0.2456	0.001067	0.7308	532.7	2182.9	2715.6	1.6005	5.4573	7.0578
405	0.2854	0.001072	0.6349	554.0	2168.6	2722.6	1.6532	5.3546	7.0078
410	0.3302	0.001077	0.5537	575.3	2154.0	2729.3	1.7054	5.2537	6.9591
415	0.3806	0.001082	0.4846	596.7	2139.1	2735.8	1.7572	5.1545	6.9117
420	0.4370	0.001087	0.4256	618.2	2123.9	2742.1	1.8085	5.0570	6.8655
425	0.4999	0.001093	0.3750	639.8	2108.4	2748.2	1.8594	4.9611	6.8205
430	0.5699	0.001099	0.3314	661.4	2092.7	2754.1	1.9099	4.8667	6.7766
435	0.6474	0.001104	0.2938	683.1	2076.6	2759.7	1.9599	4.7737	6.7336
440	0.7332	0.001110	0.2612	705.0	2060.0	2765.0	2.0096	4.6820	6.6916
445	0.8277	0.001117	0.2328	726.9	2043.2	2770.1	2.0590	4.5914	6.6504
450	0.9315	0.001123	0.2080	749.0	2025.9	2774.9	2.1080	4.5020	6.6100
455	1.045	0.001130	0.1864	771.1	2008.2	2779.3	2.1567	4.4136	6.5703
460	1.170	0.001137	0.1673	793.4	1990.1	2783.5	2.2050	4.3263	6.5313
465	1.306	0.001144	0.1506	815.7	1971.6	2787.3	2.2530	4.2399	6.4929
470	1.454	0.001152	0.1358	838.2	1952.6	2790.8	2.3007	4.1544	6.4551
475	1.615	0.001159	0.1227	860.8	1933.0	2793.8	2.3482	4.0695	6.4177
480	1.789	0.001167	0.1111	883.5	1913.0	2796.5	2.3953	3.9855	6.3808
490	2.181	0.001184	0.09150	929.3	1871.4	2800.7	2.4887	3.8193	6.3080
500	2.637	0.001202	0.07585	975.6	1827.5	2803.1	2.5813	3.6550	6.2363
510	3.163	0.001222	0.06323	1022.6	1781.0	2803.6	2.6731	3.4921	6.1652
520	3.766	0.001244	0.05296	1070.4	1731.7	2802.1	2.7644	3.3301	6.0945
530	4.453	0.001267	0.04454	1119.1	1679.1	2798.2	2.8555	3.1681	6.0236
540	5.233	0.001293	0.03758	1168.9	1622.9	2791.8	2.9466	3.0055	5.9521
550	6.112	0.001322	0.03179	1219.9	1562.7	2782.6	3.0382	2.8413	5.8795
560	7.100	0.001355	0.02694	1272.5	1497.8	2770.3	3.1306	2.6746	5.8052
570	8.206	0.001391	0.02284	1326.9	1427.5	2754.4	3.2241	2.5044	5.7285
580	9.439	0.001433	0.01934	1383.3	1350.9	2734.2	3.3193	2.3291	5.6484
590	10.81	0.001482	0.01635	1442.3	1266.6	2708.9	3.4167	2.1468	5.5635
600	12.33	0.001540	0.01375	1504.6	1172.5	2677.1	3.5174	1.9543	5.4717
610	14.02	0.001611	0.01146	1571.1	1065.6	2636.7	3.6231	1.7468	5.3699
620	15.88	0.001704	0.009422	1644.3	939.6	2583.9	3.7370	1.5154	5.2524
630	17.95	0.001837	0.007532	1729.3	781.4	2510.7	3.8671	1.2404	5.1075
640	20.25	0.002076	0.005626	1842.9	550.5	2393.4	4.0389	0.8602	4.8991
647.29	22.089	0.003155	0.003155	2098.8	0.0	2098.8	4.4289	0.0	4.4289

PROPERTIES OF SATURATED WATER

P MPa	T K	volume, m³/kg		enthalpy, kJ/kg			entropy, kJ/(kg·K)		
		v_f	v_g	h_f	h_{fg}	h_g	s_f	s_{fg}	s_g
0.00080	276.92	0.001000	159.7	15.4	2492.4	2507.8	0.0559	9.0007	9.0566
0.0010	280.13	0.001000	129.2	28.6	2485.1	2513.7	0.1034	8.8714	8.9748
0.0012	282.81	0.001000	108.7	39.7	2479.0	2518.7	0.1429	8.7654	8.9083
0.0014	285.13	0.001001	93.92	49.3	2473.6	2522.9	0.1768	8.6754	8.8522
0.0016	287.17	0.001001	82.76	57.8	2468.9	2526.7	0.2065	8.5972	8.8037
0.0018	288.99	0.001001	74.03	65.5	2464.5	2530.0	0.2330	8.5280	8.7610
0.0020	290.65	0.001002	67.00	72.4	2460.6	2533.0	0.2569	8.4659	8.7228
0.0025	294.23	0.001002	54.25	87.5	2452.1	2539.6	0.3083	8.3340	8.6423
0.0030	297.23	0.001003	45.67	100.1	2445.0	2545.1	0.3510	8.2258	8.5768
0.0040	302.12	0.001004	34.80	120.7	2433.2	2553.9	0.4197	8.0541	8.4738
0.0050	306.03	0.001005	28.19	137.2	2423.8	2561.0	0.4740	7.9203	8.3943
0.0060	309.31	0.001007	23.74	151.0	2415.9	2566.9	0.5191	7.8105	8.3296
0.0080	314.66	0.001009	18.10	173.7	2402.8	2576.5	0.5915	7.6364	8.2279
0.010	318.96	0.001010	14.67	191.8	2392.4	2584.2	0.6488	7.5006	8.1494
0.012	322.57	0.001012	12.36	207.1	2383.5	2590.6	0.6964	7.3891	8.0855
0.014	325.70	0.001013	10.69	220.3	2375.8	2596.1	0.7371	7.2946	8.0317
0.016	328.47	0.001015	9.433	231.9	2369.1	2601.0	0.7728	7.2124	7.9852
0.018	330.96	0.001016	8.445	242.4	2362.9	2605.3	0.8045	7.1397	7.9442
0.020	333.22	0.001017	7.649	251.9	2357.4	2609.3	0.8332	7.0745	7.9077
0.025	338.12	0.001020	6.204	272.6	2345.1	2617.7	0.8947	6.9359	7.8306
0.030	342.26	0.001022	5.229	289.9	2334.9	2624.8	0.9458	6.8220	7.7678
0.040	349.02	0.001026	3.993	318.3	2318.0	2636.3	1.0279	6.6413	7.6692
0.050	354.48	0.001030	3.240	341.3	2304.1	2645.4	1.0930	6.5001	7.5931
0.060	359.09	0.001033	2.732	360.6	2292.4	2653.0	1.1471	6.3841	7.5312
0.080	366.65	0.001038	2.087	392.3	2273.0	2665.3	1.2344	6.1994	7.4338
0.10	372.78	0.001043	1.694	418.0	2257.0	2675.0	1.3038	6.0548	7.3586
0.101325	373.14	0.001043	1.673	419.5	2256.1	2675.6	1.3079	6.0462	7.3541
0.12	377.96	0.001047	1.428	439.7	2243.4	2683.1	1.3617	5.9356	7.2973
0.14	382.46	0.001051	1.237	458.6	2231.4	2690.0	1.4115	5.8341	7.2456
0.16	386.47	0.001054	1.091	475.5	2220.5	2696.0	1.4553	5.7456	7.2009
0.18	390.09	0.001058	0.9775	490.8	2210.6	2701.4	1.4945	5.6670	7.1615
0.20	393.38	0.001061	0.8857	504.7	2201.5	2706.2	1.5300	5.5963	7.1263
0.25	400.59	0.001067	0.7187	535.2	2181.3	2716.5	1.6068	5.4451	7.0519
0.30	406.70	0.001073	0.6058	561.2	2163.7	2724.9	1.6710	5.3201	6.9911
0.40	416.78	0.001084	0.4625	604.3	2133.8	2738.1	1.7755	5.1196	6.8951
0.50	425.01	0.001093	0.3749	639.8	2108.4	2748.2	1.8594	4.9611	6.8205
0.60	432.00	0.001101	0.3157	670.1	2086.3	2756.4	1.9299	4.8293	6.7592
0.80	443.59	0.001115	0.2404	720.7	2048.0	2768.7	2.0451	4.6169	6.6620
1.0	453.06	0.001127	0.1944	762.5	2015.1	2777.6	2.1378	4.4479	6.5857
1.2	461.14	0.001139	0.1633	798.5	1985.9	2784.4	2.2160	4.3065	6.5225
1.4	468.22	0.001149	0.1408	830.2	1959.4	2789.6	2.2838	4.1847	6.4685
1.6	474.56	0.001159	0.1238	858.8	1934.8	2793.6	2.3440	4.0770	6.4210
1.8	480.30	0.001168	0.1104	884.9	1911.8	2796.7	2.3981	3.9805	6.3786
2.0	485.57	0.001176	0.09963	908.9	1890.2	2799.1	2.4474	3.8927	6.3401
2.5	497.15	0.001197	0.07998	962.4	1840.2	2802.6	2.5549	3.7018	6.2567
3.0	507.05	0.001216	0.06668	1008.7	1795.0	2803.7	2.6461	3.5400	6.1861
4.0	523.55	0.001252	0.04978	1087.6	1713.4	2801.0	2.7968	3.2725	6.0693
5.0	537.14	0.001286	0.03944	1154.5	1639.4	2793.9	2.9206	3.0520	5.9726
6.0	548.79	0.001319	0.03244	1213.7	1570.2	2783.9	3.0271	2.8613	5.8884
7.0	559.03	0.001352	0.02737	1267.4	1504.3	2771.7	3.1216	2.6909	5.8125
8.0	568.22	0.001385	0.02352	1317.0	1440.5	2757.5	3.2073	2.5351	5.7424
10.	584.22	0.001453	0.01803	1407.9	1316.4	2724.3	3.3600	2.2533	5.6133
11.	591.30	0.001489	0.01599	1450.2	1255.0	2705.2	3.4296	2.1224	5.5520
12.	597.90	0.001527	0.01426	1491.2	1193.2	2684.4	3.4960	1.9956	5.4916
13.	604.09	0.001567	0.01278	1531.1	1130.7	2661.8	3.5599	1.8717	5.4316
14.	609.90	0.001610	0.01149	1570.4	1066.8	2637.2	3.6220	1.7490	5.3710
16.	620.59	0.001710	0.009307	1648.9	931.3	2580.2	3.7441	1.5007	5.2448
18.	630.22	0.001840	0.007492	1731.4	777.4	2508.8	3.8703	1.2336	5.1039
20.	638.96	0.002041	0.005836	1828.5	581.0	2409.5	4.0172	0.9093	4.9265
22.089	647.29	0.003155	0.003155	2098.8	0.0	2098.8	4.4289	0.0	4.4289

PROPERTIES OF GASEOUS WATER

P,MPa (T$_{sat}$,K)		sat	350	400	450	T,K 500	550	600	650	700
0.0010 (280.1)	v,m³/kg	129.2	161.5	184.6	207.7	230.7	253.8	276.9	300.0	323.1
	h,kJ/kg	2513.7	2644.4	2739.0	2834.7	2931.8	3030.2	3130.1	3231.7	3334.8
	s,kJ/(kg·K)	8.9748	9.3913	9.6439	9.8693	10.0737	10.2614	10.4353	10.5978	10.7506
	u,kJ/kg	2384.5	2482.9	2554.4	2627.1	2701.0	2776.4	2853.2	2931.7	3011.7
0.0020 (290.7)	v,m³/kg	67.00	80.73	92.28	103.8	115.4	126.9	138.4	150.0	161.5
	h,kJ/kg	2533.0	2644.3	2738.9	2834.7	2931.7	3030.2	3130.1	3231.6	3334.8
	s,kJ/(kg·K)	8.7228	9.0710	9.3238	9.5493	9.7538	9.9414	10.1153	10.2779	10.4307
	u,kJ/kg	2399.0	2482.8	2554.4	2627.0	2701.0	2776.4	2853.2	2931.7	3011.7
0.0040 (302.1)	v,m³/kg	34.80	40.35	46.13	51.91	57.68	63.45	69.22	74.99	80.76
	h,kJ/kg	2553.9	2644.0	2738.8	2834.6	2931.7	3030.1	3130.1	3231.6	3334.8
	s,kJ/(kg·K)	8.4738	8.7504	9.0035	9.2292	9.4338	9.6215	9.7954	9.9579	10.1108
	u,kJ/kg	2414.7	2482.6	2554.2	2627.0	2700.9	2776.3	2853.2	2931.6	3011.7
0.0070 (312.2)	v,m³/kg	20.53	23.04	26.35	29.66	32.96	36.25	39.55	42.85	46.15
	h,kJ/kg	2572.0	2643.5	2738.5	2834.4	2931.5	3030.0	3130.0	3231.6	3334.7
	s,kJ/(kg·K)	8.2750	8.4911	8.7447	8.9707	9.1753	9.3631	9.5371	9.6996	9.8525
	u,kJ/kg	2428.3	2482.2	2554.0	2626.8	2700.8	2776.3	2853.2	2931.6	3011.7
0.010 (319.0)	v,m³/kg	14.67	16.12	18.44	20.75	23.07	25.38	27.69	29.99	32.30
	h,kJ/kg	2584.2	2643.0	2738.2	2834.2	2931.4	3030.0	3130.0	3231.5	3334.7
	s,kJ/(kg·K)	8.1494	8.3254	8.5796	8.8058	9.0106	9.1984	9.3724	9.5349	9.6878
	u,kJ/kg	2437.5	2481.8	2553.8	2626.7	2700.8	2776.2	2853.1	2931.6	3011.7
0.020 (333.2)	v,m³/kg	7.649	8.044	9.210	10.37	11.53	12.68	13.84	14.99	16.15
	h,kJ/kg	2609.3	2641.4	2737.3	2833.7	2931.0	3029.7	3129.7	3231.3	3334.5
	s,kJ/(kg·K)	7.9077	8.0019	8.2579	8.4849	8.6901	8.8781	9.0522	9.2148	9.3678
	u,kJ/kg	2456.3	2480.6	2553.1	2626.3	2700.5	2776.0	2852.9	2931.4	3011.6
0.040 (349.0)	v,m³/kg	3.993	4.005	4.595	5.179	5.759	6.339	6.917	7.495	8.073
	h,kJ/kg	2636.3	2638.2	2735.5	2832.5	2930.3	3029.1	3129.3	3231.0	3334.3
	s,kJ/(kg·K)	7.6692	7.6747	7.9344	8.1631	8.3690	8.5574	8.7318	8.8945	9.0476
	u,kJ/kg	2476.6	2478.0	2551.7	2625.4	2699.9	2775.6	2852.6	2931.2	3011.3

P, MPa (T$_{sat}$,K)		750	800	850	900	T,K 950	1000	1050	1100	1150
0.0010 (280.1)	v,m³/kg	346.1	369.2	392.3	415.4	438.4	461.5	484.6	507.7	530.7
	h,kJ/kg	3439.6	3546.1	3654.3	3764.3	3876.0	3989.5	4104.7	4221.7	4340.5
	s,kJ/(kg·K)	10.8952	11.0327	11.1639	11.2896	11.4104	11.5268	11.6392	11.7481	11.8536
	u,kJ/kg	3093.5	3176.9	3262.0	3348.9	3437.6	3528.0	3620.2	3714.1	3809.7
0.0020 (290.7)	v,m³/kg	173.1	184.6	196.1	207.7	219.2	230.8	242.3	253.8	265.4
	h,kJ/kg	3439.6	3546.1	3654.3	3764.3	3876.0	3989.5	4104.7	4221.7	4340.5
	s,kJ/(kg·K)	10.5753	10.7128	10.8440	10.9697	11.0905	11.2069	11.3193	11.4282	11.5337
	u,kJ/kg	3093.5	3176.9	3262.0	3348.9	3437.6	3528.0	3620.2	3714.1	3809.7
0.0040 (302.1)	v,m³/kg	86.53	92.30	98.07	103.8	109.6	115.4	121.1	126.9	132.7
	h,kJ/kg	3439.6	3546.1	3654.3	3764.3	3876.0	3989.5	4104.7	4221.7	4340.5
	s,kJ/(kg·K)	10.2554	10.3929	10.5241	10.6498	10.7706	10.8870	10.9994	11.1083	11.2138
	u,kJ/kg	3093.4	3176.9	3262.0	3348.9	3437.6	3528.0	3620.1	3714.1	3809.7
0.0070 (312.2)	v,m³/kg	49.45	52.74	56.04	59.34	62.63	65.93	69.23	72.52	75.82
	h,kJ/kg	3439.5	3546.0	3654.3	3764.3	3876.0	3989.5	4104.7	4221.7	4340.5
	s,kJ/(kg·K)	9.9971	10.1346	10.2658	10.3915	10.5123	10.6287	10.7412	10.8500	10.9556
	u,kJ/kg	3093.4	3176.9	3262.0	3348.9	3437.6	3528.0	3620.1	3714.1	3809.7
0.010 (319.0)	v,m³/kg	34.61	36.92	39.23	41.54	43.84	46.15	48.46	50.77	53.07
	h,kJ/kg	3439.5	3546.0	3654.3	3764.2	3876.0	3989.5	4104.7	4221.7	4340.4
	s,kJ/(kg·K)	9.8324	9.9699	10.1011	10.2269	10.3477	10.4641	10.5765	10.6854	10.7910
	u,kJ/kg	3093.4	3176.8	3262.0	3348.9	3437.5	3528.0	3620.1	3714.1	3809.7
0.020 (333.2)	v,m³/kg	17.30	18.46	19.61	20.77	21.92	23.07	24.23	25.38	26.54
	h,kJ/kg	3439.4	3545.9	3654.2	3764.2	3875.9	3989.4	4104.7	4221.7	4340.4
	s,kJ/(kg·K)	9.5124	9.6499	9.7812	9.9069	10.0277	10.1442	10.2566	10.3655	10.4710
	u,kJ/kg	3093.3	3176.8	3261.9	3348.8	3437.5	3527.9	3620.1	3714.0	3809.7
0.040 (349.0)	v,m³/kg	8.650	9.228	9.805	10.38	10.96	11.54	12.11	12.69	13.27
	h,kJ/kg	3439.2	3545.7	3654.0	3764.0	3875.8	3989.3	4104.6	4221.6	4340.3
	s,kJ/(kg·K)	9.1923	9.3299	9.4611	9.5869	9.7077	9.8242	9.9366	10.0455	10.1511
	u,kJ/kg	3093.1	3176.6	3261.8	3348.7	3437.4	3527.8	3620.0	3714.0	3809.6

PROPERTIES OF GASEOUS WATER

P,MPa (T$_{sat}$,K)		sat	400	450	500	550	600	650	700	750
0.070 (363.1)	v,m³/kg	2.365	2.617	2.953	3.287	3.619	3.950	4.281	4.612	4.942
	h,kJ/kg	2659.6	2732.7	2830.8	2929.1	3028.3	3128.7	3230.5	3333.8	3438.8
	s,kJ/(kg·K)	7.4789	7.6707	7.9019	8.1090	8.2980	8.4727	8.6357	8.7889	8.9337
	u,kJ/kg	2494.0	2549.5	2624.1	2699.0	2774.9	2852.1	2930.8	3011.0	3092.9
0.101325 (373.1)	v,m³/kg	1.673	1.802	2.036	2.268	2.498	2.727	2.956	3.185	3.413
	h,kJ/kg	2675.6	2729.7	2829.0	2927.9	3027.4	3128.0	3229.9	3333.4	3438.4
	s,kJ/(kg·K)	7.3541	7.4942	7.7281	7.9365	8.1261	8.3012	8.4644	8.6177	8.7627
	u,kJ/kg	2506.0	2547.2	2622.7	2698.1	2774.3	2851.6	2930.4	3010.7	3092.6
0.20 (393.4)	v,m³/kg	0.8857	0.9024	1.025	1.144	1.262	1.379	1.495	1.612	1.728
	h,kJ/kg	2706.2	2720.2	2823.2	2924.0	3024.6	3125.8	3228.2	3332.0	3437.3
	s,kJ/(kg·K)	7.1263	7.1616	7.4044	7.6168	7.8085	7.9847	8.1486	8.3024	8.4477
	u,kJ/kg	2529.0	2539.7	2618.3	2695.2	2772.2	2850.1	2929.1	3009.7	3091.8
0.40 (416.8)	v,m³/kg	0.4625		0.5053	0.5671	0.6273	0.6866	0.7455	0.8040	0.8624
	h,kJ/kg	2738.1		2811.0	2916.0	3018.8	3121.5	3224.8	3329.2	3435.0
	s,kJ/(kg·K)	6.8951		7.0634	7.2848	7.4808	7.6594	7.8248	7.9795	8.1255
	u,kJ/kg	2553.1		2608.9	2689.1	2767.9	2846.8	2926.6	3007.6	3090.0
0.70 (438.1)	v,m³/kg	0.2729		0.2822	0.3197	0.3552	0.3899	0.4240	0.4579	0.4915
	h,kJ/kg	2763.1		2791.3	2903.4	3010.0	3114.8	3219.5	3325.0	3431.5
	s,kJ/(kg·K)	6.7072		6.7709	7.0073	7.2104	7.3928	7.5605	7.7168	7.8637
	u,kJ/kg	2572.1		2593.7	2679.6	2761.3	2841.9	2922.7	3004.4	3087.4
1.0 (453.1)	v,m³/kg	0.1944			0.2206	0.2464	0.2712	0.2955	0.3194	0.3432
	h,kJ/kg	2777.6			2890.2	3000.9	3108.0	3214.2	3320.7	3428.0
	s,kJ/(kg·K)	6.5857			6.8223	7.0333	7.2198	7.3898	7.5476	7.6956
	u,kJ/kg	2583.2			2669.6	2754.5	2836.8	2918.8	3001.3	3084.8
2.0 (485.6)	v,m³/kg	0.09963			0.1044	0.1191	0.1326	0.1454	0.1578	0.1701
	h,kJ/kg	2799.1			2840.5	2968.4	3084.5	3196.1	3306.2	3416.1
	s,kJ/(kg·K)	6.3401			6.4242	6.6683	6.8704	7.0491	7.2122	7.3639
	u,kJ/kg	2599.8			2631.8	2730.2	2819.4	2905.3	2990.5	3075.9

P, MPa (T$_{sat}$,K)		800	850	900	950	1000	1050	1100	1150	1200
0.070 (363.1)	v,m³/kg	5.272	5.602	5.932	6.262	6.592	6.922	7.251	7.581	7.911
	h,kJ/kg	3545.4	3653.8	3763.8	3875.6	3989.1	4104.4	4221.5	4340.2	4460.7
	s,kJ/(kg·K)	9.0713	9.2027	9.3284	9.4493	9.5658	9.6783	9.7872	9.8927	9.9953
	u,kJ/kg	3176.4	3261.6	3348.6	3437.3	3527.7	3619.9	3713.9	3809.5	3906.9
0.101325 (373.1)	v,m³/kg	3.641	3.870	4.098	4.326	4.554	4.781	5.009	5.237	5.465
	h,kJ/kg	3545.1	3653.5	3763.6	3875.4	3989.0	4104.3	4221.3	4340.1	4460.6
	s,kJ/(kg·K)	8.9004	9.0317	9.1576	9.2785	9.3950	9.5075	9.6164	9.7220	9.8245
	u,kJ/kg	3176.2	3261.4	3348.4	3437.1	3527.6	3619.8	3713.8	3809.4	3906.8
0.20 (393.4)	v,m³/kg	1.844	1.959	2.075	2.191	2.306	2.422	2.537	2.653	2.768
	h,kJ/kg	3544.2	3652.7	3762.9	3874.8	3988.5	4103.8	4220.9	4339.7	4460.3
	s,kJ/(kg·K)	8.5856	8.7172	8.8432	8.9642	9.0808	9.1933	9.3023	9.4079	9.5105
	u,kJ/kg	3175.5	3260.8	3347.9	3436.7	3527.2	3619.4	3713.4	3809.1	3906.6
0.40 (416.8)	v,m³/kg	0.9206	0.9787	1.037	1.095	1.153	1.210	1.268	1.326	1.384
	h,kJ/kg	3542.2	3651.1	3761.5	3873.6	3987.4	4102.9	4220.1	4339.0	4459.6
	s,kJ/(kg·K)	8.2639	8.3959	8.5221	8.6433	8.7601	8.8728	8.9818	9.0875	9.1901
	u,kJ/kg	3174.0	3259.6	3346.8	3435.8	3526.4	3618.7	3712.8	3808.6	3906.0
0.70 (438.1)	v,m³/kg	0.5250	0.5584	0.5917	0.6249	0.6581	0.6912	0.7244	0.7575	0.7905
	h,kJ/kg	3539.3	3648.6	3759.4	3871.8	3985.8	4101.5	4218.9	4337.9	4458.6
	s,kJ/(kg·K)	8.0029	8.1354	8.2621	8.3836	8.5006	8.6135	8.7226	8.8284	8.9312
	u,kJ/kg	3171.8	3257.7	3345.2	3434.4	3525.2	3617.7	3711.8	3807.7	3905.2
1.0 (453.1)	v,m³/kg	0.3668	0.3902	0.4137	0.4370	0.4603	0.4836	0.5068	0.5300	0.5532
	h,kJ/kg	3536.4	3646.1	3757.3	3870.0	3984.3	4100.1	4217.6	4336.8	4457.6
	s,kJ/(kg·K)	7.8356	7.9686	8.0957	8.2175	8.3348	8.4478	8.5571	8.6631	8.7659
	u,kJ/kg	3169.6	3255.9	3343.6	3433.0	3524.0	3616.6	3710.8	3806.8	3904.4
2.0 (485.6)	v,m³/kg	0.1821	0.1941	0.2060	0.2178	0.2295	0.2413	0.2530	0.2646	0.2763
	h,kJ/kg	3526.5	3637.8	3750.2	3863.9	3979.0	4095.5	4213.5	4333.1	4454.2
	s,kJ/(kg·K)	7.5064	7.6413	7.7698	7.8928	8.0108	8.1245	8.2343	8.3406	8.4437
	u,kJ/kg	3162.2	3249.6	3338.3	3428.3	3519.9	3613.0	3707.6	3803.8	3901.6

PROPERTIES OF GASEOUS WATER

P,MPa (T_{sat},K)		sat	600	650	T,K 700	750	800	900	1000	1100
3.0 (507.1)	v,m³/kg	0.06668	0.08628	0.09532	0.1040	0.1124	0.1206	0.1367	0.1526	0.1684
	h,kJ/kg	2803.7	3059.6	3177.3	3291.3	3404.0	3516.5	3743.1	3973.7	4209.4
	s,kJ/(kg·K)	6.1861	6.6516	6.8402	7.0091	7.1646	7.3098	7.5767	7.8196	8.0442
	u,kJ/kg	2603.7	2800.7	2891.4	2979.4	3066.9	3154.7	3332.8	3515.8	3704.3
4.0 (523.6)	v,m³/kg	0.04978	0.06304	0.07024	0.07699	0.08349	0.08981	0.1021	0.1142	0.1261
	h,kJ/kg	2801.0	3033.0	3157.8	3276.1	3391.6	3506.3	3735.8	3968.3	4205.3
	s,kJ/(kg·K)	6.0693	6.4847	6.6846	6.8600	7.0194	7.1674	7.4378	7.6827	7.9085
	u,kJ/kg	2601.8	2780.8	2876.8	2968.1	3057.7	3147.0	3327.4	3511.7	3701.1
6.0 (548.8)	v,m³/kg	0.03244	0.03958	0.04507	0.04998	0.05459	0.05901	0.06750	0.07571	0.08375
	h,kJ/kg	2783.9	2973.8	3116.3	3244.4	3366.3	3485.5	3721.2	3957.5	4197.0
	s,kJ/(kg·K)	5.8884	6.2201	6.4486	6.6385	6.8067	6.9605	7.2382	7.4872	7.7154
	u,kJ/kg	2589.3	2736.3	2845.9	2944.5	3038.8	3131.4	3316.2	3503.3	3694.5
8.0 (568.2)	v,m³/kg	0.02352	0.02759	0.03239	0.03643	0.04011	0.04359	0.05018	0.05648	0.06260
	h,kJ/kg	2757.5	2904.1	3071.1	3210.9	3340.0	3464.0	3706.2	3946.6	4188.7
	s,kJ/(kg·K)	5.7424	5.9938	6.2617	6.4691	6.6472	6.8073	7.0927	7.3459	7.5766
	u,kJ/kg	2569.4	2683.3	2812.1	2919.5	3019.1	3115.3	3304.8	3494.8	3687.8
10. (584.2)	v,m³/kg	0.01803	0.02008	0.02468	0.02825	0.03141	0.03434	0.03979	0.04494	0.04992
	h,kJ/kg	2724.3	2818.3	3021.4	3175.6	3312.6	3442.0	3691.0	3935.6	4180.3
	s,kJ/(kg·K)	5.6133	5.7722	6.0983	6.3270	6.5162	6.6833	6.9767	7.2344	7.4676
	u,kJ/kg	2544.0	2617.5	2774.6	2893.1	2998.5	3098.7	3293.1	3486.2	3681.2
15. (615.4)	v,m³/kg	0.01034		0.01404	0.01723	0.01975	0.02196	0.02593	0.02956	0.03301
	h,kJ/kg	2610.1		2868.5	3077.4	3239.6	3384.3	3652.0	3907.7	4159.4
	s,kJ/(kg·K)	5.3090		5.7192	6.0295	6.2536	6.4404	6.7559	7.0254	7.2653
	u,kJ/kg	2455.0		2658.0	2818.9	2943.5	3054.9	3263.0	3464.3	3664.3
20. (639.0)	v,m³/kg	0.00584		0.00790	0.01156	0.01386	0.01575	0.01900	0.02188	0.02456
	h,kJ/kg	2409.5		2625.1	2961.0	3159.4	3323.0	3611.7	3879.3	4138.5
	s,kJ/(kg·K)	4.9265		5.2616	5.7622	6.0363	6.2477	6.5881	6.8702	7.1172
	u,kJ/kg	2292.8		2467.1	2729.9	2882.2	3007.9	3231.6	3441.8	3647.3

P, MPa (T_{sat},K)		700	750	800	850	T,K 900	950	1000	1050	1100
30.	v,m³/kg	0.00543	0.00786	0.00951	0.01087	0.01208	0.01318	0.01421	0.01518	0.01612
	h,kJ/kg	2633.3	2973.5	3189.4	3367.6	3528.0	3678.1	3821.6	3960.6	4096.5
	s,kJ/(kg·K)	5.1776	5.6490	5.9280	6.1442	6.3276	6.4900	6.6373	6.7729	6.8993
	u,kJ/kg	2470.4	2737.6	2904.0	3041.4	3165.7	3282.8	3395.4	3505.1	3612.8
40.	v,m³/kg	0.00260	0.00483	0.00640	0.00760	0.00863	0.00954	0.01039	0.01117	0.01192
	h,kJ/kg	2221.6	2752.8	3043.7	3258.4	3441.6	3607.8	3763.3	3911.6	4054.6
	s,kJ/(kg·K)	4.5363	5.2720	5.6483	5.9089	6.1185	6.2982	6.4578	6.6025	6.7357
	u,kJ/kg	2117.4	2559.5	2787.8	2954.3	3096.4	3226.0	3347.9	3464.7	3577.8
50.	v,m³/kg	0.00203	0.00323	0.00459	0.00567	0.00658	0.00738	0.00811	0.00878	0.00941
	h,kJ/kg	2074.8	2535.1	2893.2	3147.2	3354.5	3537.3	3705.1	3862.8	4013.2
	s,kJ/(kg·K)	4.2943	4.9293	5.3926	5.7009	5.9380	6.1358	6.3080	6.4619	6.6019
	u,kJ/kg	1973.0	2373.7	2663.9	2863.5	3025.2	3168.1	3299.6	3423.8	3542.6
60.	v,m³/kg	0.00183	0.00251	0.00350	0.00444	0.00526	0.00597	0.00661	0.00720	0.00775
	h,kJ/kg	2013.6	2387.9	2754.9	3039.5	3269.1	3468.0	3647.8	3814.7	3972.3
	s,kJ/(kg·K)	4.1795	4.6954	5.1697	5.5152	5.7779	5.9930	6.1776	6.3405	6.4872
	u,kJ/kg	1903.6	2237.5	2544.7	2772.8	2953.8	3109.9	3251.2	3382.7	3507.3
70.	v,m³/kg	0.00172	0.00217	0.00287	0.00364	0.00435	0.00498	0.00556	0.00609	0.00658
	h,kJ/kg	1977.8	2301.9	2644.3	2941.8	3188.5	3401.4	3592.2	3767.9	3932.5
	s,kJ/(kg·K)	4.1031	4.5498	4.9920	5.3530	5.6353	5.8656	6.0615	6.2329	6.3861
	u,kJ/kg	1857.6	2150.3	2443.7	2687.2	2884.2	3052.6	3203.2	3341.9	3472.0
80.	v,m³/kg	0.00164	0.00197	0.00248	0.00310	0.00371	0.00427	0.00479	0.00527	0.00571
	h,kJ/kg	1953.8	2248.4	2563.0	2858.7	3115.3	3339.0	3539.4	3722.9	3893.9
	s,kJ/(kg·K)	4.0448	4.4510	4.8571	5.2159	5.5094	5.7514	5.9571	6.1362	6.2953
	u,kJ/kg	1822.6	2090.5	2364.3	2610.8	2818.6	2997.2	3156.1	3301.5	3436.9
100.	v,m³/kg	0.00153	0.00176	0.00207	0.00247	0.00291	0.00335	0.00377	0.00416	0.00453
	h,kJ/kg	1923.7	2186.1	2461.2	2736.7	2995.5	3230.7	3444.2	3640.0	3821.8
	s,kJ/(kg·K)	3.9567	4.3186	4.6735	5.0077	5.3037	5.5581	5.7772	5.9684	6.1375
	u,kJ/kg	1770.5	2010.4	2254.1	2489.8	2704.5	2895.7	3067.3	3223.4	3368.4

PROPERTIES OF LIQUID WATER

P MPa		400	425	450	475	500	525	550	575	600
	P_{sat},MPa	0.2456	0.4999	0.9315	1.615	2.637	4.098	6.112	8.806	12.33
sat	ρ,kg/m^3	937.35	915.08	890.25	862.64	831.71	796.64	756.18	708.38	649.40
	h,kJ/kg	532.69	639.71	748.98	860.80	975.65	1094.63	1219.93	1354.82	1504.56
	s,kJ/(kg·K)	1.60049	1.85933	2.10801	2.34815	2.58128	2.80995	3.03821	3.27144	3.51742
	u,kJ/kg	532.43	639.17	747.93	858.93	972.48	1089.49	1211.84	1342.38	1485.57
0.50	ρ,kg/m^3	937.51	915.08							
	h,kJ/kg	532.82	639.71							
	s,kJ/(kg·K)	1.60020	1.85933							
	u,kJ/kg	532.29	639.17							
0.70	ρ,kg/m^3	937.62	915.22							
	h,kJ/kg	532.94	639.84							
	s,kJ/(kg·K)	1.59999	1.85914							
	u,kJ/kg	532.19	639.07							
1.0	ρ,kg/m^3	937.79	915.41	890.30						
	h,kJ/kg	533.12	640.02	749.01						
	s,kJ/(kg·K)	1.59968	1.85884	2.10793						
	u,kJ/kg	532.06	638.93	747.89						
1.4	ρ,kg/m^3	938.01	915.66	890.58						
	h,kJ/kg	533.37	640.27	749.20						
	s,kJ/(kg·K)	1.59928	1.85843	2.10740						
	u,kJ/kg	531.88	638.74	747.63						
2.0	ρ,kg/m^3	938.33	916.03	890.99	862.93					
	h,kJ/kg	533.76	640.64	749.50	860.92					
	s,kJ/(kg·K)	1.59868	1.85779	2.10661	2.34748					
	u,kJ/kg	531.63	638.46	747.26	858.60					
3.0	ρ,kg/m^3	938.86	916.63	891.66	863.70	832.04				
	h,kJ/kg	534.42	641.26	750.01	861.24	975.68				
	s,kJ/(kg·K)	1.59771	1.85672	2.10529	2.34578	2.58049				
	u,kJ/kg	531.23	637.98	746.64	857.77	972.08				
5.0	ρ,kg/m^3	939.90	917.80	892.99	865.23	833.88	797.71			
	h,kJ/kg	535.77	642.49	751.04	861.95	975.97	1094.50			
	s,kJ/(kg·K)	1.59579	1.85454	2.10267	2.34248	2.57633	2.80757			
	u,kJ/kg	530.45	637.04	745.44	856.18	969.97	1088.23			
7.0	ρ,kg/m^3	940.93	918.96	894.30	866.74	835.70	800.06	757.63		
	h,kJ/kg	537.13	643.73	752.08	862.71	976.34	1094.30	1219.41		
	s,kJ/(kg·K)	1.59390	1.85237	2.10006	2.33927	2.57233	2.80247	3.03517		
	u,kJ/kg	529.69	636.11	744.25	854.64	967.96	1085.55	1210.18		
10.	ρ,kg/m^3	942.45	920.66	896.23	868.97	838.39	803.48	762.36	711.24	
	h,kJ/kg	539.18	645.59	753.67	863.91	976.99	1094.16	1217.91	1353.16	
	s,kJ/(kg·K)	1.59110	1.84912	2.09618	2.33455	2.56651	2.79513	3.02530	3.26566	
	u,kJ/kg	528.57	634.73	742.51	852.40	965.06	1081.72	1204.79	1339.10	
14.	ρ,kg/m^3	944.45	922.89	898.75	871.89	841.87	807.86	768.28	720.13	656.02
	h,kJ/kg	541.93	648.10	755.82	865.57	977.99	1094.20	1216.32	1348.37	1499.43
	s,kJ/(kg·K)	1.58742	1.84484	2.09110	2.32843	2.55903	2.78578	3.01295	3.24764	3.50461
	u,kJ/kg	527.11	632.93	740.24	849.52	961.36	1076.87	1198.09	1328.92	1478.08
20.	ρ,kg/m^3	947.40	926.15	902.43	876.12	846.90	814.10	776.50	731.86	675.64
	h,kJ/kg	546.09	651.88	759.11	868.19	979.70	1094.61	1214.62	1342.80	1485.18
	s,kJ/(kg·K)	1.58199	1.83852	2.08365	2.31954	2.54829	2.77251	2.99579	3.22363	3.46589
	u,kJ/kg	524.98	630.29	736.95	845.36	956.08	1070.04	1188.87	1315.48	1455.58
30.	ρ,kg/m^3	952.15	931.39	908.31	882.86	854.83	823.75	788.76	748.41	700.23
	h,kJ/kg	553.10	658.28	764.75	872.87	983.09	1096.17	1213.36	1336.77	1469.95
	s,kJ/(kg·K)	1.57321	1.82824	2.07165	2.30546	2.53159	2.75225	2.97029	3.18966	3.41631
	u,kJ/kg	521.60	626.07	731.72	838.89	948.00	1059.75	1175.33	1296.68	1427.11
50.	ρ,kg/m^3	961.23	941.29	919.30	895.30	869.22	840.82	809.63	774.92	735.63
	h,kJ/kg	567.28	671.32	776.46	882.95	991.08	1101.29	1214.33	1331.34	1454.04
	s,kJ/(kg·K)	1.55640	1.80868	2.04904	2.27933	2.50117	2.71624	2.92655	3.13458	3.34342
	u,kJ/kg	515.27	618.20	722.07	827.10	933.56	1041.83	1152.57	1266.82	1386.07
100.	ρ,kg/m^3	982.01	963.53	943.46	921.97	899.14	875.01	849.47	822.32	793.27
	h,kJ/kg	603.30	705.01	807.50	910.95	1015.43	1121.02	1227.92	1336.47	1447.18
	s,kJ/(kg·K)	1.51781	1.76443	1.99876	2.22248	2.43683	2.64289	2.84180	3.03479	3.22326
	u,kJ/kg	501.47	601.22	701.51	802.48	904.21	1006.73	1110.20	1214.86	1321.12

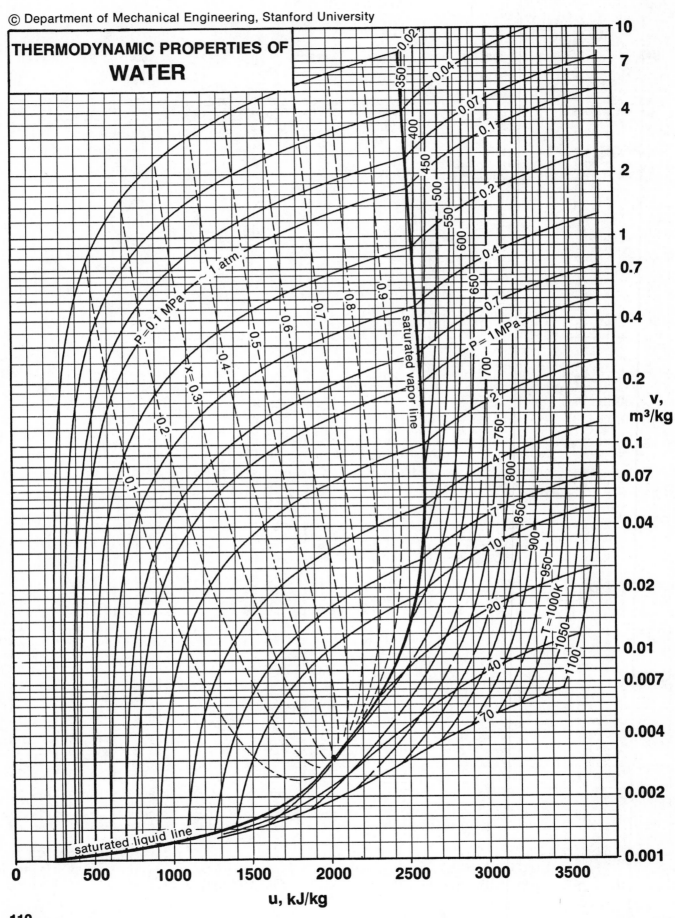

THERMODYNAMIC PROPERTIES OF
WATER

v, m³/kg

u, kJ/kg

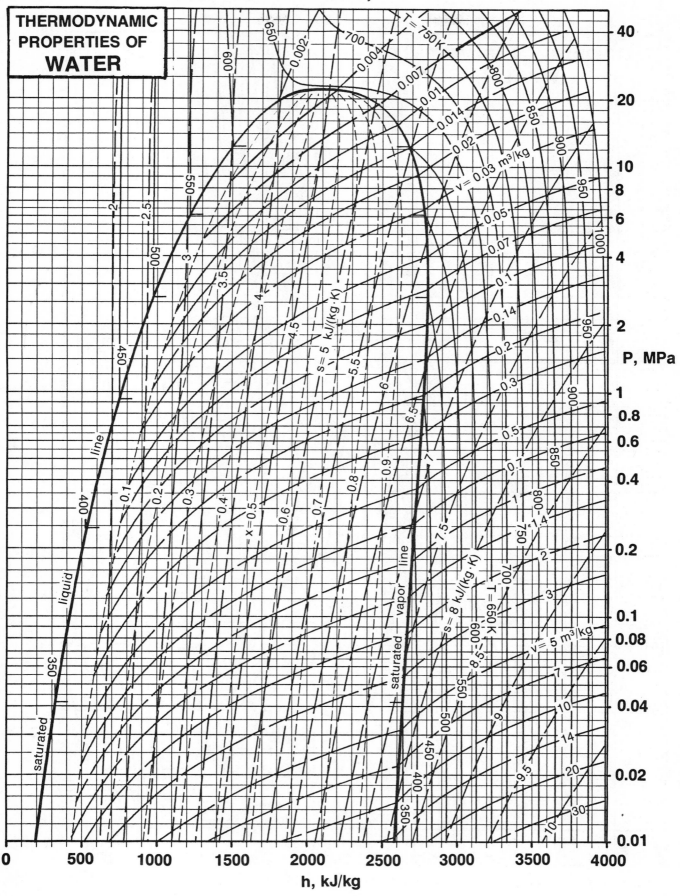

© Department of Mechanical Engineering, Stanford University

THERMODYNAMIC PROPERTIES OF WATER

P, MPa

h, kJ/kg

111

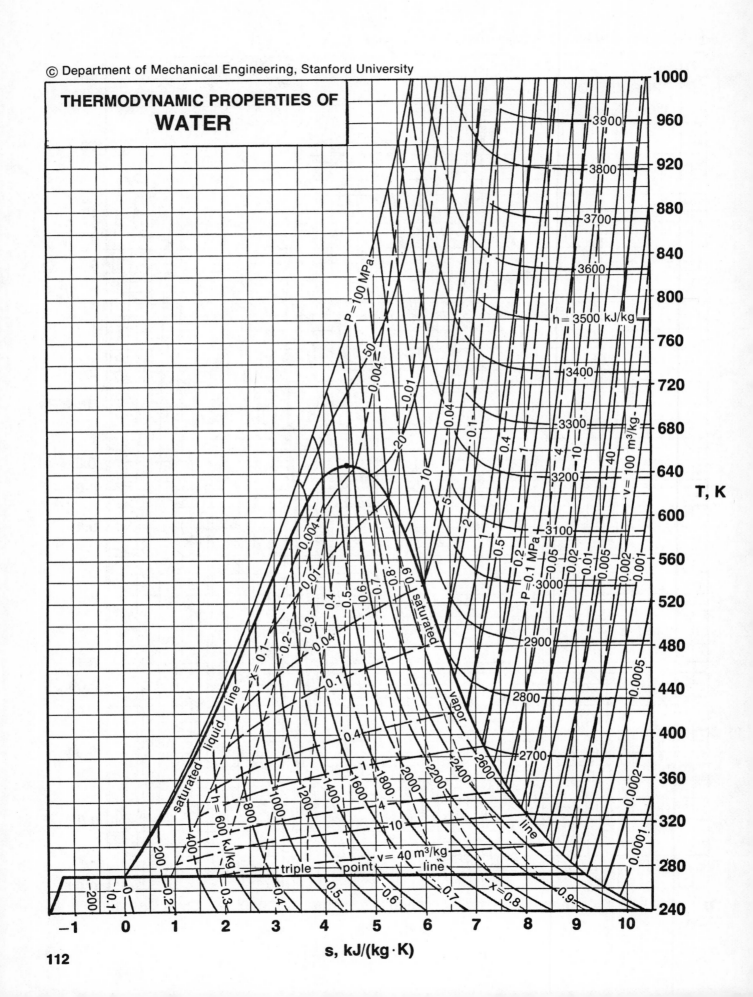

THERMODYNAMIC PROPERTIES OF
WATER

s, kJ/(kg·K)

T, K

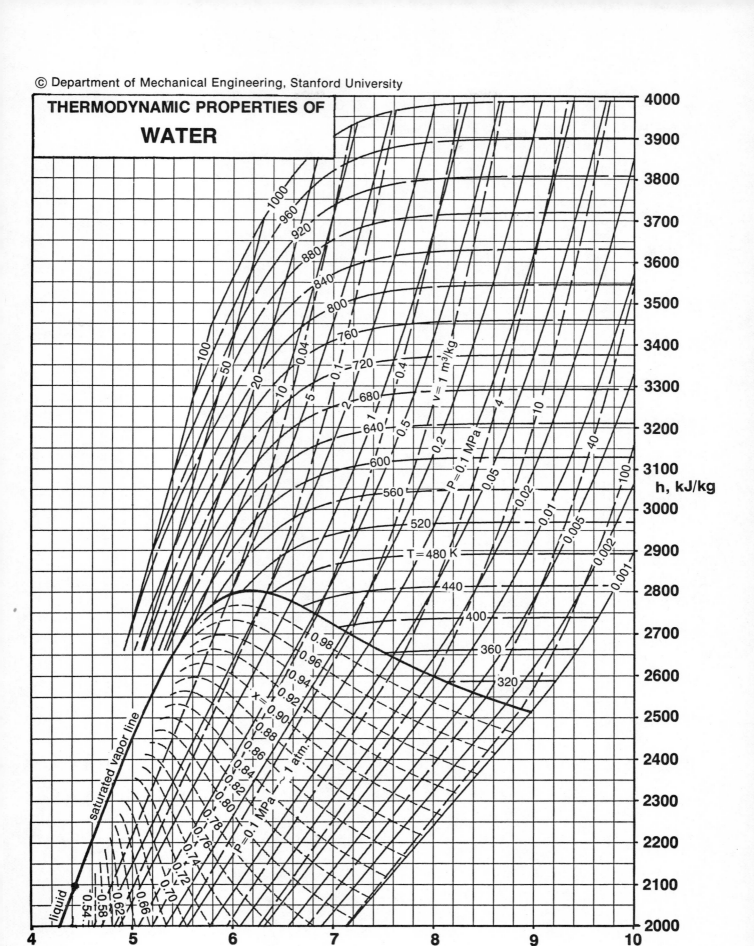

THERMODYNAMIC PROPERTIES OF
WATER

h, kJ/kg

s, kJ/(kg·K)

Section 2
Computational Equations and Methods

This section describes the basic methods for obtaining equations relating the various thermodynamic properties. A general structure for computerization of these equations is recommended. The equations used for the substances included herein are listed; the constants in these equations, for each substance, are given in Section 3.

Section 2
Computational Equations and Methods

A. *General Approach*

The calculation of the thermodynamic properties of a simple compressible substance requires expressions of two types: (1) a P-ρ-T equation, and (2) an equation for c_v at low density (ideal gas), generally denoted by $c_v^0(T)$. The manner in which this information is used will now be outlined.

The internal energy of a simple compressible substance is generally expressible as

$$u = u(T, v) \tag{1}$$

Differentiating and using the definition $c_v = (\partial u / \partial T)_v$,

$$du = c_v dT + \left(\frac{\partial u}{\partial v}\right)_T dv \tag{2}$$

An important thermodynamic relationship, derived in most thermodynamics texts*, is

$$\left(\frac{\partial u}{\partial v}\right)_T = T\left(\frac{\partial P}{\partial T}\right)_v - P \tag{3}$$

Substituting Eqn. (3) in Eqn. (2), integrating over the path shown in Fig. 1, and using $dv = -d\rho/\rho^2$, one finds

$$u = \int_{T_0}^{T} c_v^0(T)dT + \int_0^\rho \frac{1}{\rho^2}\left[P - T\left(\frac{\partial P}{\partial T}\right)_\rho\right] d\rho + u_0 \tag{4}$$

Note that the first integration is carried out at zero density, allowing c_v to be replaced by c_v^0, and that the second integration is carried out at constant temperature. T_0 is a chosen reference temperature. The constant u_0 is simply a term used to set the datum for u as desired.

The P-ρ-T data are usually fit to an appropriate equation, or perhaps by a set of equations over connecting regions. In general, these are of the form

$$P = \rho RT + F(\rho, T) \tag{5}$$

and $F = 0(\rho^2)$ as $\rho \to 0$, so that ideal-gas behavior is obtained at low densities. If $F = 0(\rho^2)$, then the second integral in Eqn. (4) vanishes as $\rho \to 0$, giving the ideal-gas behavior for u.

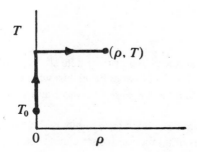

Fig. 1
Note that the first integration is
at zero density and the second is
at constant temperature.

---

* See, for example, Reynolds, W. C., and Perkins, H. C., *Engineering Thermodynamics*, Second Edition, McGraw-Hill, 1977, p. 266.

The entropy is determined from the Gibbs equation,

$$ds = \frac{1}{T}\, du + \frac{P}{T}\, dv \tag{6}$$

Using Eqns. (2) and (3),

$$ds = \frac{c_v}{T}\, dT - \frac{1}{\rho^2}\left(\frac{\partial P}{\partial T}\right)_\rho d\rho \tag{7}$$

It is useful to add and subtract a term $-R\,d\rho/\rho$ from Eqn. (7). Then, integrating on the path of Fig. 1,

$$s = \int_{T_0}^{T} \frac{c_v^0(T)}{T}\, dT - R \ln \rho + \int_0^\rho \frac{1}{\rho^2}\left[\rho R - \left(\frac{\partial P}{\partial T}\right)_\rho\right] d\rho + s_0 \tag{8}$$

Here s_0 is a constant that can be chosen to set the datum for s as desired. Since $F = 0(\rho^2)$, the second integral in Eqn. (8) will vanish at zero density, and the ideal gas behavior for s is obtained as $\rho \to 0$.

Given analytical expressions for $P(\rho, T)$ and $c_v^0(T)$, the values of P, u, s, and h can be calculated for specified values of T and ρ. The equations used are given in Tables 2.1 and 2.2. The equation used for each substance, and the constants for that substance, are given in Section 3. A short table of unusual integrals arising in the u and s integrations is given in Table 2.5.

B. *Fitting the Data*

Various workers use different P-ρ-T expressions and obtain their fits in different ways. The equations always involve a number of constants that are determined by a least-squares fit of P-ρ-T data.

Note that, from Eqn. (4), $h_{fg} = u_{fg} + Pv_{fg}$ involves only the P-ρ-T function and does not depend upon the specific heat data. Hence, in addition to the obvious use of P-ρ-T data, many workers also incorporate h_{fg} data in the P-ρ-T curvefit.

The least-squares P-ρ-T fits are usually subjected to some constraints. Values of the second virial coefficient

$$B \equiv \left(\frac{\partial[P/(\rho R T)]}{\partial \rho}\right)_T \Bigg|_{\rho = 0} \tag{9}$$

at selected temperatures are often used as constraints on the fit. Most workers also use constraints at the critical point,

$$P = P_c \tag{10a}$$

$$\left(\frac{\partial P}{\partial \rho}\right)_T = 0 \qquad \text{at } T = T_c, \qquad \rho = \rho_c \tag{10b}$$

$$\left(\frac{\partial^2 P}{\partial \rho^2}\right)_T = 0 \tag{10c}$$

When these constraints are not imposed, the resulting P-ρ-T surface has a critical state slightly different from the experimental point. Some workers accept this error in the interest of better fitting elsewhere. It is now generally believed that the critical point is a point of non-analyticity in the P-ρ-T surface, and so there is some justification for not imposing the derivative constraints.

The author experimented with a variety of P-ρ-T fits and methods for a number of substances. Slight changes in weighting can make significant changes in the resulting thermodynamic tables and graphs, especially when one is attempting to fit the entire P-ρ-T surface with a single equation. It is particularly important to have very smooth "data" for the densities in the liquid region. For this reason, many workers have first fit the saturated liquid density to appropriate equations and then used these equations to generate smooth liquid density "data" accurate to six digits.

118

C. Saturation Data

Phase equilibrium points (saturated liquid/vapor) can be determined from the P-ρ-T surface by finding those points which, at the same T and P, have the same value of the Gibbs function $g = h - Ts$. From Eqns. (4) and (6), one can see that the difference in Gibbs function between any two states at the same T and P depends only upon the P-ρ-T surface, and is independent of c_v^0. The author wrote a program to do this calculation, and developed saturation pressure-temperature information this way for several substances. However, it is more convenient for graph and table construction, and for engineering calculations, to have separate equations for the saturation pressure and for the density of the saturated liquid. In cases where the original worker did not give these expressions, the author developed them using the phase equilibrium program described above to generate the "data," which was then used in a least-squares fit to an appropriate equation.

The enthalpy of vaporization, h_{fg}, is calculated from the Clapeyron equation*,

$$h_{fg} = Tv_{fg} \frac{dP_{sat}}{dT_{sat}} \tag{11}$$

The entropy of vaporization is given by

$$s_{fg} = h_{fg}/T \tag{12}$$

D. Summary: The Four Basic Equations

Four equations are given for each substance. These are:

(1) *Pressure-density-temperature*

$$P = P(\rho, T)$$

(2) *Ideal gas specific heat*

$$c_v^0 = c_v^0(T)$$

(3) *Sauration pressure*

$$P_{sat} = P_{sat}(T_{sat})$$

(4) *Saturated liquid density*

$$\rho_f = \rho_f(T_{sat})$$

Tables 2.1–2.4 give the equations, and the Tables in Section 3 indicate which equation was used for each substance and the constants for that substance. All constants have been converted to SI from the values given in the original papers. Numerous typographical errors in the constants in these papers have been corrected. Note that P is in Pa, T is in K, ρ is in m^3/kg, c_v^0 is in J/(kg · K), and u is in J/kg.

E. Basic Computer Programs

Given the equations and values for the constants, it is a simple matter for any user to prepare computer programs that will yield P, u, s, and h as functions of T and v. It is useful to have three programs for each substance, and the author used the following (replace xxx by a substance identification code):

(1) Pxxx(T,P,V,U,H,S)

When called for input T, v, calculates P, u, h, and s.

(2) Dxxx(T,DF)

When called for input T, calculates the saturated liquid density ρ_f = DF.

(3) Sxxx(T,P,DPDT)

When called for the input T, calculates the saturation pressure P and the derivative dP_{sat}/dT_{sat} = DPDT.

---

* Reynolds, W. C., and Perkins, H. C., *Engineering Thermodynamics,* 2nd Ed., McGraw-Hill, 1977, p. 270.

The author also wrote a utility routine, PROP(T,P,V,U,H,S,NOP,PXXX), which may be called with any two properties specified and with the trial values for T and v, to calculate the unspecified properties as indicated by the option parameter NOP. This FORTRAN program is listed in the Appendix. A second utility program, SAT(T,P,DPDT,NOP,SXXX), listed in the Appendix can be used to calculate $P_{sat}(T)$ or $T_{sat}(P)$ and dP_{sat}/dT_{sat}.

In preparing a Pxxx program, it is convenient to write the P-ρ-T equation as

$$P = \rho RT + \sum_{i=1}^{N} C_i(T)H_i(\rho) \tag{13}$$

Then, denoting

$$C_i' = dC_i/dT \tag{14a}$$

$$I_i = \int_0^\rho \frac{1}{\rho^2} H_i(\rho)d\rho \tag{14b}$$

Eqn. (4) becomes

$$u = \int_{T_0}^{T} c_v^0(T)dT + \sum_{i=1}^{N} [C_i - TC_i']I_i + u_0 \tag{15}$$

and Eqn. (8) is

$$s = \int_{T_0}^{T} \frac{c_v^0(T)}{T} dT - R\ln\rho - \sum_{i=1}^{N} C_i'I_i + s_0 \tag{16}$$

F. *Special Treatment in the Liquid Region*

In order to force the tabulated saturation tables to satisfy exactly the phase equilibrium condition $g_f = g_g$, the following procedure was used:

(1) The saturation pressure and dP_{sat}/dT_{sat} were calculated at a given T using Sxxx.

(2) The saturated vapor properties v_g, u_g, h_g, and s_g were calculated using PROP for the specified T and P.

(3) The liquid density was calculated using Dxxx.

(4) h_{fg} and s_{fg} were calculated using Eqns. (11) and (12), and then the properties of the saturated liquid (h_f and s_f) were calculated by subtraction from h_g and s_g.

In cases where the P-ρ-T equation is valid in the liquid regime, a call of PROP for v_f and T so determined would not give precisely the same values for P, h_f, and s_f as calculated by the above process. In particular, P could be off considerably since P is very strongly dependent upon ρ in the liquid region. However, a call of PROP for the saturation T and P and a trial liquid density will give a value of ρ_f not very different (perhaps in the third or fourth digit) from that determined from Dxxx, and the values of u, h, and s yielded by this PROP call will be very close to those calculated for the saturated liquid by steps 1–4 above. For smoothness in the liquid region, only a small correction is required, and the following was used in constructing the tables:

$$f = f_p + \left(f_{es} - f_{ps}\right)\left(\frac{\ln P_c - \ln P}{\ln P_c - \ln P_s}\right) \quad P < P_c; \quad f = f_p \quad P > P_c \tag{17}$$

Here f is any property (ρ, u, h, or s) in the compressed liquid region, f_p is the value calculated from PROP for the specified T and P, f_{ps} is the value of f_p at the saturation point at the specified T, f_{es} is the saturation value at T, calculated by steps 1–4 above, P_c is the critical pressure, and P_s is the saturation pressure at T. Note that the correction is zero at the critical pressure and above.

Users requiring very accurate and consistent values, for example in availability analysis, may find it desirable to make this correction. The compressed-liquid tables presented herein cannot be reproduced exactly unless this correction is employed.

G. *Datum States*

For each substance, the constants u_0 and s_0 were chosen to make the saturated liquid enthalpy and entropy zero at a convenient datum temperature T_0. The values of T_0, u_0, and s_0 are listed with the constants in Section 3. The datum for the psychrometric chart is determined by the datum states for air and water, and hence this chart is fully consistent with the air and water tables and graphs herein.

H. *Graph and Table Preparation*

All graphs presented here were drawn directly by computer programs using a CALCOMP plotter. Type was added by hand before photo-reduction. In order to eliminate all errors of typesetting and proofreading, the numbers in the tables were all set in type by computer, exactly as calculated by the various programs. Tabulated equation constants are precisely as used in the computerized property programs.

I. *Air Properties*

The properties of air were developed by the author from those of N_2, O_2, and A using the principle of corresponding states. Thus, at low densities the air properties agree with those calculated from the base components using ideal gas mixture theory.

The properties of air at low densities (ideal gas with variable specific heat) are given in a separate table. The function $\phi(T)$ and $\psi(T)$ are defined such that

$$s = \psi(T) - R \ln \rho = \phi(T) + R \ln P \tag{18}$$

The functions P_r and V_r are such that, for an isentropic process,

$$\frac{P_1}{P_2} = \frac{P_{r_1}}{P_{r_2}} \tag{19}$$

$$\frac{v_1}{v_2} = \frac{V_{r_1}}{V_{r_2}} \tag{20}$$

Note that the datum state for air is determined by those for N_2, O_2, and A. Thus, the low density tables are consistent with the other air graphs and tables herein, but do *not* have a datum of 0K.

J. *Psychrometric Chart*

The psychrometric chart was developed using the equations given by Reynolds, W. C., and Perkins, H. C., *Engineering Thermodynamics,* Second Edition, McGraw-Hill, 1977, pp. 393–397.

Table 2.1
P-v-T Equations

Constants not given values in the tables in Section 3 are zero for that substance.

(P-1)

$$P = \frac{RT}{v - b} + \sum_{i=2}^{5} \frac{1}{(v - b)^i} \left(A_i + B_i T + C_i e^{-\kappa T/T_c}\right) + \frac{A_6 + B_6 T + C_6 e^{-\kappa T/T_c}}{e^{\alpha v}(1 + c e^{\alpha v})}$$

NOTE: When using Eqn. (P-1), the term $-R \ln \rho$ in Eqn. (8) is replaced by $+R \ln (v - b)$, and the term ρR in the integrand is replaced by $R/(v - b)$.

(P-2)

$$P = \rho RT + \left(B_0 RT - A_0 - \frac{C_0}{T^2} + \frac{D_0}{T^3} - \frac{E_0}{T^4}\right) \rho^2 + \left(bRT - a - \frac{d}{T}\right) \rho^3 + \alpha \left(a + \frac{d}{T}\right) \rho^6$$

$$+ c \frac{\rho^3}{T^2} (1 + \gamma \rho^2) e^{-\gamma \rho^2}$$

(P-3)

$$P = \rho RT + \rho^2 \sum_{i=1}^{5} A_i T^{2-i} + \rho^3 \sum_{i=6}^{8} A_i T^{7-i} + \rho^4 (A_9 T + A_{10}) + \rho^5 (A_{11} T + A_{12}) + \rho^6 A_{13}$$

$$+ \left[\rho^3 \sum_{i=14}^{16} A_i T^{12-i} + \rho^5 \sum_{i=17}^{19} A_i T^{15-i}\right] e^{-\gamma \rho^2}$$

(P-4)

$$P = \rho RT + \rho^2 \left[A_1 T + A_2 T^{1/2} + \sum_{i=3}^{5} A_i T^{3-i}\right] + \rho^3 \sum_{i=6}^{9} A_i T^{7-i} + \rho^4 \sum_{i=10}^{12} A_i T^{11-i} + \rho^5 A_{13}$$

$$+ \rho^6 (A_{14}/T + A_{15}/T^2) + \rho^7 A_{16}/T + \rho^8 (A_{17}/T + A_{18}/T^2) + \rho^9 A_{19}/T^2$$

$$+ \left[\rho^3 (A_{20}/T^2 + A_{21}/T^3) + \rho^5 (A_{22}/T^2 + A_{23}/T^4) + \rho^7 (A_{24}/T^2 + A_{25}/T^3)\right.$$

$$+ \rho^9 (A_{26}/T^2 + A_{27}/T^4) + \rho^{11} (A_{28}/T^2 + A_{29}/T^3)$$

$$\left.+ \rho^{13} (A_{30}/T^2 + A_{31}/T^3 + A_{32}/T^4)\right] e^{-\gamma \rho^2}$$

(P-5)

$$P = \rho RT + \rho^2 \sum_{i=1}^{9} A_i T^{2-(i-1)/2} + \rho^3 \sum_{i=10}^{17} A_i T^{1-(i-10)/2} + \rho^4 \sum_{i=18}^{21} A_i T^{1/2-(i-18)} + \rho^5 \sum_{i=22}^{27} A_i T^{1/2-(i-22)/4}$$

$$+ \rho^6 (A_{28} + A_{29}/T) + \left[\rho^3 (A_{30} + A_{31}/T + A_{32}/T^2) + \rho^5 (A_{33} + A_{34}/T + A_{35}/T^2)\right] e^{-\gamma \rho^2}$$

(P-6)

$$P = \rho RT \left[1 + \rho Q + \rho^2 \left(\frac{\partial Q}{\partial \rho} \right)_T \right]$$

used with one of the Q equations below:

(Q-1)   (used with P-6):

$$Q = \sum_{i=1}^{9} \sum_{j=1}^{6} A_{ij} \rho^{i-1} (\tau - \tau_c)^{j-1} \qquad \tau = T_a/T$$

(Q-2)   (used with P-6):

$$Q = (\tau - \tau_c) \sum_{j=1}^{7} (\tau - \tau_{aj})^{j-2} \left[\sum_{i=1}^{8} A_{ij} (\rho - \rho_{aj})^{i-1} + e^{-E\rho} \sum_{i=9}^{10} A_{ij} \rho^{i-9} \right]$$
$$\tau = T_a/T$$
$$\tau_{a1} = \tau_c; \qquad \tau_{aj} = 2.5, \; j > 1$$

(P-7)

$$P = \rho RT + \rho^2 B(T) + \rho^3 C(T) + \rho^4 D(T) + \rho^5 E(T)$$
$$B = -T^2 \exp(A_1 + A_2/T)$$
$$C = T \exp(A_3 + A_4/T + A_5/T^2)$$
$$D = -T \exp(A_6 + A_7/T + A_8/T^2)$$
$$E = A_9 T$$

(P-8)

$$P = \frac{RT}{v - b} - \frac{\alpha}{v(v + b)T^{1/2}}$$

NOTE: When using Eqn. (P-8), the term $- R \ln \rho$ in Eqn. (8) is replaced by $+ R \ln (v - b)$, and the term ρR in the integrand is replaced by $R/(v - b)$.

(P-9)

$$P = \rho RT - \rho^2 T \exp(A_1 + A_2/T + A_3 \ln T)$$

(P-10)

$$P = \rho RT + \rho^2 \sum_{i=1}^{4} A_i T^{2-i} + \rho^3 \sum_{i=5}^{9} A_i T^{7-i} + \rho^4 (A_{10} T + A_{11}) + \rho^5 A_{12}/T + \rho^6 A_{13}$$
$$+ (A_{14}/T^2 + A_{15}/T^3)\rho^3 e^{-\gamma\rho^2} + (A_{16}/T^2 + A_{17}/T^3)\rho^5 e^{-\gamma\rho^2}$$

(P-11)

$$P = \rho RT + \rho^2 B_1(T) + \rho^3 B_2(T) + \rho^4 B_3(T)$$
$$B_1 = (A_1 T + A_2 T^2 + A_3 T^3 + A_4 T^4) e^{\alpha/T}$$
$$B_2 = (A_5 T + A_6 T^2 + A_7 T^3) e^{\alpha/T}$$
$$B_3 = (A_8 T + A_9 T^2) e^{\alpha/T}$$

Table 2.2
c_v^0 Equations

Constants not given values in the tables in Section 3 are zero for that substance.

(C-0)

$$c_v^0 = G_1$$

(C-1)

$$c_v^0 = \sum_{i=1}^{4} G_i T^{i-1} + G_5/T^2$$

(C-2)

$$c_v^0 = \sum_{i=1}^{N} G_i T^{i-1}$$

(C-3)

$$c_v^0 = G_1 + G_2 T^{1/3} + G_3 T^{2/3} + G_4 T + G_5 \, e^{\beta/T} \left[\frac{\beta/T}{e^{\beta/T} - 1} \right]^2$$

(C-4)

$$c_v^0 = \sum_{i=1}^{7} G_i T^{i-4} + G_8 \, e^{\beta/T} \left[\frac{\beta/T}{e^{\beta/T} - 1} \right]^2$$

(C-5)

$$c_v^0 = G_1 \qquad\qquad\qquad T \leq T_1$$

$$= \sum_{i=1}^{12} G_i \left[\ln\,(T/T_1) \right]^{i-1} \quad T_1 \leq T \leq T_2$$

$$= \sum_{i=13}^{17} G_i \left[\ln\,(T/T_2) \right]^{i-13} \quad T \geq T_2$$

(C-6)

$$c_v^0 = \sum_{i=1}^{6} G_i T^{i-2}$$

(C-7)

$$c_v^0 = G_1 + G_2 \, \frac{e^{-\beta/T}}{T^2}$$

Table 2.3
Saturation Pressure Equations

Constants not given values in the tables in Section 3 are zero for that substance.

(S-1)

$$\ln P = F_1 + F_2/T + F_3 \ln T + F_4 T + F_5 \frac{(\gamma - T)}{T} \ln (\gamma - T)$$

(S-2)

$$\ln (P/P_c) = \left(\frac{T_c}{T} - 1\right) \sum_{i=1}^{8} F_i \left(\frac{T}{T_P} - 1\right)^{i-1}$$

(S-3)

$$\ln (P/P_t) = F_1 X + F_2 X^2 + F_3 X^3 + F_4 X (1 - X)^\alpha$$
$$X = (1 - T_t/T)/(1 - T_t/T_c)$$

(S-4)

$$\ln P = F_1/T + F_2 + F_3 T + F_4 (T_c - T)^\alpha + F_5 T^3 + F_6 T^4 + F_7 T^5 + F_8 T^6 + F_9 \ln T$$

(S-5)

$$\ln P = \sum_{i=1}^{10} F_i T^{2-i}$$

(S-6)

$$\ln (P/P_c) = (1 - T/T_c) \times \sum_{i=1}^{8} F_i \left[a(T - T_p) \right]^{i-1}$$

(S-7)

$$\ln P = F_1 + F_2/T + F_3 \ln T$$

(S-8)

$$\ln P = F_1 + F_2/T + F_3 \ln T + F_4 T + F_5 T^2 + F_6 T^3$$

(S-9)

$$\ln P = F_1 + F_2/T + F_3 \ln T + F_4/T^2$$

(S-10)

$$\ln P = F_1 + F_2/T + F_3 T + F_4 T^2$$

(S-11)

$$\ln (P/P_c) = F_1 X + F_2 X^2 + F_3 \ln (T/T_c)$$
$$X = \left(\frac{1}{T_c} - \frac{1}{T}\right)$$

Table 2.4
Saturated Liquid Density Equations

Constants not given values in the tables in Section 3 are zero for that substance.

(D-1)

$$\rho_f = \sum_{i=1}^{5} D_i X^{(i-1)/3} + D_6 X^{1/2} + D_7 X^2$$

$$X = 1 - T/T_c$$

(D-2)

$$\rho_f = \sum_{i=1}^{6} D_i X^{(i-1)/3}$$

$$X = 1 - T/T_c$$

(D-3)

$$\frac{\rho_f - \rho_c}{\rho_t - \rho_c} = w^\alpha \exp\left[D_1 \left(1 - w^{2/3}\right) + D_2 \left(1 - w^{4/3}\right) + D_3 \left(1 - w^2\right) \right]$$

$$w = (T_c - T)/(T_c - T_t)$$

(D-4)

$$\rho_f = \rho_c + D_1 X^\alpha + \sum_{i=1}^{6} D_{i+1} X^{1+(i-1)/3}$$

$$X = 1 - T/T_c$$

(D-5)

$$\rho_f = \rho_c \left[1 + \sum_{i=1}^{N} D_i \left(1 - T/T_c\right)^{i/3} \right]$$

(D-6)

$$\rho_f = \sum_{i=1}^{4} D_i \left(T - T_p\right)^{i-1}$$

(D-7)

$$\rho_f = D_1 + D_2 X + D_3 X^\alpha + D_4 X^2$$

$$X = 1 - T/T_c$$

(D-8)

$$\rho_f = D_1 + D_2 X + D_3 X^2$$

$$X = T - T_p$$

Table 2.5
Useful Integrals

(1)

$$W_n(z) = \int_0^z x^{2n+1} e^{-\gamma x^2} \, dx = -\frac{z^{2n}}{2\gamma} e^{-\gamma z^2} + \frac{n}{2\gamma} W_{n-1}(z)$$

$$W_0(z) = \frac{1}{2\gamma} \left(1 - e^{-\gamma z^2} \right)$$

(2)

$$\int_\infty^z \frac{e^{-2\alpha x}}{e^{-\alpha x} + c} \, dx = \frac{1}{\alpha} \left[c \ln \left(1 + \frac{1}{c} e^{-\alpha z} \right) - e^{-\alpha z} \right]$$

(3)

$$I_n(z) = \int_1^z (\ln x)^n \, dx = x(\ln x)^n - n \, I_{n-1}(z)$$

$$I_0(z) = z - 1$$

(4)

$$\int_1^z \frac{1}{x} (\ln x)^n \, dx = \frac{1}{n+1} (\ln z)^{n+1}$$

Table 2.6
Equation Sources

Numbers refer to references given at the end of this table.

Substance	P-ρ-T	P_{sat}	ρ_f	c_v^0	c_v^0 range
Air	†	1	1	†	50–2000 K
Ammonia	2	2*	2*	3*	50–1500 K
Argon	4	4*	4*	‡	‡
Butane	5	5*	5*	6*	200–1500 K
Carbon Dioxide	4	4*	4*	6*	50–1500 K
Cesium	7	7	7	8*	500–2500 K
Ethane	5	5*	5*	6*	100–1500 K
Ethylene	9	9	9	9	100–1000 K
Helium	10	10	10	‡	‡
Heptane	5	5*	5*	6*	200–1000 K
Hexane	5	5*	5*	6*	200–1000 K
Hydrogen (para)	11	11	11	11*	10–5000 K
Isobutane	5	5*	5*	6*	200–1500 K
Isopentane	5	5*	5*	6*	200–1500 K
Lithium	12*	12*	12*	8*	800–3000 K
Mercury	12*	12*	12*	12*	400–1600 K
Methane	13	13	13	13	50–1700 K
Neon	14	14	14	‡	‡
Nitrogen	15	15	15	15	50–2000 K
Octane	5	5*	5*	6*	200–1000 K
Oxygen	15	15	15	15	50–2000 K
Pentane	5	5*	5*	6*	200–1000 K
Potassium	16	16	16	8*	500–2500 K
Propane	5	5*	5*	6*	50–1500 K
Propyl Alcohol	17	17	17*	17	300–700 K
Propylene	9	9	9	9	115–800 K
Refrigerant 11	18, 19	18, 19	18, 19	18, 19	100–700 K
Refrigerant 12	18	18	18	18	200–650 K
Refrigerant 13	18	18	18	18	150–600 K
Refrigerant 14	18	18	18	18	125–600 K
Refrigerant 22	18, 20	18, 20	18, 20	18, 20	100–600 K
Refrigerant 23	18	18	18	18	200–650 K
Refrigerant 114	21, 18	21, 18	21, 18	21, 18	200–500 K
Refrigerant C-318	22, 18	22, 18	22, 18	22, 18	250–600 K
Refrigerant 500	18	18	18	18	200–600 K
Refrigerant 502	23	23	23	23	100–600 K
Refrigerant 503	24	24	24	24	150–600 K
Rubidium	25	26*	27*	8*	300–3000 K
Sodium	28	28	28	8*	300–2500 K
Water	29	29	29*	29	250–1600 K

* Data derived from the indicated reference was fitted by the present author. For saturation data this involved determination of the phase equilibrium points from the P-ρ-T equation; the calculated points were then fit to an appropriate saturation equation.

† Constructed from O_2, N_2, A equations using the principle of corresponding states.

‡ Monatomic gas with $c_v^0 = 1.5$ R at all temperatures.

Table 2.6 (continued)

1. Din, F., *Thermodynamic Functions of Gases,* V. 2, Butterworth Scientific Publications, London, 1956.
2. Haar, L., and Gallagher, J. S., "Thermodynamic Properties of Ammonia," *J. Phys. Chem. Ref. Data,* V. 7, No. 30, 1978, p. 635.
3. Haar, L., "Thermodynamic Properties of Ammonia as an Ideal Gas," *J. Research NBS,* V. 72A, 1968, p. 207.
4. Bender, E., "Equations of State Exactly Representing the Phase Behavior of Pure Substances," *Proc. 5th Symposium on Thermophysical Properties,* ASME, 1970, p. 227.
5. Starling, K. E., *Fluid Thermodynamic Properties for Light Petroleum Substances,* Gulf Publishing Co., 1973.
6. American Petroleum Institute, Project 44, "Selected Values of Physical Properties of Hydrocarbons and Related Compounds," 1953.
7. Ewing, C. T., Stone, J. P., Spann, J. R., and Miller, R. R., "High Temperature Properties of Cesium," *J. Chem. Engrg. Data,* V. 11, No. 4, October 1966, p. 473.
8. Evans, W. H., Jacobson, R., Munson, T. R., and Wagman, D. D., "Thermodynamic Properties of the Alkali Metals," *J. Res. NBS,* V. 55, No. 2, August 1955, p. 83.
9. Bender., E., "Equations of State for Ethylene and Propylene," *Cryogenics,* V. 15, 1975, p. 667.
10. McCarty, R. D., "Thrmodynamic Properties of Helium 4 from 2 to 1500 K at Pressures to 10^8 Pa," *J. Chem. Phys. Ref. Data,* V. 2, No. 4, 1973, p. 923.
11. Roder, H. M., and McCarty, R. D., "A Modified Benedict-Webb-Rubin Equation of State for Para-hydrogen-2," NBS Report NBSIR 75−814, June 1975.
12. Vargaftik, N. B., *Tables of the Thermophysical Properties of Liquids and Gases.* Second Edition, Hemisphere Publishing Co., Washington, 1975.
13. McCarty, R. D., "A Modified Benedict-Webb-Rubin Equation of State for Methane Using Recent Experimental Data," *Cryogenics,* V. 14, 1974, p. 276.
14. McCarty, R. D., and Stewart, R. B., "Thermodynamic Properties of Neon from 25 to 300 K between 0.1 and 200 Atmospheres," *Third Symposium on Thermophysical Properties,* ASME, 1965, p. 84.
15. Jacobsen, R. T., Stewart, R. B., and Myers, A. F., "An Equation of State for Oxygen and Nitrogen," *Advances in Cryogenic Engrg.,* V. 18, 1972, p. 248.
16. Ewing, C. T., Stone, J. P., Spann, J. R., and Miller, R. R., "High Temperature Properties of Potassium," *J. Chem. Engrg. Data,* V. 11, No. 4, October 1966, p. 460.
17. Martin, J. J., Campbell, J. A., and Seidel, E. M., "Thermodynamic Properties of N−Propyl Alcohol," *J. Chem. Engrg. Data,* V. 8, No. 4, October 1963, p. 560.
18. Downing, R. C., "Refrigerant Equations," *ASHRAE Paper 2313,* Trans. ASHRAE, V. 80. Part II, 1974, p. 158.
19. E. I. DuPont de Nemours & Co., Bulletin T-11, November 1972.
20. E. I. DuPont de Nemours & Co., Bulletin T-22, November 1972.
21. Martin, J. J., "Thermodynamic Properties of Dichlortetrafluoromethane," *J. Chem. Engrg. Data,* V. 5, No. 3, July 1960, p. 334.
22. Martin, J. J., "Thermodynamic Properties of Perfluorocyclobutane," *J. Chem. Engrg. Data,* V. 7, No. 1, January 1962, p. 68.
23. E. I. DuPont de Nemours & Co., Bulletin T-502, August 1969.
24. E. I. DuPont de Nemours & Co., Bulletin T-503, June 1968.
25. Stone, J. P., *et al.,* "Predicted High-Temperature Properties of Rubidium," *J. Chem. Engrg. Data,* V. 12, No. 3, July 1967, p. 352.
26. Bhise, V. S., and Bonilla, C. F., "The Vapor Pressure and Critical Point of Rubidium," *Proc. 6th Symposium on Thermophysical Properties,* ASME, 1973, p. 362.
27. Chung, J-W, and Bonilla, C. F., "High Temperature Saturated Phase Densities of Rubidium, and the Critical Properties of Rubidium," *Proc. 6th Symposium on Thermophysical Properties,* ASME, 1973, p. 397.
28. Ewing, C. T., Stone, J. P., Spann, J. R., and Miller, R. R., "High Temperature Properties of Sodium," *J. Chem. Engrg. Data,* V. 1, No. 4, October 1966, p. 468.
29. Keenan, J. H., Keyes, F. G., Hill, P. C., and Moore, J. G., *Steam Tables,* John Wiley and Sons, Inc., New York, 1969.

Section 3
Constants in the Computational Equations

This section indicates which of the equations in Section 2 were used for each substance and gives the constants for that substance. The computational equations should be used with great caution beyond the range of the graphs and tables herein. In no case should the equations be used for densities greater than those covered by the graphs for that substance. If property values are needed in the subcooled liquid region, and the equations are not valid in this region, use of the incompressible liquid approximation is recommended. At low densities the equations can be used with fair confidence to temperatures above those covered by the graphs, provided that the temperatures are within the range of the c_v^0 fit given in Table 2.6.

AIR

The mixture model has the following mol fractions
N_2 - 0.7809 O_2 - 0.2095   A - 0.0096
This is a single-substance approximation

M = 28.96 kg/kmol
T_c = 132.50 K
P_c = 3.77 MPa
ρ_c = 343.3 kg/m^3
The datum is fixed by N_2, O_2, and A

Constants for T in K, ρ in kg/m^3, P in Pa, c_v in J/(kg·K)

P-ρ-T Eqn. P-4

R = 287.0686
A_1 = 1.55623098409137x10^{-1}
A_2 = 1.25288666202326x10^1
A_3 =-2.92541568638838x10^2
A_4 = 4.29432480725523x10^3
A_5 =-5.58450959675108x10^5
A_6 = 3.92054480883008x10^{-4}
A_7 =-4.40985641881347x10^{-2}
A_8 = 5.86387178724129x10^{-4}
A_9 = 7.97411385439405x10^4
A_{10} = 9.88045320906742x10^{-9}
A_{11} = 2.97999237261289x10^{-4}
A_{12} =-6.81783040959070x10^{-2}
A_{13} = 2.02551630992042x10^{-7}
A_{14} =-1.62724281849497x10^{-7}
A_{15} =-1.06340143152999x10^{-4}
A_{16} = 3.51428501875049x10^{-10}

A_{17} =-1.70388092279449x10^{-13}
A_{18} = 5.91103444646786x10^{-11}
A_{19} =-1.05363473794348x10^{-14}
A_{20} =-7.32732651196979x10^4
A_{21} =-5.42674649924748x10^5
A_{22} =-4.48935466142735x10^{-1}
A_{23} = 2.81453138446295x10^2
A_{24} =-8.83132042791851x10^{-7}
A_{25} =-1.32229814838386x10^{-5}
A_{26} =-2.16521865046609x10^{-12}
A_{27} =-1.47835008246593x10^{-9}
A_{28} =-6.93219849301501x10^{-19}
A_{29} = 6.06743598768355x10^{-17}
A_{30} =-3.20538718135891x10^{-24}
A_{31} =-4.73178337355130x10^{-23}
A_{32} = 3.83950822306912x10^{-22}
γ = 5.97105475117183x10^{-6}

P_{sat} Eqn.S-11 along dew line

P_c = 3.77436x10^6
F_1 = 8.52176441x10^1
F_2 =-2.66657734x10^4
F_3 = 5.46923993

ρf Eqn. D-2 along bubble line

D_1 = 3.43300000x10^2
D_2 = 3.01809400x10^2
D_3 = 4.96457200x10^2
D_4 = 5.01113000x10^2
D_5 =-5.44617300x10^2

P_{sat} Eqn.S-11 along bubble line

P_c = 3.77436x10^6
F_1 = 1.69881524x10^3
F_2 = 4.40210939x10^4
F_3 =-7.61593848

c_v determined by mixture
The entropy of mixing is 174.519 J/(kg·K)

AMMONIA

M = 17.03 kg/kmol
T_c = 406.80 K
P_c = 11.627 MPa
ρ_c = 237.64 kg/m^3
T_0 = 200 K

Constants for T in K, ρ in kg/m^3, P in Pa, c_v in J/(kg·K)

P-ρ-T from Eqn.Q-1

R = 488.20981
$A_{1,1}$ =-6.453022304053x10^{-3}
$A_{2,1}$ = 8.080094367688x10^{-6}
$A_{3,1}$ = 1.032994880724x10^{-9}
$A_{4,1}$ =-8.948264632008x10^{-12}
$A_{5,1}$ =-6.692285882015x10^{-14}
$A_{6,1}$ = 2.473417459954x10^{-16}
$A_{7,1}$ =-3.065578854310x10^{-19}
$A_{8,1}$ = 1.617910033375x10^{-22}
$A_{9,1}$ =-2.782168879368x10^{-26}
$A_{1,2}$ =-1.371992677050x10^{-2}
$A_{2,2}$ = 1.435692000561x10^{-5}
$A_{3,2}$ = 5.584395580933x10^{-8}
$A_{4,2}$ =-1.697777441391x10^{-10}
$A_{5,2}$ =-1.753943775320x10^{-15}
$A_{6,2}$ = 2.999839155475x10^{-16}
$A_{7,2}$ = 2.411655109855x10^{-20}
$A_{8,2}$ =-5.074780704643x10^{-22}
$A_{9,2}$ = 2.988129173133x10^{-25}
$A_{1,3}$ =-8.100620315713x10^{-3}
$A_{2,3}$ =-4.505297669943x10^{-5}
$A_{3,3}$ = 4.920166508177x10^{-7}
$A_{4,3}$ =-1.236532371672x10^{-9}
$A_{5,3}$ = 2.085533713355x10^{-13}
$A_{6,3}$ = 4.509080578790x10^{-15}
$A_{7,3}$ =-9.323356799989x10^{-18}
$A_{8,3}$ = 8.139470397409x10^{-21}
$A_{9,3}$ =-2.772597352058x10^{-24}
$A_{1,4}$ =-4.880096421085x10^{-3}
$A_{2,4}$ =-1.661889985705x10^{-4}
$A_{3,4}$ = 1.737835999473x10^{-6}

$A_{4,4}$ =-7.812161168317x10^{-9}
$A_{5,4}$ = 2.134894661440x10^{-11}
$A_{6,4}$ =-3.798084988179x10^{-14}
$A_{7,4}$ = 4.272409853059x10^{-17}
$A_{8,4}$ =-2.745871062656x10^{-20}
$A_{9,4}$ = 7.668928677925x10^{-24}
$A_{1,5}$ =-1.202877562682x10^{-2}
$A_{2,5}$ = 3.790895022982x10^{-5}
$A_{3,5}$ =-3.087491526377x10^{-8}
$A_{4,5}$ = 1.779548269140x10^{-12}
$A_{5,5}$ = 0.0
$A_{6,5}$ = 0.0
$A_{7,5}$ = 0.0
$A_{8,5}$ = 0.0
$A_{9,5}$ = 0.0
$A_{1,6}$ = 6.806345929616x10^{-3}
$A_{2,6}$ =-4.073020833373x10^{-5}
$A_{3,6}$ = 7.148353041627x10^{-8}
$A_{4,6}$ =-3.897461095850x10^{-11}
$A_{5,6}$ = 0.0
$A_{6,6}$ = 0.0
$A_{7,6}$ = 0.0
$A_{8,6}$ = 0.0
$A_{9,6}$ = 0.0
T_a = 500
τ_c = 1.2333498

P_{sat} Eqn. S-2

F_1 =-6.7232038
F_2 =-1.4928492x10^{-3}
F_3 =-2.1966350
F_4 = 1.8152441x10^{-1}
F_5 = 3.4255443x10^{-1}
F_6 =-1.2772013x10^1
F_7 =-5.8344087x10^1
F_8 =-6.5163169x10^1
T_P = 300.

ρ_f Eqn. D-2

D_1 = 2.3763863x10^2
D_2 = 2.2030340x10^2
D_3 = 1.1999997x10^3
D_4 =-1.9145612x10^3
D_5 = 1.7358862x10^3
D_6 =-5.5587491x10^2

c_v Eqn. C-2

G_1 = 1.469259288x10^3
G_2 = 2.411085448x10^{-1}
G_3 =-7.038236532x10^{-3}
G_4 = 5.157906857x10^{-5}
G_5 =-1.209815448x10^{-7}
G_6 = 1.440829341x10^{-10}
G_7 =-9.429402197x10^{-14}
G_8 = 3.229595395x10^{-17}
G_9 =-4.528318341x10^{-21}
u_0 = 1.3814023x10^6
s_0 = 6.2092055x10^3

ARGON

M = 39.948 kg/kmol
T_c = 150.70 K
P_c = 4.8649 MPa
ρ_c = 513.00 kg/m^3
T_0 = 83.8 K

Constants for T in K, ρ in kg/m^3, P in Pa, c_v in J/(kg·K)

P-ρ-T Eqn. P-3

R = 208.128
A_1 = 1.9825921x10^{-1} A_{11} =-2.1572754x10^{-10}
A_2 =-8.1733119x10^1 A_{12} = 1.6544141x10^{-7}
A_3 = 1.7777470x10^3 A_{13} =-2.8142112x10^{-11}
A_4 =-8.2406544x10^5 A_{14} = 8.2532059x10^1
A_5 = 3.1666098x10^7 A_{15} =-9.1538377x10^3
A_6 =-4.4202671x10^{-5} A_{16} =-1.8340752x10^6
A_7 = 6.2161420x10^{-2} A_{17} =-3.3858136x10^{-3}
A_8 = 1.1443248 A_{18} = 1.5532886
A_9 = 4.7797520x10^{-7} A_{19} =-6.7479568x10^1
A_{10} =-1.9645227x10^{-4} γ = 3.5x10^{-6}

P_{sat} Eqn. S-2

F_1 =-5.340410
F_2 =-2.371280x10^{-1}
F_3 =-9.490142x10^{-1}
F_4 = 1.187040
F_5 =-5.889895
F_6 = 5.627790
F_7 = 2.674117x10^1
F_8 =-6.661814x10^1
T_P = 100.
P_c = 4.86492x10^6

ρf Eqn. D-2

D_1 = 5.129994x10^2
D_2 = 8.358137x10^2
D_3 = 1.195878x10^3
D_4 =-3.196858x10^3
D_5 = 4.502276x10^3
D_6 =-2.086375x10^3

c_v Eqn. C-0

c_v = 312.192
u_0 = 1.4935540x10^5
s_0 = 2.2706700x10^3

BUTANE

M = 58.12 kg/kmol
T_c = 423.95 K
P_c = 3.7183 MPa
ρ_c = 204.00 kg/m^3
T_0 = 200 K

Constants for T in K, ρ in kg/m^3, P in Pa, c_v in J/(kg·K)

P-ρ-T Eqn. P-2

R = 1.430797x10^2
B_0 = 1.681913x10^{-3}
A_0 = 2.588747x10^2
C_0 = 3.374153x10^7
D_0 = 4.544053x10^8
E_0 = 1.749633x10^9
b = 1.054551x10^{-5}
a = 6.081677x10^{-1}
d = 1.728889x10^2
c = 1.846013x10^5
α = 4.968935x10^{-9}
γ = 8.700251x10^{-6}

P_{sat} Eqn. S-2

F_1 =-6.4773780
F_2 =-3.0579064x10^{-2}
F_3 =-2.0756011
F_4 = 9.3845364x10^{-1}
F_5 =-5.7943269
F_6 =-5.2770385
F_7 = 2.6036457x10^1
F_8 = 6.2752788x10^1
T_P = 300.
P_c = 3.7180959x10^6

ρf Eqn. D-2

D_1 = 2.0399757x10^2
D_2 = 5.0903116x10^2
D_3 = 7.0925596x10^2
D_4 =-1.9959517x10^3
D_5 = 1.7838737x10^3
D_6 =-3.6126335x10^2

c_v Eqn. C-6

G_1 = 9.4817634x10^3
G_2 = 3.9633418x10^2
G_3 = 2.8576075
G_4 = 4.8802965x10^{-3}
G_5 =-6.4100047x10^{-6}
G_6 = 2.0651236x10^{-9}
u_0 = 4.2760753x10^5
s_0 = 1.8916540x10^3

CARBON DIOXIDE

M = 44.01 kg/kmol
T_c = 304.21 K
P_c = 7.3834 MPa
ρ_c = 464.00 kg/m³
T_0 = 216.54 K

Constants for T in K, ρ in kg/m³, P in Pa, c_v in J/(kg·K)

P-ρ-T Eqn. P-3

R = 188.918
A_1 = 2.2488558x10⁻¹ A_{16} =-2.9186718x10⁹
A_2 =-1.3717965x10² A_{17} = 2.4358627x10⁻²
A_3 =-1.4430214x10⁴ A_{18} =-3.7546530x10¹
A_4 =-2.9630491x10⁶ A_{19} = 1.1898141x10⁴
A_5 =-2.0606039x10⁸ γ = 5.0x10⁻⁶
A_6 = 4.5554393x10⁻⁵
A_7 = 7.7042840x10⁻²
A_8 = 4.0602371x10¹ ρ_f Eqn. D-2
A_9 = 4.0029509x10⁻⁷
A_{10} =-3.9436077x10⁻⁴ D_1 = 4.6400009x10²
A_{11} = 1.2115286x10⁻¹⁰ D_2 = 6.7938129x10²
A_{12} = 1.0783386x10⁻⁷ D_3 = 1.4776836x10³
A_{13} = 4.3962336x10⁻¹¹ D_4 =-3.1267676x10³
A_{14} =-3.6505545x10⁴ D_5 = 3.6397656x10³
A_{15} = 1.9490511x10⁷ D_6 =-1.3437098x10³

P_{sat} Eqn. S-2

F_1 =-6.5412610
F_2 =-2.7914636x10⁻¹
F_3 =-3.4716202
F_4 =-3.4989637
F_5 =-1.9770948x10¹
F_6 = 1.3922839x10²
F_7 =-2.7670389x10²
F_8 =-7.0510251x10³
P_c = 7.38350x10⁶
T_P = 250.

c_v Eqn. C-6

G_1 = 8.726361x10³
G_2 = 1.840040x10²
G_3 = 1.914025
G_4 =-1.667825x10⁻³
G_5 = 7.305950x10⁻⁷
G_6 =-1.255290x10⁻¹⁰
u_0 = 3.2174105x10⁵
s_0 = 2.1396056x10³

CESIUM

M = 132.91 kg/kmol
T_c = 2047.79 K
P_c = 11.73 MPa
ρ_c = 420.5 kg/m³
T_0 = 800 K

Constants for T in K, ρ in kg/m³, P in Pa, c_v in J/(kg·K)

P-ρ-T Eqn. P-7 A_7 = 1.125708x10³
                      A_8 = 0.0
R = 62.5559 A_9 = 1.826843x10⁻⁶ ρ_f Eqn. D-6
A_1 =-1.127493x10¹
A_2 = 5.116856x10³ P_{sat} Eqn. S-7 D_1 = 1.865883x10³
A_3 =-3.465370 D_2 =-5.051594x10⁻¹
A_4 =-6.820129x10³ F_1 = 2.473601x10¹ D_3 =-8.747735x10⁻⁵
A_5 = 7.693051x10⁶ F_2 =-9.006562x10³ T_P = 255.370 K
A_6 =-9.216489 F_3 =-5.329000x10⁻¹

c_v Eqn. C-7

G_1 = 9.386710x10¹
G_2 = 1.804957x10¹¹
β = 17383.33
u_0 = 4.7798663x10⁵
s_0 = 6.0099922x10²

ETHANE

M = 30.07 kg/kmol
T_c = 305.88 K
P_c = 5.0102 MPa
ρ_c = 217.59 kg/m³
T_0 = 150 K

Constants for T in K, ρ in kg/m³, P in Pa, c_v in J/(kg·K)

P-ρ-T Eqn. P-2 P_{sat} Eqn. S-2 ρf Eqn. D-2 c_v Eqn. C-6

R = 2.767735x10² F_1 =-5.9040507 D_1 = 2.1758939x10² G_1 = 2.6209109x10⁴
B_0 = 1.716337x10⁻³ F_2 = 2.6293983x10⁻³ D_2 = 3.9512352x10² G_2 = 3.9731855x10²
A_0 = 4.000173x10² F_3 =-1.6989361 D_3 =-4.1074978x10² G_3 = 2.0372154
C_0 = 2.711853x10⁷ F_4 = 2.5761218x10⁻¹ D_4 = 2.0021645x10³ G_4 = 6.3813897x10⁻³
D_0 = 1.314084x10⁹ F_5 =-9.6655814x10⁻¹ D_5 =-3.2750407x10³ G_5 =-7.2185581x10⁻⁶
E_0 = 4.162885x10¹⁰ F_6 = 3.7608925 D_6 = 1.9447815x10³ G_6 = 2.2048025x10⁻⁹
b = 1.343479x10⁻⁵ F_7 =-6.2752642 u_0 = 4.9861617x10⁵
a = 1.385571 F_8 =-2.5027513x10¹ s_0 = 3.1934536x10³
d = 2.412543x10¹ T_p = 200.
c = 1.301434x10⁵ P_c = 5.0106051x10⁶
α = 8.159501x10⁻⁹
γ = 1.293618x10⁻⁵

ETHYLENE

M = 28.054 kg/kmol
T_c = 282.65 K
P_c = 5.0750 MPa
ρ_c = 216.67 kg/m³
T_0 = 150 K

Constants for T in K, ρ in kg/m³, P in Pa, c_v in J/(kg·K)

P-ρ-T Eqn. P-3

R = 296.367 A_{16} = 6.383210497x10⁹
A_1 = 6.199009568x10⁻¹ A_{17} =-3.452285470 P_{sat} Eqn. S-2 c_v Eqn. C-2
A_2 =-5.480331377x10² A_{18} = 2.067324621x10³
A_3 = 5.939028162x10⁴ A_{19} =-2.179125512x10⁵ F_1 =-5.8351826 G_1 = 1.0657565x10³
A_4 =-2.978456992x10⁷ γ = 2.1x10⁻⁵ F_2 =-1.0535323x10⁻¹ G_2 =-2.5996503
A_5 = 1.410862498x10⁹ F_3 =-1.4231237 G_3 = 3.0370139x10⁻¹
A_6 = 2.099253547x10⁻³ F_4 =-4.2199146x10⁻¹ G_4 = 7.5775277x10⁻⁵
A_7 =-3.023961281x10⁻¹ ρf Eqn. D-2 F_5 =-1.8385922 G_5 =-2.5613127x10⁻⁷
A_8 = 2.126582512x10² F_6 = 1.1504786x10¹ G_6 = 3.5699585x10⁻¹
A_9 = 4.064840279x10⁻⁶ D_1 = 2.1667533x10² F_7 =-1.5509321x10¹ G_7 =-2.3618747x10⁻¹
A_{10} =-4.409410402x10⁻³ D_2 = 2.7238643x10² F_8 =-1.0601457x10² G_8 = 6.1095297x10⁻¹
A_{11} = 4.569939966x10⁻¹⁰ D_3 = 6.7325682x10² P_c = 5.07500x10⁶ u_0 = 4.6760769x10⁵
A_{12} = 6.188244460x10⁻⁶ D_4 =-1.2879223x10³ T_p = 200. s_0 = 3.2657141x10³
A_{13} = 5.116189590x10⁻¹⁰ D_5 = 1.3553807x10³
A_{14} = 5.920592324x10⁴ D_6 =-4.6055649x10²
A_{15} =-3.868585434x10⁷

HELIUM 4

M = 4.0026 kg/kmol
T_c = 5.2014 K
P_c = 0.22746 MPa
ρ_c = 69.64 kg/m^3
T_0 = 2.177 K

Constants for T in K, ρ in kg/m^3, P in Pa, c_v in J/(kg·K)

P-ρ-T Eqn. P-5

R = 2077.22578699

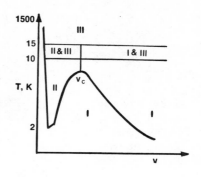

Region I

A_1 =-2.63717841606x10^{-4}
A_2 =-5.79620044301x10^{-2}
A_3 = 6.04727743809
A_4 = 3.86500111589x10^1
A_5 =-2.75796664744x10^2
A_6 =-4.96960774707x10^2
A_7 = 2.04341052964x10^3
A_8 =-2.66595676810x10^3
A_9 = 1.07968703317x10^3
A_{10} = 2.33740311250x10^{-1}
A_{11} =-5.14034417722
A_{12} = 3.08419481342x10^1
A_{13} =-1.67047385071x10^2
A_{14} = 5.24045883077x10^2
A_{15} =-8.07915654647x10^2
A_{16} = 6.31099960781x10^2
A_{17} =-2.45791511511x10^2
A_{18} = 1.47668657398x10^{-2}
A_{19} =-2.53062442742x10^{-1}
A_{20} = 7.33463898526x10^{-1}
A_{21} = 2.92163822280x10^{-1}
A_{22} = 4.07953759561x10^{-3}
A_{23} =-3.73905300971x10^{-2}
A_{24} = 1.36171997779x10^{-1}
A_{25} =-2.47415495892x10^{-1}
A_{26} = 2.33727221372x10^{-1}
A_{27} =-9.44142746383x10^{-2}
A_{28} =-3.72006192405x10^{-6}
A_{29} = 1.59283523218x10^{-5}
A_{30} = 7.75248537108
A_{31} =-4.13169817472x10^1
A_{32} = 5.40743659299x10^1
A_{33} = 5.34172600153x10^{-4}
A_{34} =-1.05413018834x10^{-3}
A_{35} =-8.82580260817x10^{-4}
γ = 1.56047072875x10^{-4}

Region II

A_1 =-2.63717841606x10^{-4}
A_2 =-5.79620044301x10^{-2}
A_3 = 6.04727743809
A_4 = 3.86500111589x10^1
A_5 =-2.75796664744x10^2
A_6 =-4.96960774707x10^2
A_7 = 2.04341052964x10^3
A_8 =-2.66595676810x10^3
A_9 = 1.07968703317x10^3
A_{10} = 3.23316248529x10^{-2}
A_{11} = 2.01417823467
A_{12} =-3.20336592218x10^1
A_{13} = 1.17952847254x10^2
A_{14} =-2.72064513304x10^2
A_{15} =, 8.06705554799x10^2
A_{16} =-6.34863771449x10^2
A_{17} = 4.23944026969x10^2
A_{18} =-1.26804959063x10^{-2}
A_{19} = 5.58960362485x10^{-2}
A_{20} = 5.81328684698x10^{-1}
A_{21} =-1.03365680210
A_{22} =-1.01057001312x10^{-3}
A_{23} = 8.40859671873x10^{-3}
A_{24} =-2.48181422872x10^{-2}
A_{25} = 3.24270326025x10^{-2}
A_{26} =-1.04566294786x10^{-2}
A_{27} =-1.05412341221x10^{-2}
A_{28} =-1.04201749588x10^{-6}
A_{29} = 1.09726080203x10^{-5}
A_{30} = 1.24933778088x10^1
A_{31} =-1.41252424541x10^2
A_{32} =-2.38228039845x10^2
A_{33} = 2.65139980533x10^{-4}
A_{34} =-3.33310756017x10^{-3}
A_{35} =-2.41601688592x10^{-3}
γ = 3.12094145751x10^{-5}

Region III

A_1 =-2.63717841606x10^{-4}
A_2 =-5.79620044301x10^{-2}
A_3 = 6.04727743809
A_4 = 3.86500111589x10^1
A_5 =-2.75796664744x10^2
A_6 =-4.96960774707x10^2
A_7 = 2.04341052964x10^3
A_8 =-2.66595676810x10^3
A_9 = 1.07968703317x10^3
A_{10} =-5.69281410539x10^{-2}
A_{11} = 2.54082433493
A_{12} =-4.33612764494x10^1
A_{13} = 2.32901880818x10^2
A_{14} =-6.88289870860x10^2
A_{15} = 2.12493828516x10^3
A_{16} =-2.69258356337x10^3
A_{17} = 1.42625846393x10^3
A_{18} = 7.76178949940x10^{-4}
A_{19} = 6.75967782095x10^{-2}
A_{20} = 9.09992115812x10^{-2}
A_{21} =-3.81211874106x10^{-1}
A_{22} =-2.30068006523x10^{-5}
A_{23} = 4.02950826349x10^{-5}
A_{24} = 1.07511466109x10^{-3}
A_{25} =-4.93747339170x10^{-3}
A_{26} = 1.11576934297x10^{-2}
A_{27} =-1.23679512941x10^{-2}
A_{28} =-3.64745210287x10^{-7}
A_{29} = 1.02807881652x10^{-5}
A_{30} = 8.98703364016
A_{31} =-2.28140026278x10^2
A_{32} = 5.33588707469
A_{33} = 1.06067862115x10^{-4}
A_{34} =-4.46441499497x10^{-3}
A_{35} = 3.80683087199x10^{-3}
γ = 3.12094145751x10^{-5}

P_{sat} Eqn. S-5

F_1 =-3.9394635287
F_2 = 1.3925998798x10^2
F_3 =-1.6407741565x10^3
F_4 = 1.1974557102x10^4
F_5 =-5.5283309818x10^4
F_6 = 1.6621956504x10^5
F_7 =-3.2521282840x10^5
F_8 = 3.9884322750x10^5
F_9 =-2.7771806992x10^5
F_{10} = 8.3395204183x10^4

ρ_f Eqn. D-2

D_1 = 6.9640000000x10^1
D_2 = 1.2874326484x10^2
D_3 =-4.3128217346x10^2
D_4 = 1.7851911824x10^3
D_5 =-3.3509624489x10^3
D_6 = 3.0344215824x10^3
D_7 =-1.0981289602x10^3

c_v Eqn. C-0

c_v = 3115.85
u_0 = 1.8712207x10^4
s_0 = 1.0812833x10^4

HEPTANE

M = 100.20 kg/kmol
T_c = 537.68 K
P_c = 2.6199 MPa
ρ_c = 197.60 kg/m³
T_0 = 300 K

Constants for T in K, ρ in kg/m³, P in Pa, c_v in J/(kg·K)

P-ρ-T Eqn. P-2	P_{sat} Eqn. S-2	ρf Eqn. D-2	c_v Eqn. C-6
R = 8.299504x10¹	F_1 = -7.2298764	D_1 = 1.9760405x10²	G_1 = 1.1925213x10⁵
B_0 = 2.246032x10⁻³	F_2 = 3.8607475x10⁻¹	D_2 = 8.9451237x10²	G_2 = -7.7231363x10²
A_0 = 2.082990x10²	F_3 = -3.4216472	D_3 = -1.1462908x10³	G_3 = 7.4463527
C_0 = 5.085746x10⁷	F_4 = 4.6274432x10⁻¹	D_4 = 1.7996947x10³	G_4 = -3.0888167x10⁻³
D_0 = 3.566396x10⁹	F_5 = -9.7926124	D_5 = -1.7250843x10³	u_0 = 3.4058439x10⁵
E_0 = 1.622168x10⁹	F_6 = -4.2058094x10¹	D_6 = 9.7088329x10²	s_0 = 1.1080254x10³
b = 1.065237x10⁻⁵	F_7 = 7.5468678x10¹		
a = 5.987922x10⁻¹	F_8 = 3.1758992x10²		
d = 7.736602	T_P = 400.		
c = 1.929386x10⁵	P_c = 2.6197435x10⁶		
α = 5.291379x10⁻⁹			
γ = 9.611604x10⁻⁶			

HEXANE

M = 86.18 kg/kmol
T_c = 506.13 K
P_c = 2.9265 MPa
ρ_c = 191.63 kg/m³
T_0 = 250 K

Constants for T in K, ρ in kg/m³, P in Pa, c_v in J/(kg·K)

P-ρ-T Eqn. P-2	P_{sat} Eqn. S-2	ρf Eqn. D-2	c_v Eqn. C-6
R = 9.650393x10¹	F_1 = -7.0231374	D_1 = 1.9162870x10²	G_1 = 1.2149350x10⁵
B_0 = 1.928741x10⁻³	F_2 = -2.1827311x10⁻¹	D_2 = -3.2794532x10²	G_2 = -7.8379325x10²
A_0 = 1.640433x10²	F_3 = -1.9928180	D_3 = 6.2017594x10³	G_3 = 7.4139795
C_0 = 5.875423x10⁷	F_4 = 3.9897963x10⁻¹	D_4 = -1.4823173x10⁴	G_4 = -3.0234462x10⁻³
D_0 = 3.426013x10⁹	F_5 = 1.0736773x10¹	D_5 = 1.4904295x10⁴	u_0 = 3.8436664x10⁵
E_0 = 2.159373x10¹¹	F_6 = 1.5436086x10²	D_6 = -5.1866270x10³	s_0 = 1.3669737x10³
b = 1.548178x10⁻⁵	F_7 = 4.7486454x10²		
a = 1.139100	F_8 = 5.0555122x10²		
d = 4.769149x10¹	T_P = 400.		
c = 2.576318x10⁵	P_c = 2.9263747x10⁶		
α = 3.689017x10⁻⁹			
γ = 7.805367x10⁻⁶			

HYDROGEN (PARA)

M = 2.0159 kg/kmol
T_c = 32.938 K
P_c = 1.2838 MPa
ρ_c = 31.36 kg/m^3
T_0 = 13.8 K

Constants for T in K, ρ in kg/m^3, P in Pa, c_v in J/(kg·K)

P-ρ-T Eqn. P-4

R = 4124.299539
A_1 = 1.150470519352900x10^1
A_2 = 1.055427998826072x10^3
A_3 =-1.270685949968568x10^4
A_4 = 7.287844527295619x10^4
A_5 =-7.448780703363973x10^5
A_6 = 2.328994151810363x10^{-1}
A_7 =-1.635308393739296x10^1
A_8 = 3.730678064960389x10^3
A_9 = 6.299667723184813x10^5
A_{10} = 1.210920358305697x10^{-3}
A_{11} = 1.753651095884817
A_{12} =-1.367022988058101x10^2
A_{13} =-6.869936641299885x10^{-3}
A_{14} = 3.644494201750974x10^{-2}
A_{15} =-2.559784772600182
A_{16} =-4.038855202905836x10^{-4}
A_{17} = 1.485396303520942x10^{-6}
A_{18} = 4.243613981060742x10^{-4}
A_{19} =-2.307910113586888x10^{-6}
A_{20} =-6.082192173879582x10^5
A_{21} =-1.961080967486886x10^6
A_{22} =-5.786932854076408x10^2
A_{23} = 2.799129504191752x10^4
A_{24} =-2.381566558300913x10^{-1}
A_{25} = 8.918796032452872x10^{-1}
A_{26} =-6.985739539036644x10^{-5}

A_{27} =-7.339554179182899x10^{-3}
A_{28} =-5.597033440289980x10^{-9}
A_{29} = 8.842130160884514x10^{-8}
A_{30} =-2.655507264539047x10^{-12}
A_{31} =-4.544474518140164x10^{-12}
A_{32} = 9.818775257001922x10^{-11}
γ = 1.008854772x10^{-3}

P_{sat} Eqn. S-3

F_1 = 3.05300134164
F_2 = 2.80810925813
F_3 =-6.55461216567x10^{-1}
F_4 = 1.59514439374
α = 1.5814454428
T_t = 13.8
P_t = 7042.09

ρf Eqn. D-4

D_1 = 4.8645813003x10^1
D_2 =-3.4779278180x10^1
D_3 = 4.0776538192x10^2
D_4 =-1.1719787304x10^3
D_5 = 1.6213924400x10^3
D_6 =-1.1531096683x10^3
D_7 = 3.3825492039x10^2
α = 0.3479

c_v Eqn. C-5

G_1 = 6.1934792x10^3
G_2 = 2.9490437x10^2
G_3 =-1.5401979x10^3
G_4 =-4.9176101x10^3
G_5 = 6.8957165x10^4
G_6 =-2.2282185x10^5
G_7 = 3.7990059x10^5
G_8 =-3.7094216x10^5
G_9 = 2.1326792x10^5
G_{10} =-7.1519411x10^4
G_{11} = 1.2971743x10^4
G_{12} =-9.8533014x10^2
G_{13} = 1.0434776x10^4
G_{14} =-3.9144179x10^2
G_{15} = 5.8277696x10^2
G_{16} = 6.5409163x10^2
G_{17} =-1.8728847x10^2
T_1 = 35.0
T_2 = 400.0
u_0 = 3.9275114x10^5
s_0 = 2.3900333x10^4

ISOBUTANE

$M = 58.12\,kg/kmol$
$T_c = 409.07\ K$
$P_c = 3.6846\ MPa$
$\rho_c = 194.51\ kg/m^3$
$T_0 = 200\ K$

Constants for T in K, ρ in kg/m^3, P in Pa, c_v in $J/(kg \cdot K)$

P-ρ-T Eqn. P-2

$R = 1.430797 \times 10^2$
$B_0 = 2.018128 \times 10^{-3}$
$A_0 = 2.964140 \times 10^2$
$C_0 = 2.489763 \times 10^7$
$D_0 = 1.163672 \times 10^9$
$E_0 = 6.371519 \times 10^{10}$
$b = 9.906333 \times 10^{-6}$
$a = 4.100261 \times 10^{-1}$
$d = 1.029360 \times 10^2$
$c = 1.072632 \times 10^5$
$\alpha = 5.253972 \times 10^{-9}$
$\gamma = 8.208362 \times 10^{-6}$

P_{sat} Eqn. S-2

$F_1 = -6.3016457$
$F_2 = 2.1880736 \times 10^{-1}$
$F_3 = -1.1288158$
$F_4 = 2.2391095$
$F_5 = 1.0653363$
$F_6 = 9.3322720$
$F_7 = 2.4836848 \times 10^1$
$F_8 = 3.7187854 \times 10^1$
$T_p = 300.$
$P_c = 3.6845470 \times 10^6$

ρ_f Eqn. D-2

$D_1 = 1.9450561 \times 10^2$
$D_2 = -9.1725345 \times 10^1$
$D_3 = 2.4446128 \times 10^3$
$D_4 = -2.7219989 \times 10^3$
$D_5 = 1.9324597 \times 10^2$
$D_6 = 8.7037158 \times 10^2$

c_v Eqn. C-6

$G_1 = 1.7563902 \times 10^5$
$G_2 = -1.7524300 \times 10^3$
$G_3 = 1.1642389 \times 10^1$
$G_4 = -1.0197170 \times 10^{-2}$
$G_5 = 4.9006615 \times 10^{-6}$
$G_6 = -9.8234416 \times 10^{-10}$
$u_0 = 3.9342075 \times 10^5$
$s_0 = 1.8189390 \times 10^3$

ISOPENTANE

$M = 72.15\,kg/kmol$
$T_c = 460.98\ K$
$P_c = 3.4089\ MPa$
$\rho_c = 216.38\ kg/m^3$
$T_0 = 200\ K$

Constants for T in K, ρ in kg/m^3, P in Pa, c_v in $J/(kg \cdot K)$

P-ρ-T Eqn. P-2

$R = 1.152638 \times 10^2$
$B_0 = 1.105421 \times 10^{-3}$
$A_0 = 1.845091 \times 10^2$
$C_0 = 3.639545 \times 10^7$
$D_0 = 1.257944 \times 10^9$
$E_0 = 1.186733 \times 10^{10}$
$b = 1.485342 \times 10^{-5}$
$a = 9.127686 \times 10^{-1}$
$d = 8.666134 \times 10^1$
$c = 1.779602 \times 10^5$
$\alpha = 3.991801 \times 10^{-9}$
$\gamma = 8.788781 \times 10^{-6}$

P_{sat} Eqn. S-2

$F_1 = -6.6220707$
$F_2 = 5.5018040 \times 10^{-1}$
$F_3 = -1.9645926$
$F_4 = 8.8295088 \times 10^{-1}$
$F_5 = -1.0240822$
$F_6 = -4.4620424$
$F_7 = 7.9209958$
$F_8 = -8.6762249 \times 10^{-1}$
$T_p = 300.$
$P_c = 3.4088951 \times 10^6$

ρ_f Eqn. D-2

$D_1 = 2.1637787 \times 10^2$
$D_2 = 5.1544885 \times 10^2$
$D_3 = 1.0103369 \times 10^2$
$D_4 = 3.0133300 \times 10^2$
$D_5 = -1.2696332 \times 10^3$
$D_6 = 1.1035964 \times 10^3$

c_v Eqn. C-6

$G_1 = 2.4294906 \times 10^4$
$G_2 = -2.4667775 \times 10^2$
$G_3 = 6.4031034$
$G_4 = -2.3405578 \times 10^{-3}$
$u_0 = 3.8740774 \times 10^5$
$s_0 = 1.5693410 \times 10^3$

LITHIUM

M = 6.940 kg/kmol
T_c = 3800. K
P_c = 97. MPa
ρ_c = 100.0 kg/m³
T_0 = 1200 K

Constants for T in K, ρ in kg/m³, P in Pa, c_v in J/(kg·K)

P-ρ-T Eqn. P-11

R = 1198.03
α = 13600.
A_1 =-2.64858978
A_2 = 5.06645144x10⁻³
A_3 =-3.62080009x10⁻⁶
A_4 = 7.65377978x10⁻¹⁰
A_5 = 2.69807364
A_6 = 4.63946177x10⁻³
A_7 =-2.62591228x10⁻⁶
A_8 =-2.41803055x10¹
A_9 = 1.14363000x10⁻²

P_{sat} Eqn. S-9

F_1 = 6.6203879x10¹
F_2 =-3.1762765x10⁴
F_3 =-4.9740144
F_4 = 4.5310417x10⁶

ρ_f Eqn. D-8

D_1 = 4.4089743x10²
D_2 =-1.0458647x10⁻¹
D_3 = 7.1186130x10⁻⁶
T_p = 1200.

c_v Eqn. C-7

G_1 = 1.7991x10³
G_2 = 1.6790x10¹²
β = 21458.
u_0 = 2.0172606x10⁷
s_0 = 1.0090462x10⁴

MERCURY

M = 200.6 kg/kmol
T_c = 1763. K
P_c = 153. MPa
ρ_c = 5500.6 kg/m³
T_0 = 400 K

Constants for T in K, ρ in kg/m³, P in Pa, c_v in J/(kg·K)

P-ρ-T Eqn. P-9

R = 41.4453
A_1 = 1.0333788x10¹
A_2 =-3.1209537x10²
A_3 =-2.0794980

P_{sat} Eqn. S-9

F_1 = 2.3632090x10¹
F_2 =-7.0426208x10³
F_3 =-1.2074398x10⁻¹
F_4 =-5.8060290x10⁴

ρ_f Eqn. D-8

D_1 = 1.2813607x10⁴
D_2 =-2.4530519
D_3 =-2.6672681x10⁻⁴
T_p = 600.

c_v Eqn. C-0

c_v = 62.168
u_0 = 2.8533557x10⁵
s_0 = 5.5681521x10²

METHANE

M = 16.043 kg/kmol
T_c = 190.555 K
P_c = 4.5988 MPa
ρ_c = 160.43 kg/m^3
T_0 = 90.68 K

Constants for T in K, ρ in kg/m^3, P in Pa, c_v in J/(kg·K)

P-ρ-T Eqn. P-4

R = 5.18253475866x10^2
A_1 =-7.25929210183
A_2 = 4.13766054566x10^2
A_3 =-6.32167316855x10^3
A_4 = 3.34015577724x10^5
A_5 =-1.68253379982x10^7
A_6 = 1.87884851902x10^{-2}
A_7 =-1.18673201223x10^1
A_8 = 2.09062618015x10^3
A_9 =-4.07532656958x10^5
A_{10} =-5.73917603241x10^{-5}
A_{11} = 4.37711441593x10^{-2}
A_{12} =-4.38766500673
A_{13} = 1.13524630779x10^{-5}
A_{14} =-5.07028240949x10^{-5}
A_{15} = 2.28002199522x10^{-2}
A_{16} = 9.25611329590x10^{-9}

A_{17} = 1.33865662546x10^{-10}
A_{18} =-1.65439044196x10^{-7}
A_{19} = 1.81030980110x10^{-10}
A_{20} = 5.45753645958x10^5
A_{21} =-3.63192281933x10^7
A_{22} = 4.81463473761
A_{23} = 1.56633022620x10^5
A_{24} = 7.89977010972x10^{-5}
A_{25} = 1.39993881210x10^{-2}
A_{26} =-1.70656092212x10^{-11}
A_{27} =-4.55256623445x10^{-5}
A_{28} =-2.29314170748x10^{-14}
A_{29} = 8.31548197665x10^{-12}
A_{30} = 6.84673626259x10^{-20}
A_{31} =-4.70845544152x10^{-17}
A_{32} = 5.21465091383x10^{-16}
γ = 3.72992471469x10^{-5}

P_{sat} Eqn. S-3

P_t = 11743.5675
F_1 = 4.77748580
F_2 = 1.76065363
F_3 =-5.67888940x10^{-1}
F_4 = 1.32786231
α = 1.5

ρ_f Eqn. D-3

ρ_t = 451.562
D_1 =-1.78860165x10^{-1}
D_2 = 4.83847500x10^{-2}
D_3 =-1.84898700x10^{-2}
α = 0.36
T_t = 90.68

c_v Eqn. C-3

G_1 = 1.34740610x10^3
G_2 = 1.35512060x10^2
G_3 =-2.93910458x10^1
G_4 = 2.12774600
G_5 = 2.44656600x10^3

β = 2009.152
u_0 = 4.9716032x10^5
s_0 = 5.2782638x10^3

NEON

M = 20.183 kg/kmol
T_c = 44.40 K
P_c = 2.6537 MPa
ρ_c = 483.00 kg/m^3
T_0 = 24.54 K

Constants for T in K, ρ in kg/m^3, P in Pa, c_v in J/(kg·K)

P-ρ-T Eqn. P-10

R = 411.9344
A_1 = 4.28769078x10^{-1}
A_2 =-4.17471396x10^1
A_3 =-1.53675385x10^3
A_4 = 2.17043833x10^4
A_5 =-1.25523983x10^{-6}
A_6 = 5.23734403x10^{-5}
A_7 = 3.18297378x10^{-2}
A_8 = 1.53034563
A_9 =-7.68816484x10^{-1}

A_{10} = 8.69816636x10^{-7}
A_{11} =-8.65562359x10^{-5}
A_{12} =-8.49266257x10^{-7}
A_{13} = 4.19873205x10^{-11}
A_{14} = 2.38547521x10^2
A_{15} =-1.04435003x10^4
A_{16} =-1.98253591x10^{-3}
A_{17} = 7.09558991x10^{-2}
γ = 1.35894020x10^{-5}

P_{sat} Eqn. S-10

F_1 = 2.2072726x10^1
F_2 =-2.4428125x10^2
F_3 =-8.2113869x10^{-2}
F_4 = 9.4657431x10^{-4}

ρ_f Eqn. D-2

D_1 = 4.8300000x10^2
D_2 = 7.2815914x10^2
D_3 = 4.9773532x10^2
D_4 =-4.3525200x10^2
D_5 = 3.2839095x10^2

c_v Eqn. C-0

c_v = 617.76

u_0 = 7.9550895x10^4
s_0 = 4.2415156x10^3

NITROGEN

M = 28.0134 kg/kmol
T_c = 126.200 K
P_c = 3.4000 MPa
ρ_c = 314.03 kg/m³
T_0 = 63.15 K

Constants for T in K, ρ in kg/m³, P in Pa, c_v in J/(kg·K)

P-ρ-T Eqn. P-4

R = 2.96790515164171x10²
A_1 = 1.75889959256970x10⁻¹
A_2 = 1.38197604384933x10¹
A_3 =-3.14918412133921x10²
A_4 = 4.40300150239380x10³
A_5 =-5.45358971644916x10⁵
A_6 = 4.84413320182919x10⁻⁴
A_7 =-5.18964416491365x10⁻²
A_8 = 6.57265859197103x10⁻⁴
A_9 = 8.51299771713314x10⁴
A_{10} = 1.33459405162578x10⁻⁸
A_{11} = 3.83381319826746x10⁻⁴
A_{12} =-8.35421151028455x10⁻²
A_{13} = 2.84874912286101x10⁻⁷
A_{14} =-2.38296116270360x10⁻⁷
A_{15} =-1.48321912935764x10⁻⁴
A_{16} = 5.62605853190540x10⁻¹⁰
A_{17} =-2.98201050924595x10⁻¹³
A_{18} = 9.85319087685241x10⁻¹¹
A_{19} =-1.92002176056468x10⁻¹⁴
A_{20} =-7.82250103373122x10⁴
A_{21} =-5.51801778744598x10⁵
A_{22} =-5.72781957607352x10⁻¹

A_{23} = 3.25760529488327x10²
A_{24} =-1.34659309828737x10⁻⁶
A_{25} =-1.92036423064911x10⁻⁵
A_{26} =-3.94564337674524x10⁻¹²
A_{27} =-2.44388245328965x10⁻⁹
A_{28} =-1.50970602460077x10⁻¹⁸
A_{29} = 1.25854885346038x10⁻¹⁶
A_{30} =-8.34271144923969x10⁻²⁴
A_{31} =-1.17299202018417x10⁻²²
A_{32} = 9.06544823455730x10⁻²²
γ = 7.13602531283233x10⁻⁶

P_{sat} Eqn. S-4

F_1 = 8.3944094440x10³
F_2 =-1.8785191705x10³
F_3 =-7.2822291650
F_4 = 1.0228509660x10⁻²
F_5 = 5.5560638250x10⁻⁴
F_6 =-5.9445446620x10⁻⁶
F_7 = 2.7154339320x10⁻⁸
F_8 =-4.8795359040x10⁻¹¹
F_9 = 5.0953608240x10²
α = 1.95

ρf Eqn. D-2

D_1 = 3.1402991x10²
D_2 = 4.4111015x10²
D_3 = 9.4622994x10²
D_4 =-2.9067111x10³
D_5 = 4.4785979x10³
D_6 =-2.2746914x10³

c_v Eqn. C-4

G_1 =-2.18203473713518x10⁵
G_2 = 1.01573580096247x10⁴
G_3 =-1.65504721657240x10²
G_4 = 7.43175999190430x10²
G_5 =-5.14605623546025x10⁻³
G_6 = 5.18347156760489x10⁻⁶
G_7 =-1.05922170493616x10⁻⁹
G_8 = 2.98389393363817x10²
β = 3353.40610
u_0 = 1.9662281x10⁵
s_0 = 3.2882374x10³

OCTANE

M = 114.22 kg/kmol
T_c = 567.51 K
P_c = 2.3997 MPa
ρ_c = 181.05 kg/m³
T_0 = 300 K

Constants for T in K, ρ in kg/m³, P in Pa, c_v in J/(kg·K)

P-ρ-T Eqn. P-2

R = 7.280376x10¹
B_0 = 2.661451x10⁻³
A_0 = 1.682414x10²
C_0 = 6.334511x10⁷
D_0 = 2.791813x10⁹
E_0 = 6.796298x10⁹
b = 3.163488x10⁻⁶
a = 1.481799x10⁻¹
d = 1.162525x10²
c = 2.230527x10⁵
α = 5.634268x10⁻⁹
γ = 6.568151x10⁻⁶

P_{sat} Eqn. S-2

F_1 =-7.4537707
F_2 = 1.0592936
F_3 =-2.7218674
F_4 = 2.4984120
F_5 = 5.0654376
F_6 = 2.8024876x10¹
F_7 = 5.0827052x10¹
F_8 =-3.9836446x10¹
T_P = 400.
P_c = 2.3996292x10⁶

ρf Eqn. D-2

D_1 = 1.8105379x10²
D_2 =-2.3535183x10³
D_3 = 1.7830977x10⁴
D_4 =-3.8108204x10⁴
D_5 = 3.4999123x10⁴
D_6 =-1.1666436x10⁴

c_v Eqn. C-6

G_1 = 4.0859678x10⁴
G_2 =-3.2250398x10²
G_3 = 6.6958265
G_4 =-2.6759063x10⁻³
u_0 = 3.4468913x10⁵
s_0 = 1.0494787x10³

OXYGEN

M = 31.9994 kg/kmol
T_c = 154.581 K
P_c = 5.0429 MPa
ρ_c = 436.15 kg/m^3
T_0 = 54.34 K

Constants for T in K, ρ in kg/m^3, P in Pa, c_v in J/(kg$\cdot$K)

P-ρ-T Eqn. P-4

R = 2.59820853437877x10^2
A_1 =-4.26396872798684x10^{-1}
A_2 = 3.48334938784107x10^1
A_3 =-5.77516910418738x10^2
A_4 = 2.40961751553325x10^4
A_5 =-1.23332307855543x10^6
A_6 = 3.73585286319658x10^{-4}
A_7 =-1.70178244046465x10^{-1}
A_8 =-3.33226903068473x10^{-4}
A_9 = 8.61334799901291x10^3
A_{10} =-6.80394661057309x10^{-7}
A_{11} = 7.09583347162704x10^{-4}
A_{12} =-5.73905688255053x10^{-2}
A_{13} =-1.92123080811409x10^{-7}
A_{14} = 3.11764722329504x10^{-8}
A_{15} =-8.09463854745591x10^{-6}
A_{16} =-2.22562296356501x10^{-11}
A_{17} = 9.18401045361994x10^{-15}
A_{18} = 5.75758417511114x10^{-12}
A_{19} =-2.10752269644774x10^{-15}
A_{20} = 3.62884761272184x10^3
A_{21} =-1.23317754317110x10^6
A_{22} =-5.03800414800672x10^{-2}
A_{23} = 3.30686173177055x10^2
A_{24} =-5.26259633964252x10^{-8}
A_{25} = 5.53075442383100x10^{-6}
A_{26} =-2.71042853363688x10^{-13}
A_{27} =-1.65732450675251x10^{-9}
A_{28} =-5.82711196409204x10^{-20}
A_{29} = 4.42953322148281x10^{-17}
A_{30} =-2.95529679136244x10^{-25}
A_{31} =-1.92361786708846x10^{-23}
A_{32} = 9.43758410350413x10^{-23}
γ = 5.46895508389297x10^{-6}

P_{sat} Eqn.S-4

F_1 =-5.5819320390x10^2
F_2 =-1.0966262185x10^2
F_3 =-8.3456211630x10^{-2}
F_4 = 2.6603644330x10^{-3}
F_5 = 1.6875023830x10^{-5}
F_6 =-2.1262477120x10^{-7}
F_7 = 9.5741096780x10^{-10}
F_8 =-1.6617640450x10^{-12}
F_9 = 2.7545605710x10^1
α = 1.91576

ρf Eqn. D-2

D_1 = 4.3615175x10^2
D_2 = 7.5897189x10^2
D_3 =-4.2576866x10^2
D_4 = 2.3487106x10^3
D_5 =-3.0474660x10^3
D_6 = 1.4850169x10^3

c_v Eqn. C-4

G_1 =-1.29442711174062x10^6
G_2 = 5.98231747005341x10^4
G_3 =-8.97850772730944x10^2
G_4 = 6.55236176900400x10^2
G_5 =-1.13131252131570x10^{-2}
G_6 = 3.49810702442228x10^{-6}
G_7 = 4.21065222886885x10^{-9}
G_8 = 2.67997030050139x10^2
β = 2239.18105
u_0 = 2.2826740x10^5
s_0 = 3.2714925x10^3

PENTANE

$M = 72.15$ kg/kmol
$T_c = 467.00$ K
$P_c = 3.2396$ MPa
$\rho_c = 196.67$ kg/m^3
$T_0 = 250$ K

Constants for T in K, ρ in kg/m^3, P in Pa, c_v in J/(kg·K)

P-ρ-T Eqn. P-2 P_{sat} Eqn. S-2 ρ_f Eqn. D-2 c_v Eqn. C-6

$R = 1.152638 \times 10^2$ $F_1 = -6.8086867$ $D_1 = 1.9667315 \times 10^2$ $G_1 = 1.2766578 \times 10^5$
$B_0 = 2.114907 \times 10^{-3}$ $F_2 = -8.1097531 \times 10^{-1}$ $D_2 = 2.7200889 \times 10^2$ $G_2 = -8.2486411 \times 10^2$
$A_0 = 2.638332 \times 10^2$ $F_3 = -2.0780180$ $D_3 = 2.2915110 \times 10^3$ $G_3 = 7.4242679$
$C_0 = 3.567863 \times 10^7$ $F_4 = 1.6335436 \times 10^1$ $D_4 = -5.6090395 \times 10^3$ $G_4 = -2.9601101 \times 10^{-3}$
$D_0 = 9.008177 \times 10^8$ $F_5 = 1.2800516 \times 10^2$ $D_5 = 5.4614858 \times 10^3$ $u_0 = 3.7830502 \times 10^5$
$E_0 = 1.922074 \times 10^{10}$ $F_6 = 4.8994794 \times 10^2$ $D_6 = -1.7170116 \times 10^3$ $s_0 = 1.4741582 \times 10^3$
$b = 1.243400 \times 10^{-5}$ $F_7 = 8.6353004 \times 10^2$
$a = 7.244518 \times 10^{-1}$ $F_8 = 5.9111580 \times 10^2$
$d = 9.641415 \times 10^1$ $T_P = 400.$
$c = 1.865119 \times 10^5$ $P_c = 3.2395335 \times 10^6$
$\alpha = 4.578423 \times 10^{-9}$
$\gamma = 8.879302 \times 10^{-6}$

POTASSIUM

$M = 39.10$ kg/kmol
$T_c = 2173.$ K
$P_c = 16.7$ MPa
$\rho_c = 202.0$ kg/m^3
$T_0 = 800$ K

Constants for T in K, ρ in kg/m^3, P in Pa, c_v in J/(kg·K)

P-ρ-T Eqn. P-7

$R = 212.642$ P_{sat} Eqn. S-7 ρ_f Eqn. D-6 c_v Eqn. C-7
$A_1 = -9.423507$
$A_2 = 6.256252 \times 10^3$ $F_1 = 2.534696 \times 10^1$ $D_1 = 8.452642 \times 10^2$ $G_1 = 3.190816 \times 10^2$
$A_3 = -6.167816$ $F_2 = -1.040679 \times 10^4$ $D_2 = -2.161777 \times 10^{-1}$ $G_2 = 2.274636 \times 10^{12}$
$A_4 = 8.168676 \times 10^3$ $F_3 = -5.356000 \times 10^{-1}$ $D_3 = -2.727342 \times 10^{-5}$ $\beta = 21875.$
$A_5 = 0.0$ $D_4 = 4.652311 \times 10^{-9}$ $u_0 = 1.9289316 \times 10^6$
$A_6 = -1.059937 \times 10^1$ $T_P = 255.372$ K $s_0 = 1.9189911 \times 10^3$
$A_7 = 1.005948 \times 10^4$

PROPANE

$M = 44.09$ kg/kmol
$T_c = 369.82$ K
$P_c = 4.2362$ MPa
$\rho_c = 197.38$ kg/m^3
$T_0 = 200$ K

Constants for T in K, ρ in kg/m^3, P in Pa, c_v in J/(kg·K)

P-ρ-T Eqn. P-2

$R = 1.887326 \times 10^2$
$B_0 = 1.366892 \times 10^{-3}$
$A_0 = 2.579108 \times 10^2$
$C_0 = 3.401044 \times 10^7$
$D_0 = 1.076728 \times 10^9$
$E_0 = 3.375879 \times 10^{10}$
$b = 1.096523 \times 10^{-5}$
$a = 7.856721 \times 10^{-1}$
$d = 1.639769 \times 10^2$
$c = 1.661103 \times 10^5$
$\alpha = 5.728034 \times 10^{-9}$
$\gamma = 9.157270 \times 10^{-6}$

P$_{sat}$ Eqn. S-2

$F_1 = -6.2309993$
$F_2 = -4.4226860 \times 10^{-1}$
$F_3 = -1.8839624$
$F_4 = 3.6383362 \times 10^{-1}$
$F_5 = 1.5177354 \times 10^1$
$F_6 = 1.1216551 \times 10^2$
$F_7 = 2.7635840 \times 10^2$
$F_8 = 2.3585357 \times 10^2$
$T_P = 300.$
$P_c = 4.2359300 \times 10^6$

ρ_f Eqn. D-2

$D_1 = 1.9738193 \times 10^2$
$D_2 = -2.1307184 \times 10^1$
$D_3 = 3.3522024 \times 10^3$
$D_4 = -7.7040243 \times 10^3$
$D_5 = 7.5224059 \times 10^3$
$D_6 = -2.5663363 \times 10^3$

c_v Eqn. C-6

$G_1 = 2.0582170 \times 10^5$
$G_2 = -1.9109547 \times 10^3$
$G_3 = 1.1622054 \times 10^1$
$G_4 = -9.7951510 \times 10^{-3}$
$G_5 = 4.5167026 \times 10^{-6}$
$G_6 = -8.6345035 \times 10^{-10}$
$u_0 = 4.2027216 \times 10^5$
$s_0 = 2.1673997 \times 10^3$

PROPYL ALCOHOL

$M = 60.09$ kg/kmol
$T_c = 536.85$ K
$P_c = 5.0751$ MPa
$\rho_c = 273.38$ kg/m^3
$T_0 = 275$ K

Constants for T in K, ρ in kg/m^3, P in Pa, c_v in J/(kg·K)

P-ρ-T Eqn. P-1

$R = 138.3559$
$b = 4.87267222 \times 10^{-4}$
$A_2 = -5.42668549 \times 10^2$
$A_3 = 9.05495750 \times 10^{-1}$
$A_4 = -1.89466294 \times 10^{-3}$
$A_5 = 1.19052690 \times 10^{-6}$
$B_2 = 3.97987297 \times 10^{-1}$
$B_3 = -4.27456287 \times 10^{-5}$
$B_4 = 0.0$
$B_5 = 1.02623102 \times 10^{-9}$
$C_2 = -1.58392320 \times 10^4$
$C_3 = 5.93029373 \times 10^1$
$C_4 = 0.0$
$C_5 = -9.12685005 \times 10^{-5}$
$\kappa = 5.0$

P$_{sat}$ Eqn. S-1

$F_1 = 7.57783301 \times 10^1$
$F_2 = -1.04990282 \times 10^4$
$F_3 = -6.03916030$
$F_4 = -5.29345072 \times 10^{-3}$
$F_5 = 7.26466630 \times 10^{-1}$
$\gamma = 544.85$

ρ_f Eqn. D-1

$D_1 = 2.733829339 \times 10^2$
$D_2 = 8.068327349 \times 10^2$
$D_3 = -1.230356060 \times 10^3$
$D_4 = 2.627253614 \times 10^3$
$D_5 = -1.592222689 \times 10^3$

c_v Eqn. C-1

$G_1 = -2.990892915 \times 10^2$
$G_2 = 6.434660263$
$G_3 = -4.040634960 \times 10^{-3}$
$G_4 = 9.853269426 \times 10^{-7}$
$u_0 = 7.9479291 \times 10^5$
$s_0 = 2.4290305 \times 10^3$

PROPYLENE

$M = 42.08$ kg/kmol
$T_c = 364.90$ K
$P_c = 4.6130$ MPa
$\rho_c = 227.00$ kg/m^3
$T_0 = 200$ K

Constants for T in K, ρ in kg/m^3, P in Pa, c_v in J/(kg·K)

P-ρ-T Eqn. P-3

$R = 197.578$
$A_1 = 7.282876415 \times 10^{-1}$
$A_2 = -6.915957872 \times 10^{2}$
$A_3 = 1.232721329 \times 10^{5}$
$A_4 = -5.363598403 \times 10^{7}$
$A_5 = 4.704449163 \times 10^{9}$
$A_6 = -1.144303984 \times 10^{-3}$
$A_7 = 1.150332286$
$A_8 = -6.358860432 \times 10^{1}$
$A_9 = 1.072352773 \times 10^{-5}$
$A_{10} = -7.396844590 \times 10^{-3}$
$A_{11} = -1.210690018 \times 10^{-8}$
$A_{12} = 1.405092248 \times 10^{-5}$
$A_{13} = -4.328660394 \times 10^{-9}$
$A_{14} = 6.680314909 \times 10^{4}$
$A_{15} = 3.816884968 \times 10^{7}$
$A_{16} = -1.503361977 \times 10^{10}$
$A_{17} = -6.299803992 \times 10^{-1}$
$A_{18} = 6.964578103 \times 10^{2}$
$A_{19} = 6.429702784 \times 10^{4}$
$\gamma = 1.5 \times 10^{-5}$

P_{sat} Eqn. S-2

$F_1 = -6.2416097$
$F_2 = 7.8213066 \times 10^{-1}$
$F_3 = -1.9298461$
$F_4 = 1.1630011$
$F_5 = 4.7498495$
$F_6 = -2.0533619 \times 10^{1}$
$F_7 = 2.9972723 \times 10^{1}$
$F_8 = -1.6098289 \times 10^{1}$
$P_c = 4.61300 \times 10^{6}$
$T_P = 200.$

ρ_f Eqn. D-2

$D_1 = 2.2699930 \times 10^{2}$
$D_2 = 3.8189547 \times 10^{2}$
$D_3 = 4.5129350 \times 10^{2}$
$D_4 = -1.1201552 \times 10^{3}$
$D_5 = 1.5497893 \times 10^{3}$
$D_6 = -6.5810211 \times 10^{2}$

c_v Eqn. C-2

$G_1 = 2.5548377 \times 10^{2}$
$G_2 = 7.5938490$
$G_3 = -4.4360027 \times 10^{-2}$
$G_4 = 1.8453395 \times 10^{-4}$
$G_5 = -3.6016319 \times 10^{-7}$
$G_6 = 3.3232608 \times 10^{-10}$
$G_7 = -1.1803270 \times 10^{-13}$
$u_0 = 4.3105132 \times 10^{5}$
$s_0 = 2.2741809 \times 10^{3}$

REFRIGERANT 11

$M = 137.38$ kg/kmol
$T_c = 471.15$ K
$P_c = 4.4092$ MPa
$\rho_c = 553.76$ kg/m^3
$T_0 = 200$ K

Constants for T in K, ρ in kg/m^3, P in Pa, c_v in J/(kg·K)

P-ρ-T Eqn. P-1

$R = 60.5223$
$b = 1.18612854 \times 10^{-4}$
$A_2 = -8.40175225 \times 10^{1}$
$A_3 = -4.25086552 \times 10^{-2}$
$A_4 = 1.76692517 \times 10^{-4}$
$A_5 = -1.54214418 \times 10^{-7}$
$A_6 = 7.29123628 \times 10^{11}$
$B_2 = 6.37728282 \times 10^{-2}$
$B_3 = 1.47201258 \times 10^{-4}$
$B_4 = -3.40248641 \times 10^{-7}$
$B_5 = 2.88102877 \times 10^{-10}$
$B_6 = -1.17554178 \times 10^{9}$
$C_2 = -9.61156884 \times 10^{2}$
$C_3 = 2.04712363$

$C_4 = 0.0$
$C_5 = -9.66486318 \times 10^{-7}$
$C_6 = -6.53078769 \times 10^{8}$
$\kappa = 4.5$
$\alpha = 9290.73$

P_{sat} Eqn. S-1

$F_1 = 9.8316515149 \times 10^{1}$
$F_2 = -5.5485169388 \times 10^{3}$
$F_3 = -1.2845967530 \times 10^{1}$
$F_4 = 1.6613313807 \times 10^{-2}$
$F_5 = 3.1360535600 \times 10^{-2}$
$\gamma = 478.93$

ρ_f Eqn. D-1

$D_1 = 5.53759545 \times 10^{2}$
$D_2 = 9.23276065 \times 10^{2}$
$D_3 = 6.98922396 \times 10^{2}$
$D_4 = -6.85969196 \times 10^{2}$
$D_5 = 5.87985153 \times 10^{2}$

c_v Eqn. C-1

$G_1 = 9.97086420 \times 10^{1}$
$G_2 = 2.10926018$
$G_3 = -2.88089444 \times 10^{-3}$
$G_4 = 1.46480528 \times 10^{-6}$
$G_5 = -4.35229529 \times 10^{5}$
$u_0 = 2.0281647 \times 10^{5}$
$s_0 = 8.7360402 \times 10^{2}$

REFRIGERANT 12

M = 120.93 kg/kmol
T_c = 385.17 K
P_c = 4.1159 MPa
ρ_c = 588.08 kg/m^3
T_0 = 200 K

Constants for T in K, ρ in kg/m^3, P in Pa, c_v in J/(kg·K)

P-ρ-T Eqn. P-1

R = 68.7480
b = 4.06366926x10^{-4}
A_2 =-9.16210126x10^1
A_3 = 1.01049598x10^{-1}
A_4 =-5.74640225x10^{-5}
A_5 = 0.0
B_2 = 7.71136428x10^{-2}
B_3 =-5.67539138x10^{-5}
B_4 = 0.0
B_5 = 4.08193371x10^{-11}
C_2 =-1.52524293x10^3
C_3 = 2.19982681
C_4 = 0.0
C_5 =-1.66307226x10^{-7}
κ = 5.475

P_{sat} Eqn. S-1

F_1 = 9.33438056x10^1
F_2 =-4.39618785x10^3
F_3 =-1.24715223x10^1
F_4 = 1.96060432x10^{-2}

ρf Eqn. D-1

D_1 = 5.580845400x10^2
D_2 = 8.544458040x10^2
D_3 = 0.0
D_4 = 2.994077103x10^2
D_5 = 0.0
D_6 = 3.521500633x10^2
D_7 =-5.047419739x10^1

c_v Eqn. C-1

G_1 = 3.389005260x10^1
G_2 = 2.507020671
G_3 =-3.274505926x10^{-3}
G_4 = 1.641736815x10^{-6}
u_0 = 1.6970187x10^5
s_0 = 8.9448764x10^2

REFRIGERANT 13

M = 104.47 kg/kmol
T_c = 302.0 K
P_c = 3.8697 MPa
ρ_c = 577.79 kg/m^3
T_0 = 150 K

Constants for T in K, ρ in kg/m^3, P in Pa, c_v in J/(kg·K)

P-ρ-T Eqn. P-1

R = 79.5900
b = 2.9965352561x10^{-4}
A_2 =-8.2852902033x10^1
A_3 = 9.8725559035x10^{-2}
A_4 =-1.0744963678x10^{-4}
A_5 = 3.4587476371x10^{-8}
A_6 = 5.0873683031x10^{11}
B_2 = 1.1326045344x10^{-1}
B_3 =-1.7124042321x10^{-4}
B_4 = 2.5233687878x10^{-7}
B_5 =-8.7021612764x10^{-11}
B_6 =-9.2279585051x10^8
C_2 =-4.8938250202x10^2
C_3 = 9.5943985617x10^{-1}
C_4 = 0.0
C_5 =-2.5327694644x10^{-7}
C_6 = 0.0
κ = 4.0
α = 10011.5625

P_{sat} Eqn. S-1

F_1 = 6.4251423714x10^1
F_2 =-3.4161026958x10^3
F_3 =-7.1723439130
F_4 = 1.0548780505x10^{-2}
F_5 = 2.8030109130x10^{-1}
γ = 303.33

ρf Eqn. D-1

D_1 = 5.77786670x10^2
D_2 = 8.71328290x10^2
D_3 = 0.0
D_4 = 1.36361900x10^2
D_5 = 0.0
D_6 = 4.14557270x10^2
D_7 = 1.53601492x10^2

c_v Eqn. C-1

G_1 = 6.7072536000x10^1
G_2 = 2.1274805520
G_3 =-1.5722103888x10^{-3}
u_0 = 1.5514713x10^5
s_0 = 1.0479552x10^3

REFRIGERANT 14

M = 88.01 kg/kmol
T_c = 227.50 K
P_c = 3.7450 MPa
ρ_c = 625.68 kg/m^3
T_0 = 125 K

Constants for T in K, ρ in kg/m^3, P in Pa, c_v in J/(kg·K)

P-ρ-T Eqn. P-1

R = 94.4698
b = 9.36417268x10^{-5}
A_2 =-5.81197516x10^1
A_3 = 7.38765401x10^{-3}
A_4 = 2.01175650x10^{-5}
A_5 =-2.92947380x10^{-8}
A_6 = 4.02572833x10^{11}
B_2 = 1.03268777x10^{-1}
B_3 = 3.87338946x10^{-5}
B_4 =-7.38580538x10^{-8}
B_5 = 1.06640391x10^{-10}
B_6 =-1.14970546x10^9
C_2 =-5.08957326x10^2
C_3 = 9.05455659x10^{-1}
C_4 = 0.0
C_5 =-3.16196531x10^{-7}
C_6 = 0.0
κ = 4.0
α = 10591.4322

P_{sat} Eqn. S-1

F_1 = 5.33277810x10^1
F_2 =-3.04975772x10^3
F_3 =-4.69017025
F_4 = 2.68565551x10^{-3}
F_5 = 7.70707795x10^{-1}
γ = 235.56

ρ_f Eqn. D-1

D_1 = 6.256826100x10^2
D_2 = 1.114382841x10^3
D_3 = 7.347063471x10^1
D_4 = 5.794158350x10^2
D_5 =-1.290928672x10^2

c_v Eqn. C-1

G_1 = 1.258381602x10^2
G_2 = 1.786415576
G_3 =-3.875045218x10^{-4}
G_4 =-7.211410935x10^{-7}
u_0 = 1.3349388x10^5
s_0 = 1.2037444x10^3

REFRIGERANT 22

M = 86.48 kg/kmol
T_c = 369.17 K
P_c = 4.9776 MPa
ρ_c = 524.77 kg/m^3
T_0 = 200 K

Constants for T in K, ρ in kg/m^3, P in Pa, c_v in J/(kg·K)

P-ρ-T Eqn. P-1

R = 96.1467
b = 1.24855636x10^{-4}
A_2 =-1.16981908x10^2
A_3 =-2.92952588x10^{-2}
A_4 = 2.41919261x10^{-4}
A_5 =-2.43458381x10^{-7}
A_6 = 9.40022615x10^{11}
B_2 = 1.16431240x10^{-1}
B_3 = 2.30319412x10^{-4}
B_4 =-6.79667708x10^{-7}
B_5 = 6.30201766x10^{-10}
B_6 =-2.07580650x10^9
C_2 =-1.18409710x10^3
C_3 = 2.48896136
C_4 = 0.0
C_5 =-1.20619716x10^{-6}
C_6 = 0.0
κ = 4.2
α = 8781.3417

P_{sat} Eqn. S-1

F_1 = 7.1554148092x10^1
F_2 =-4.8189575050x10^3
F_3 =-7.8610312200
F_4 = 9.0806824483x10^{-3}
F_5 = 4.4574670300x10^{-1}
γ = 381.17

ρ_f Eqn. D-1

D_1 = 5.24766060x10^2
D_2 = 8.75161285x10^2
D_3 = 5.88662575x10^2
D_4 =-3.57093464x10^2
D_5 = 3.27951374x10^2

c_v Eqn. C-1

G_1 = 1.17767818x10^2
G_2 = 1.69972960
G_3 =-8.83043292x10^{-4}
G_4 = 0.0
G_5 = 3.32541759x10^5
u_0 = 2.3237771x10^5
s_0 = 1.2436918x10^3

REFRIGERANT 23

M = 70.02 kg/kmol
T_c = 299.07 K
P_c = 4.8358 MPa
ρ_c = 525.02 kg/m^3
T_0 = 150 K

Constants for T in K, ρ in kg/m^3, P in Pa, c_v in J/(kg·K)

P-ρ-T Eqn. P-1

R = 118.7482
b = 7.803477230x10^{-5}
A_2 =-1.25740395x10^2
A_3 =-2.09263831x10^{-2}
A_4 = 2.16566424x10^{-4}
A_5 =-2.52905160x10^{-7}
A_6 = 5.17269509x10^{11}
B_2 = 1.67967396x10^{-1}
B_3 = 2.33504859x10^{-4}
B_4 =-6.94467544x10^{-7}
B_5 = 7.59664683x10^{-10}
B_6 =-1.38278797x10^9
C_2 =-4.29323755x10^3
C_3 = 9.96617861
C_4 = 0.0
C_5 =-4.83394763x10^{-6}
C_6 = 0.0
κ = 5.5
α = 8329.62

P_{sat} Eqn. S-8

F_1 = 6.81234858x10^2
F_2 =-1.01732931x10^4
F_3 =-1.44514230x10^2
F_4 = 1.00348278
F_5 =-1.58761756x10^{-3}
F_6 = 1.26698956x10^{-6}

ρ_f Eqn. D-1

D_1 = 5.250191523x10^2
D_2 = 1.015217930x10^3
D_3 =-4.053534286x10^2
D_4 = 2.309256114x10^3
D_5 =-1.700088257x10^3

c_v Eqn. C-1

G_1 = 3.193727465x10^2
G_2 =-5.698757731x10^{-2}
G_3 = 5.299352295x10^{-3}
G_4 =-5.994244055x10^{-6}
u_0 = 2.5215188x10^5
s_0 = 1.6322250x10^3

REFRIGERANT 114

M = 170.94 kg/kmol
T_c = 418.86 K
P_c = 3.2675 MPa
ρ_c = 581.79 kg/m^3
T_0 = 200 K

Constants for T in K, ρ in kg/m^3, P in Pa, c_v in J/(kg·K)

P-ρ-T Eqn. P-1

R = 48.6567
b = 3.6925473671x10^{-4}
A_2 =-6.4104114343x10^1
A_3 = 5.7127242624x10^{-2}
A_4 =-4.0395739859x10^{-5}
A_5 = 1.0471501742x10^{-8}
B_2 = 5.2242055542x10^{-2}
B_3 =-1.6104714461x10^{-5}
B_4 = 0.0
B_5 = 7.3702304644x10^{-12}
C_2 =-1.7638764841x10^2
C_3 = 2.7453497239x10^{-1}
C_4 = 0.0
C_5 =-6.6455468465x10^{-8}
κ = 3.0

P_{sat} Eqn. S-1

F_1 = 6.7005038032x10^1
F_2 =-6.3454579033x10^3
F_3 =-6.3086761000
F_4 = 2.8651999780x10^{-3}
F_5 = 7.8142111000x10^{-1}
γ = 426.86

ρ_f Eqn. D-1

D_1 = 5.8179555x10^2
D_2 = 9.7947995x10^2
D_3 = 0.0
D_4 = 2.6299362x10^2
D_5 = 0.0
D_6 = 2.7995448x10^2
D_7 = 1.7938077x10^1

c_v Eqn. C-1

G_1 = 7.3269x10^1
G_2 = 2.6301
G_3 =-2.2654x10^{-3}
u_0 = 1.4737318x10^5
s_0 = 6.9058908x10^2

REFRIGERANT C-318

M = 200.04 kg/kmol
T_c = 388.48 K
P_c = 2.7825 MPa
ρ_c = 619.92 kg/m^3
T_0 = 250 K

Constants for T in K, ρ in kg/m^3, P in Pa, c_v in J/(kg·K)

P-ρ-T Eqn. P-1

R = 41.5628
b = 3.75279614x10^{-4}
A_2 =-5.09125078x10^1
A_3 = 4.44191073x10^{-2}
A_4 =-2.57248397x10^{-5}
A_5 = 3.98047697x10^{-9}
B_2 = 4.76339868x10^{-2}
B_3 =-2.07196888x10^{-5}
B_4 = 0.0
B_5 = 9.73125201x10^{-12}
C_2 =-7.66941499x10^2
C_3 = 1.11357942
C_4 = 0.0
C_5 =-2.51636825x10^{-7}
κ = 5.0

P_{sat} Eqn. S-1

F_1 = 4.31929871x10^1
F_2 =-5.34749337x10^3
F_3 =-2.12840100
F_4 =-4.96359519x10^{-3}
F_5 = 6.62589800x10^{-1}
γ = 396.67

ρ_f Eqn. D-1

D_1 = 6.199159500x10^2
D_2 = 1.135043967x10^3
D_3 = 3.781929245x10^2
D_4 = 2.561227119x10^2
D_5 =-1.429552707x10^2

c_v Eqn. C-1

G_1 = 9.427759077x10^1
G_2 = 2.787714064
G_3 =-2.236127054x10^{-3}
G_4 = 5.256534892x10^{-7}
u_0 = 1.1260471x10^5
s_0 = 5.5315468x10^2

REFRIGERANT 500

M = 99.31 kg/kmol
T_c = 378.66 K
P_c = 4.4258 MPa
ρ_c = 496.57 kg/m^3
T_0 = 200 K

Constants for T in K, ρ in kg/m^3, P in Pa, c_v in J/(kg·K)

P-ρ-T Eqn. P-1

R = 83.7133
b = 3.76703749x10^{-4}
A_2 =-1.22257685x10^2
A_3 = 1.45279154x10^{-1}
A_4 =-9.13792893x10^{-5}
A_5 =-8.99528863x10^{-9}
B_2 = 1.11650804x10^{-1}
B_3 =-9.48606280x10^{-5}
B_4 = 0.0
B_5 = 1.07667125x10^{-10}
C_2 =-2.49646880x10^3
C_3 = 4.60008366
C_4 = 0.0
C_5 =-1.37460901x10^{-6}
κ = 5.475

P_{sat} Eqn. S-1

F_1 = 4.73707956x10^1
F_2 =-4.27321106x10^3
F_3 =-3.63691000
F_4 = 2.08360862x10^{-3}
F_5 = 4.62940100x10^{-1}
γ = 386.43

ρ_f Eqn. D-1

D_1 = 4.965735000x10^2
D_2 = 6.977978970x10^2
D_3 = 1.196726116x10^3
D_4 =-1.402948285x10^3
D_5 = 9.047729355x10^2

c_v Eqn. C-1

G_1 = 1.122210487x10^2
G_2 = 2.138288123
G_3 =-1.318105011x10^{-3}
u_0 = 1.9934995x10^5
s_0 = 1.0530190x10^3

REFRIGERANT 502

M = 111.64 kg/kmol
T_c = 355.31 K
P_c = 4.0747 MPa
ρ_c = 560.65 kg/m^3
T_0 = 200 K

Constants for T in K, ρ in kg/m^3, P in Pa, c_v in J/(kg·K)

P-ρ-T Eqn. P-1

P_{sat} Eqn. S-1

R = 74.4743
b = 1.04254456x10^{-4}
A_2 =-8.7633628387x10^1
A_3 = 5.8487769532x10^{-2}
A_4 =-8.9814259017x10^{-5}
A_5 = 5.7770975886x10^{-8}
A_6 =-2.6377811471x10^{11}
B_2 = 9.9521056148x10^{-2}
B_3 =-2.6206099180x10^{-5}
B_4 = 1.3240127692x10^{-7}
B_5 =-9.3160674753x10^{-11}
B_6 = 6.9270943008x10^8
C_2 =-6.5157668337x10^2
C_3 = 5.5817296336x10^{-1}
C_4 = 2.3470347290x10^{-3}
C_5 =-2.4297977885x10^{-6}
C_6 = 1.0603021861x10^{13}
κ = 4.2
c = 7.0x10^{-7}
α = 9755.2665

F_1 = 3.2652346611x10^1
F_2 =-4.5218998176x10^3
F_3 =-3.6983496000x10^{-1}
F_4 =-7.2380229337x10^{-3}
F_5 = 8.1611391000x10^{-1}
γ = 363.33

ρ_f Eqn. D-1

D_1 = 5.6064750x10^2
D_2 = 8.5673938x10^2
D_3 = 1.0230082x10^3
D_4 =-1.1225871x10^3
D_5 = 7.7656102x10^2

c_v Eqn. C-1

G_1 = 8.5490269200x10^1
G_2 = 2.2584619105
G_3 =-1.9113995193x10^{-3}
G_4 = 5.3983516293x10^{-7}
G_5 = 8.2777831437x10^4
u_0 = 1.6813807x10^5
s_0 = 9.4570295x10^2

REFRIGERANT 503

M = 87.5 kg/kmol
T_c = 292.59 K
P_c = 4.3256 MPa
ρ_c = 521.05 kg/m^3
T_0 = 150 K

Constants for T in K, ρ in kg/m^3, P in Pa, c_v in J/(kg·K)

P-ρ-T Eqn. P-8

R = 95.2533
α = 1.3139445x10^3
b = 5.5837499x10^{-4}

ρ_f Eqn. D-1

D_1 = 5.210480060x10^2
D_2 = 2.089253902x10^3
D_3 =-5.379287269x10^3
D_4 = 1.043202080x10^4
D_5 =-5.991462863x10^3

P_{sat} Eqn. S-1

F_1 = 4.40368096x10^1
F_2 =-1.99577131x10^3
F_3 =-4.49169000
F_4 = 1.22205099x10^{-2}
F_5 =-1.76710000x10^{-1}
γ = 297.04

c_v Eqn. C-1

G_1 = 1.698794100x10^2
G_2 = 1.233735242
G_3 = 1.241300119x10^{-3}
G_4 =-2.462789574x10^{-6}
u_0 = 1.6454753x10^5
s_0 = 1.1562357x10^3

RUBIDIUM

M = 85.48 kg/kmol
T_c = 2105.9 K
P_c = 13.39 MPa
ρ_c = 370.25 kg/m^3
T_0 = 1000 K

Constants for T in K, ρ in kg/m^3, P in Pa, c_v in J/(kg·K)

P-ρ-T Eqn. P-7

  R = 97.2665
  A_1 =-1.074062x10^1
  A_2 = 5.771685x10^3
  A_3 =-5.476099
  A_4 = 7.767259x10^2
  A_5 = 4.049067x10^6
  A_6 =-6.498737
  A_7 =-6.148542x10^3
  A_8 = 8.432152x10^6
  A_9 = 8.135142x10^{-6}

P_{sat} Eqn. S-9

  F_1 = 6.1540106x10^1
  F_2 =-1.9981647x10^4
  F_3 =-4.7487641
  F_4 = 3.0981909x10^6

ρ_f Eqn. D-7

  D_1 = 3.7025000x10^2
  D_2 =-5.0591467x10^3
  D_3 = 4.9774057x10^3
  D_4 = 1.4965687x10^3
  α = 0.76

c_v Eqn. C-7

  G_1 = 1.4563x10^2
  G_2 = 6.6020x10^{10}
  β = 17738.
  u_0 = 7.4868607x10^5
  s_0 = 8.7177399x10^2

SODIUM

M = 22.99 kg/kmol
T_c = 2573. K
P_c = 34.1 MPa
ρ_c = 206.2 kg/m^3
T_0 = 800 K

Constants for T in K, ρ in kg/m^3, P in Pa, c_v in J/(kg·K)

P-ρ-T Eqn. P-7

  R = 361.634
  A_1 =-9.451051
  A_2 = 8.641474x10^3
  A_3 =-7.340161
  A_4 = 1.386540x10^4
  A_5 = 0.0
  A_6 =-1.204430x10^1
  A_7 = 1.731928x10^4

P_{sat} Eqn. S-7

  F_1 = 2.690991x10^1
  F_2 =-1.276771x10^4
  F_3 =-6.134400x10^{-1}

ρ_f Eqn. D-6

  D_1 = 9.541580x10^2
  D_2 =-2.292363x10^{-1}
  D_3 =-1.490566x10^{-5}
  D_4 = 5.637890x10^{-9}
  T_P = 255.372 K

c_v Eqn. C-7

  G_1 = 5.246321x10^2
  G_2 = 1.240918x10^{12}
  β = 24350.
  u_0 = 4.1138826x10^6
  s_0 = 3.4233272x10^3

WATER

M = 18.016 kg/kmol
T_c = 647.286 K
P_c = 22.089 MPa
ρ_c = 317.0 kg/m^3
T_0 = 273.16 K

Constants for T in K, ρ in kg/m^3, P in Pa, c_v in J/(kg·K)

P-ρ-T from Q Eqn. Q-2

R = 461.51
$A_{1,1}$ = 2.9492937x10^{-2}
$A_{2,1}$ =-1.3213917x10^{-4}
$A_{3,1}$ = 2.7464632x10^{-7}
$A_{4,1}$ =-3.6093828x10^{-10}
$A_{5,1}$ = 3.4218431x10^{-13}
$A_{6,1}$ =-2.4450042x10^{-16}
$A_{7,1}$ = 1.5518535x10^{-19}
$A_{8,1}$ = 5.9728487x10^{-24}
$A_{9,1}$ =-4.1030848x10^{-1}
$A_{10,1}$ =-4.1605860x10^{-4}
$A_{1,2}$ =-5.1985860x10^{-3}
$A_{2,2}$ = 7.7779182x10^{-6}
$A_{3,2}$ =-3.3301902x10^{-8}
$A_{4,2}$ =-1.6254622x10^{-11}
$A_{5,2}$ =-1.7731074x10^{-13}
$A_{6,2}$ = 1.2748742x10^{-16}
$A_{7,2}$ = 1.3746153x10^{-19}
$A_{8,2}$ = 1.5597836x10^{-22}
$A_{9,2}$ = 3.3731180x10^{-1}
$A_{10,2}$ =-2.0988866x10^{-4}
$A_{1,3}$ = 6.8335354x10^{-3}
$A_{2,3}$ =-2.6149751x10^{-5}
$A_{3,3}$ = 6.5326396x10^{-8}
$A_{4,3}$ =-2.6181978x10^{-11}
$A_{5,3}$ = 0.0
$A_{6,3}$ = 0.0
$A_{7,3}$ = 0.0
$A_{8,3}$ = 0.0
$A_{9,3}$ =-1.3746618x10^{-1}
$A_{10,3}$ =-7.3396848x10^{-4}
$A_{1,4}$ =-1.5641040x10^{-4}
$A_{2,4}$ =-7.2546108x10^{-7}
$A_{3,4}$ =-9.2734289x10^{-9}
$A_{4,4}$ = 4.3125840x10^{-12}
$A_{5,4}$ = 0.0
$A_{6,4}$ = 0.0
$A_{7,4}$ = 0.0

$A_{8,4}$ = 0.0
$A_{9,4}$ = 6.7874983x10^{-3}
$A_{10,4}$ = 1.0401717x10^{-5}
$A_{1,5}$ =-6.3972405x10^{-3}
$A_{2,5}$ = 2.6409282x10^{-5}
$A_{3,5}$ =-4.7740374x10^{-8}
$A_{4,5}$ = 5.6323130x10^{-11}
$A_{5,5}$ = 0.0
$A_{6,5}$ = 0.0
$A_{7,5}$ = 0.0
$A_{8,5}$ = 0.0
$A_{9,5}$ = 1.3687317x10^{-1}
$A_{10,5}$ = 6.4581880x10^{-4}
$A_{1,6}$ =-3.9661401x10^{-3}
$A_{2,6}$ = 1.5453061x10^{-5}
$A_{3,6}$ =-2.9142470x10^{-8}
$A_{4,6}$ = 2.9568796x10^{-11}
$A_{5,6}$ = 0.0
$A_{6,6}$ = 0.0
$A_{7,6}$ = 0.0
$A_{8,6}$ = 0.0
$A_{9,6}$ = 7.9847970x10^{-2}
$A_{10,6}$ = 3.9917570x10^{-4}
$A_{1,7}$ =-6.9048554x10^{-4}
$A_{2,7}$ = 2.7407416x10^{-6}
$A_{3,7}$ =-5.1028070x10^{-9}
$A_{4,7}$ = 3.9636085x10^{-12}
$A_{5,7}$ = 0.0
$A_{6,7}$ = 0.0
$A_{7,7}$ = 0.0
$A_{8,7}$ = 0.0
$A_{9,7}$ = 1.3041253x10^{-2}
$A_{10,7}$ = 7.1531353x10^{-5}
E = 4.8
T_a = 1000
ρ_{a1} = 634
ρ_{aj} = 1000 for j = 2, 3,....,7

P_{sat} Eqn. s-6

F_1 =-7.4192420
F_2 = 2.9721000x10^{-1}
F_3 =-1.1552860x10^{-1}
F_4 = 8.6856350x10^{-3}
F_5 = 1.0940980x10^{-3}
F_6 =-4.3999300x10^{-3}
F_7 = 2.5206580x10^{-3}
F_8 =-5.2186840x10^{-4}
a = 0.01
T_p = 338.15 K

ρ_f Eqn. D-5

D_1 = 3.6711257
D_2 =-2.8512396x10^1
D_3 = 2.2265240x10^2
D_4 =-8.8243852x10^2
D_5 = 2.0002765x10^3
D_6 =-2.6122557x10^3
D_7 = 1.8297674x10^3
D_8 =-5.3350520x10^2

c_v Eqn. C-6

G_1 = 4.600000x10^4
G_2 = 1.011249x10^3
G_3 = 8.389300x10^{-1}
G_4 =-2.199890x10^{-4}
G_5 = 2.466190x10^{-7}
G_6 =-9.704700x10^{-11}
u_0 = 2.3750207x10^6
s_0 = 6.6965776x10^3

Section 4
Generalized Equations of State

A new generalized equation of state has been developed. The basis for this equation is described and the equation and its constants are given in this section. Four graphs of the compressibility function are given over the range from 0 to 100 critical pressures. Graphs giving the enthalpy and entropy corrections, as derived from the new equation of state, are included.

Section 4
Generalized Equations of State

A new generalized equation of state has been developed using "data" obtained from the computational equations of state of the various substances given in Section 2. Nitrogen data to 10,000 atmospheres enabled the generalized equation to be extended to over 300 critical pressures.

To the extent that the Principle of Corresponding States is valid, the new equations can be used to estimate properties beyond the ranges of equations for particular substances. The equation used for $Z = Pv/(RT)$ is given in Table 4.1 Simpler equations were tried, but these did not fit the ultra-high pressure range adequately.

The constants in the second virial coefficient $B(\tau)$ were first determined by a least-squares fit to virial coefficients calculated from the computational equations of state. The "data" points covered the range $0.4 < T/T_c < 20$ and all substances in this compilation except the liquid metals. Two constraints were applied;

$$\text{at } T/T_c = 1, \qquad B = -0.34 \tag{i}$$

$$\text{at } T/T_c = 2.5, \qquad B = 0 \tag{ii}$$

Approximately 400 points were used in the fit.

The remaining constants $A_7, \ldots, A_{33}$ were determined by least-square fits to Z values calculated from equations over a wide range of temperatures. Emphasis was placed on nitrogen data from 50K to 1200K and to pressures of 10,000 atm. Approximately 500 "data" points were used. Three constraints were applied at the critical point:

$$\left. \begin{array}{l} Z = 0.3 \\[2mm] \left(\dfrac{\partial p}{\partial r}\right)_\tau = 0 \\[2mm] \left(\dfrac{\partial^2 p}{\partial r^2}\right)_\tau = 0 \end{array} \right\} \quad \text{at } \tau = 1, \qquad r = r_c = 1/0.3$$

$$\text{(i)} \qquad \text{(ii)} \qquad \text{(iii)}$$

where $p = P/P_c$, $r = RT_c/(P_c v)$, and $\tau = T_c/T$. The value of γ was determined from the corresponding constant used in the nitrogen P-ρ-T equation.

After the constants had been determined, the saturation conditions were determined by finding points of equal temperatures, pressure, and Gibbs functions. Then, these points were fit with the equations given in Table 4.1 to provide saturation pressure and saturated liquid density equations in forms similar to those of the various substances.

The enthalpy and entropy departure functions were calculated from the Z equation using the basic analysis presented in Section 2, which leads to the following equations:

$$\frac{h^0(T) - h}{RT_c} = -\int_0^r \frac{1}{r}\left(\frac{\partial Z}{\partial \tau}\right)_r dr + (1 - Z)/\tau$$

$$\frac{s^0(T, P) - s}{R} = -\tau \int_0^r \frac{1}{r}\left(\frac{\partial Z}{\partial \tau}\right)_r dr + \int_0^r \frac{(Z - 1)}{r} dr - \ln Z$$

The values of Z predicted by the new generalized equation of state agree with the Nelson-Obert* charts, to within the accuracy of the Principle of Corresponding States. Since h and s (especially s) are very sensitive to the shape of the P-ρ-T surface, the new enthalpy and entropy departure curves differ somewhat from those of Nelson and Obert, chiefly at high densities where the Principle of Corresponding States is least valid.

---

* Nelson, L. C., and Obert, F. E., "Generalized Compressibility Charts," *Chemical Engineering*, Vol. 61, July 1954, p. 203.

Table 4.1
Generalized Equations

$$r = RT_c/(P_c v) \qquad \tau = T_c/T \qquad Z = Pv/(RT)$$

Compressibility Factor:

$$Z = 1 + rB(\tau) + r^2 \sum_{i=7}^{10} A_i \tau^{i-7} + r^3 \sum_{i=11}^{13} A_i \tau^{i-11} + r^4 A_{14} \tau + r^5 (A_{15} \tau^2 + A_{16} \tau^3) + r^6 A_{17} \tau^2$$

$$+ r^7 (A_{18} \tau + A_{19} \tau^3) + r^8 A_{20} \tau^3$$

$$+ \left\{ r^2 (A_{21} \tau^3 + A_{22} \tau^4) + r^4 (A_{23} \tau^3 + A_{24} \tau^5) + r^6 (A_{25} \tau^3 + A_{26} \tau^4) \right.$$

$$\left. + r^8 (A_{27} \tau^3 + A_{28} \tau^5) + r^{10} (A_{29} \tau^3 + A_{30} \tau^4) + r^{12} (A_{31} \tau^3 + A_{32} \tau^4 + A_{33} \tau^5) \right\} e^{-\gamma r^2}$$

where

$$B = \sum_{i=1}^{6} A_i \tau^{i-1}$$

Saturation Pressure:

$$P/P_c = \exp \left(\sum_{i=1}^{6} F_i X^i \right) \qquad X = 1 - T/T_c$$

Saturation Liquid Density:

$$r = r_c + \sum_{i=1}^{6} D_i X^{i/3} \qquad X = 1 - T/T_c$$

CONSTANTS IN THE GENERALIZED EQUATIONS

Constants in the P-v-T Eqn.

$A_1 = 6.24323840000000 \times 10^{-2}$
$A_2 = 1.27214770000000 \times 10^{-1}$
$A_3 = -9.36332330000000 \times 10^{-1}$
$A_4 = 7.01844110000000 \times 10^{-1}$
$A_5 = -3.51608960000000 \times 10^{-1}$
$A_6 = 5.64500320000000 \times 10^{-2}$
$A_7 = 2.99561469907038 \times 10^{-2}$
$A_8 = -3.18174367647130 \times 10^{-2}$
$A_9 = -1.68211055516855 \times 10^{-2}$
$A_{10} = 1.60204060081333$
$A_{11} = -1.09996740746713 \times 10^{-3}$
$A_{12} = -7.27155024312992 \times 10^{-4}$
$A_{13} = -4.52454652610146 \times 10^{-3}$
$A_{14} = 1.30468724100552 \times 10^{-3}$
$A_{15} = -2.22165128409268 \times 10^{-4}$
$A_{16} = -1.98140535655985 \times 10^{-3}$
$A_{17} = 5.97573972920861 \times 10^{-5}$
$A_{18} = -3.64135349702173 \times 10^{-6}$
$A_{19} = 8.41364845385683 \times 10^{-6}$
$A_{20} = -9.82868858821942 \times 10^{-9}$
$A_{21} = -1.57683056810249$
$A_{22} = 4.00728988907560 \times 10^{-2}$
$A_{23} = -8.45194493812845 \times 10^{-2}$
$A_{24} = -3.40931311928311 \times 10^{-3}$
$A_{25} = -1.95127049901091 \times 10^{-3}$
$A_{26} = 4.93899910978312 \times 10^{-5}$
$A_{27} = -4.93264612930464 \times 10^{-5}$
$A_{28} = 8.85666572381610 \times 10^{-7}$
$A_{29} = 5.34788029552768 \times 10^{-8}$
$A_{30} = -5.93420559192355 \times 10^{-8}$
$A_{31} = -9.06813326928540 \times 10^{-9}$
$A_{32} = 1.61822407264951 \times 10^{-9}$
$A_{33} = -3.32044793914655 \times 10^{-10}$
$\gamma = 0.0588$

Constants in the ρf Eqn.

$D_1 = 5.8300884 \times 10^{1}$
$D_2 = -3.3890207 \times 10^{2}$
$D_3 = 1.1142672 \times 10^{3}$
$D_4 = -1.9645619 \times 10^{3}$
$D_5 = 1.7835191 \times 10^{3}$
$D_6 = -6.5207296 \times 10^{2}$

Constants in the P_{sat} Eqn.

$F_1 = -5.7896051$
$F_2 = -5.5773833$
$F_3 = 1.4160472 \times 10^{1}$
$F_4 = -1.9238731 \times 10^{2}$
$F_5 = 5.5074771 \times 10^{2}$
$F_6 = -7.6116542 \times 10^{2}$

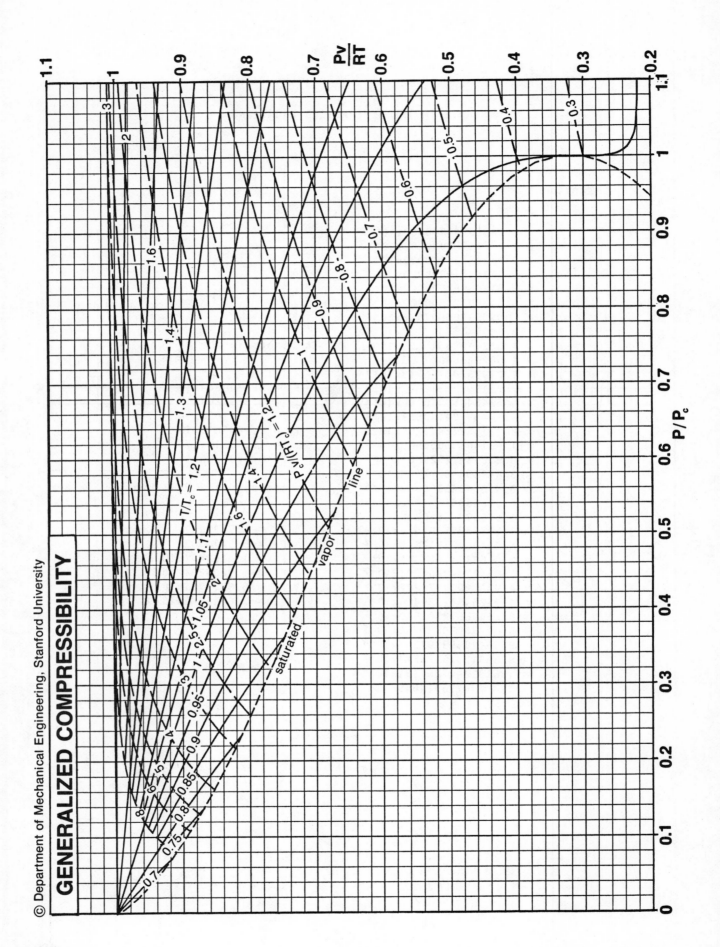

GENERALIZED COMPRESSIBILITY

© Department of Mechanical Engineering, Stanford University

160

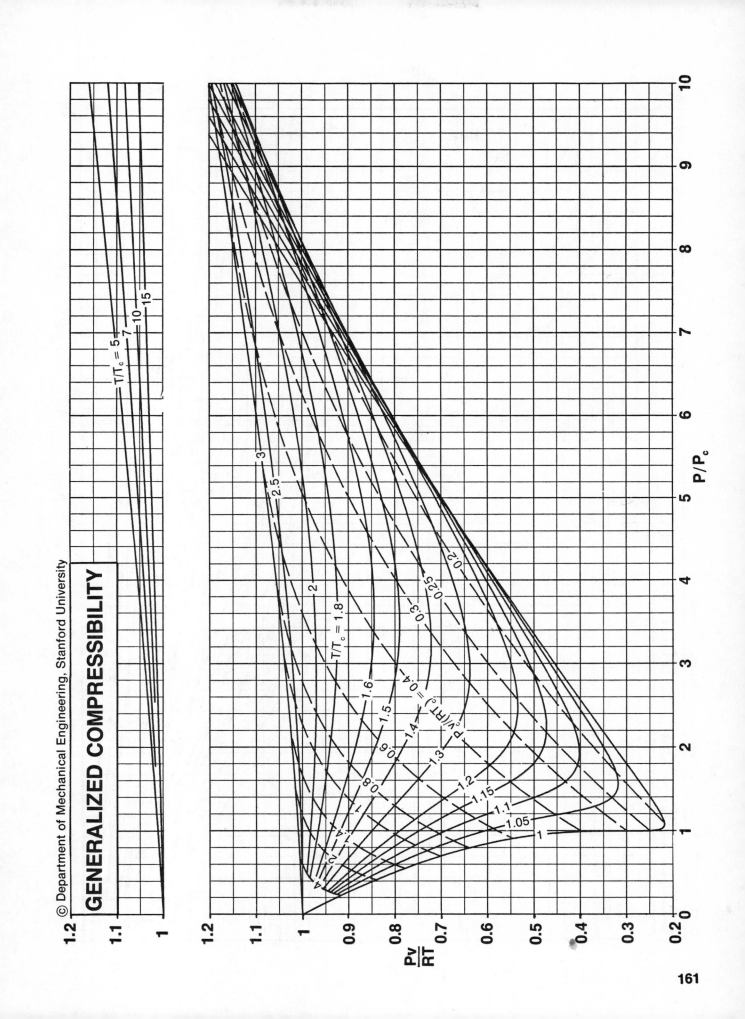

© Department of Mechanical Engineering, Stanford University

GENERALIZED COMPRESSIBILITY

$\dfrac{Pv}{RT}$

P/P_c

161

GENERALIZED COMPRESSIBILITY

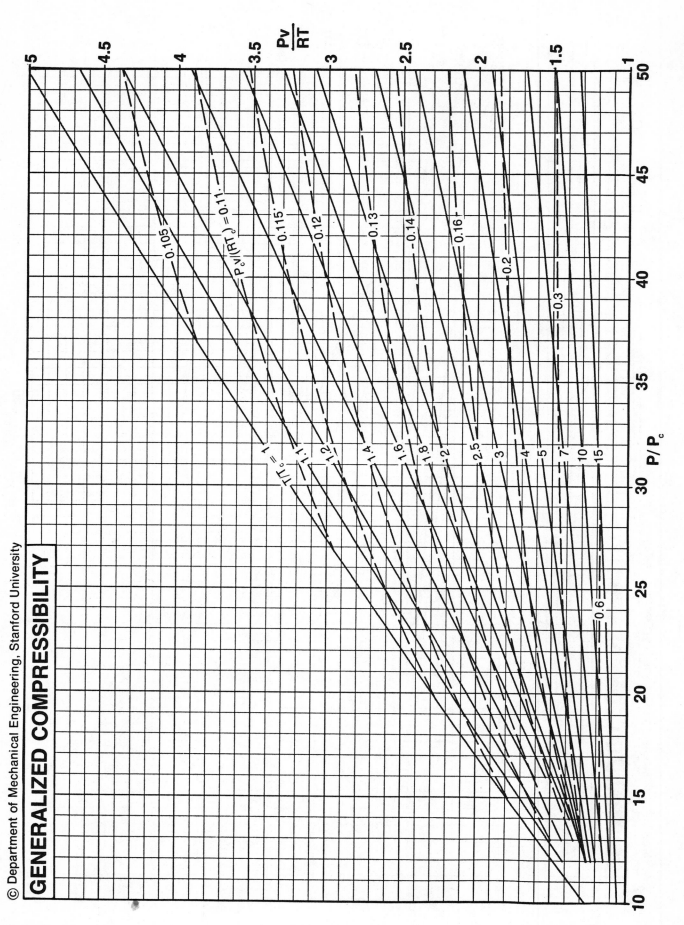

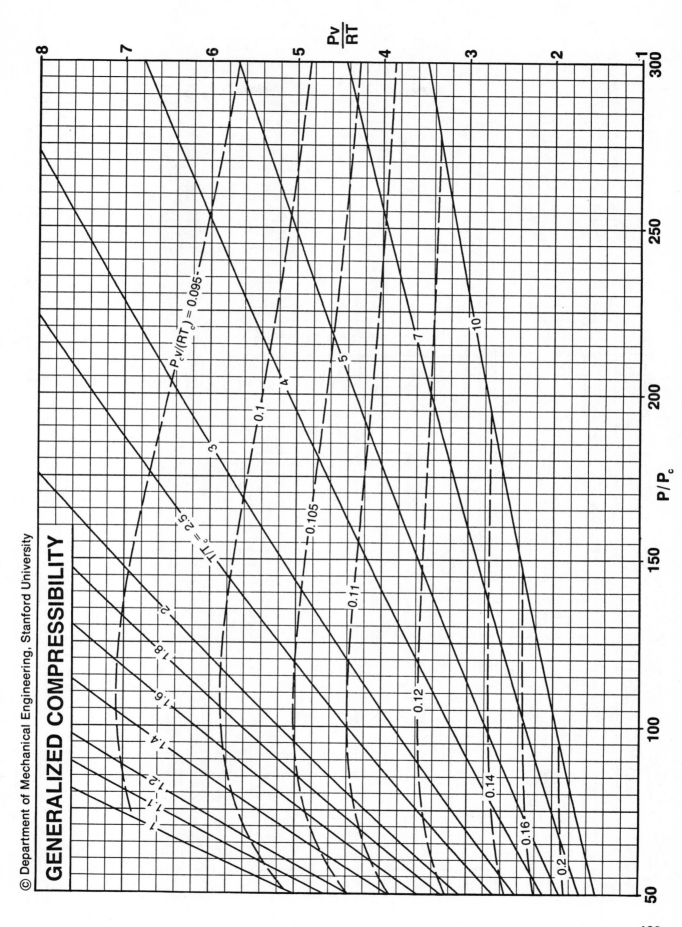

© Department of Mechanical Engineering, Stanford University

GENERALIZED COMPRESSIBILITY

163

GENERALIZED ENTHALPY

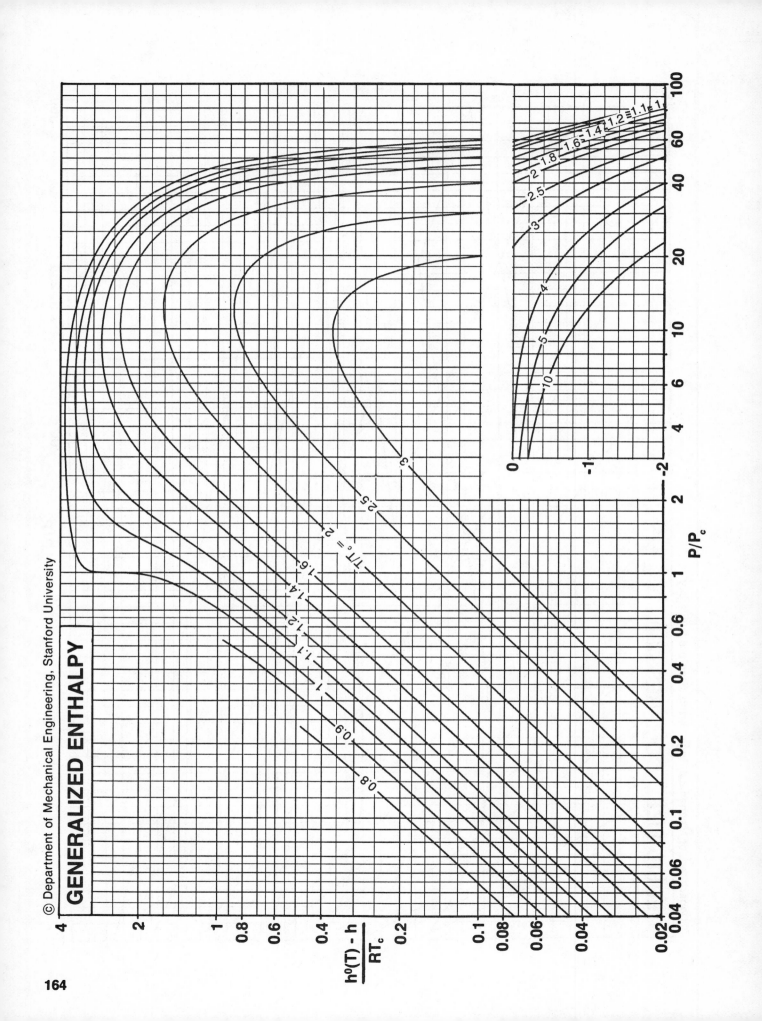

$$\frac{h^o(T) - h}{RT_c}$$

P/P_c

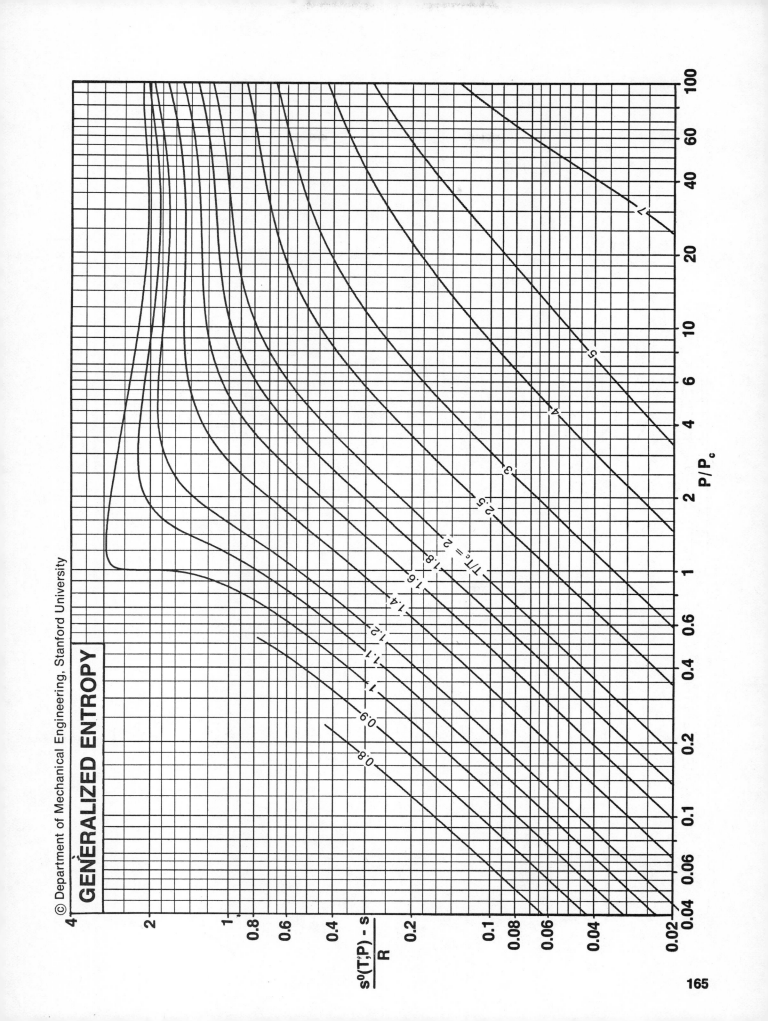

© Department of Mechanical Engineering, Stanford University

GENERALIZED ENTROPY

$$\frac{s^o(T,P) - s}{R}$$

P/P_c

$T/T_c = 2$

165

Annotated Bibliography of Important Thermodynamic Property Tabulations

Tables of Thermophysical Properties of Liquids and Gases by N. B. Vargaftik (Translation from Russian), Second Edition, Hemisphere Publishing Co., New York, 1975.

This is a very comprehensive set of tables of thermodynamics and transport properties in SI (pressures are given in bars). The tables are especially useful for gases at very high temperatures where ionization and disassociation are important. Some of the vapor phase values have been computed from statistical mechanics and therefore do not reach regions of high density. Computational methods are referenced but not included.

Fluid Thermodynamic Properties for Light Petroleum Substances, by K. E. Starling, Gulf Publishing Co., 1973.

This publication presents graphs, extensive tables, and computational equations for the principal hydrocarbons and other gases found in natural gas, all in English units. Equations for saturation conditions are not given. The P-v-T equations were not constrained to fit the critical point so in some cases the critical states are in error, by as much as 5° C. The ideal gas enthalpy and entropy were curvefit separately (rather than a single fit for c_v^0), and hence the resulting h and s equations are not quite thermodynamically consistent. This could present some problems in availability analysis where small differences between quantities of large magnitude often are important. The equations of state are all of identical form, and hence one can use them to construct the equations of state for mixtures of these substances, using mixture rules given in the publication. Computer programs are included. Thus, this is a very useful source for persons desiring to calculate the phase equilibrium conditions of arbitrary mixtures of hydrocarbons, nitrogen, and oxygen.

Steam Tables, by J. H. Keenan, F. G. Keyes, P. G. Hill, and J. G. Moore, John Wiley and Sons, Inc., New York, 1969, (available in both English and metric editions).

This is an essential reference for any person working seriously in steam power system analysis. Behind its extensive tables stand the very careful work of its authors. However, it does have one pedagogical weakness; the Gibbs functions of the liquid and vapor phases are not, as they should be, exactly equal. Hence, students who test the relationships $s_{fg} = h_{fg}/T$ find that it is not quite satisfied by these tables. Values in the present tables differ slightly from those in the *Steam Tables* because of a small correction that has been made here to insure that the tabulated values are *exactly* consistent with the above relationship.

Steam and Air Tables in SI Units, by T. F. Irvine and J. P. Hartnett, Hemisphere, Washington, 1976.

This publication presents moderately extensive tables of the Thermodynamic properties of water brief saturation tables for ammonia, refrigerant-11 and mercury, and a table of the low-density properties of air. The tabulations are in SI (pressures are given in bars). The low-density air table contains a column incorrectly labeled ''entropy'' which apparently is the function $\phi(T)$: see Equation (18) of Section 2. The equations used to generate these tables are not given. A detailed large h-s diagram for steam in SI is included in an end pocket.

Appendix
General-Purpose Computer Programs

A FORTRAN computer program for calculating the various thermodynamic properties, given two, is listed in this appendix. Also listed is a program for dealing with the sauration pressure-temperature relationships. The user will have to construct substance-specific programs that are in turn called by these general-purpose programs. The equations for the substance-specific programs are given in Section 2, and the constants for these equations are given in Section 3.

```
      SUBROUTINE PROP(T,P,V,U,H,S,NOP,PXXX)
C
C         ROUTINE FOR THERMODYNAMIC PROPERTIES EVALUATION
C
C         NOP DETERMINES THE TWO INPUT PROPERTIES. TRIAL VALUES FOR
C         T AND V MUST ALWAYS BE PROVIDED.
C         IF NOP=1, ENTER WITH T,V
C         IF NOP=2, ENTER WITH T,P, AND TRIAL V
C         IF NOP=3, ENTER WITH P,V, AND TRIAL T
C         IF NOP=4, ENTER WITH V,H, AND TRIAL T
C         IF NOP=5, ENTER WITH T,H, AND TRIAL V
C         IF NOP=6, ENTER WITH S,V, AND TRIAL T
C         IF NOP=7, ENTER WITH S,T, AND TRIAL V
C         IF NOP=8, ENTER WITH S,P, AND TRIAL T,V
C         IF NOP=9, ENTER WITH H,P, AND TRIAL T,V
C         IF NOP=10,ENTER WITH S,H, AND TRIAL T,V
C
C         THE INTERNAL PARAMETERS ERP,ERH, AND ERS CONTROL THE
C         ACCURACY OF P, H, AND S ITERATIONS.
C
C         THE USER MUST FILL COMMON BLOCK CRIT WITH THE GAS
C         CONSTANT R AND THE CRITICAL T,V,P.
C
C         PXXX(T,P,V,U,H,S) IS THE USER'S SUBSTANCE-SPECIFIC
C         ROUTINE THAT CALCULATES P,U,H,S FOR INPUT T,V.
C
C         ALL QUANTITIES ARE DOUBLE PRECISION.
C_____
C
      IMPLICIT REAL*8  (A-H,O-Z)
      DATA ERP,ERH,ERS/3*0.0001D0/
      COMMON /CRIT/  R,TC,VC,PC
C         INITIALIZATIONS
      DT=0.D0
      KBR=0
      DVBF=1.0D0
      VMIN=0.D0
      VMAX=1.0D30
      PMIN=1.0D30
      PMAX=0.D0
      DVS1=2.0D0*VC
      DVS2=0.7D0*VC
      KTR=1
C         LOOP POINT
    1 RT=R*T
      CALL PXXX(T,PX,V,UX,HX,SX)
C         TEST FOR CONVERGENCE
      GO TO (10,20,20,40,40,60,60,80,90,100),   NOP
   10 GO TO 700
   20 IF (DABS(P-PX).LT.(ERP*P))  GO TO 700
      GO TO 104
   40 IF (DABS(H-HX).LT.(ERH*RT))   GO TO 700
      GO TO 104
   60 IF (DABS(S-SX).LT.(ERS*R))  GO TO 700
      GO TO 104
   80 IF ((DABS(S-SX).LT.(ERS*R)).AND.(DABS(P-PX).LT.(ERP*P))) GO TO 700
      GO TO 104
   90 IF ((DABS(H-HX).LT.(ERH*RT)).AND.(DABS(P-PX).LT.(ERP*P)))
     1          GO TO 700
      GO TO 104
  100 IF ((DABS(S-SX).LT.(ERS*R)).AND.(DABS(H-HX).LT.(ERH*RT)))
     1   GO TO 700
      GO TO 104
  104 IF (KTR.GT.20)  GO TO 850
C         CALCULATE THE NECESSARY PARTIAL DERIVATIVES
      IF (PX.LT.0.D0)  GO TO 300
      GO TO (880,120,110,110,120,110,120,110,110,110),   NOP
C         PERTURB T
  110 DT=0.001D0*T
      T1=T+DT
      V1=V
      CALL PXXX(T1,P1,V1,U1,H1,S1)
      GO TO (880,880,140,140,880,140,880,120,120,120),   NOP
C         PERTURB V
  120 DV=0.001D0*V
      IF (V.LE.VC)  DV=-DV
      V2=V+DV
      T2=T
      CALL PXXX(T2,P2,V2,U2,H2,S2)
  140 GO TO (880,220,230,240,250,260,270,280,290,296),   NOP
```

170

```
  220 DPDV=(P2-PX)/DV
      IF (DPDV.GT.0.D0)  GO TO 300
C           THE POINT IS GOOD - UPDATE LIMITS
      IF ((PX.GT.P).AND.(V.GT.VMIN)) VMIN=V
      IF ((PX.LT.P).AND.(V.LT.VMAX))  VMAX=V
      IF (V.EQ.VMIN)  PMIN=PX
      IF (V.EQ.VMAX)  PMAX=PX
      IF (VMIN.GE.VMAX)  GO TO 840
      IF ((VMIN.GT.0.D0).AND.(VMAX.LT.1.0D30))  KBR=1
      DVBF=1.0D0
      IF (DPDV.EQ.0.D0)  GO TO 226
      DV=(P-PX)/DPDV
      DT=0.D0
      GO TO 400
C           DPDV=0 AT A GOOD POINT - TREAT BY BRACKETING
  226 DVBF=0.5D0
      GO TO 300
  230 DPDT=(P1-PX)/DT
      DT=(P-PX)/DPDT
      DV=0.D0
      GO TO 400
  240 DHDT=(H1-HX)/DT
      DT=(H-HX)/DHDT
      DV=0.D0
      GO TO 400
  250 DHDV=(H2-HX)/DV
      DV=(H-HX)/DHDV
      DT=0.D0
      GO TO 400
  260 DSDT=(S1-SX)/DT
      DT=(S-SX)/DSDT
      DV=0.D0
      GO TO 400
  270 DSDV=(S2-SX)/DV
      DV=(S-SX)/DSDV
      DT=0.D0
      GO TO 400
  280 DSDT=(S1-SX)/DT
      DSDV=(S2-SX)/DV
      DPDT=(P1-PX)/DT
      DPDV=(P2-PX)/DV
      DET=DSDT*DPDV-DPDT*DSDV
      DT=((S-SX)*DPDV-(P-PX)*DSDV)/DET
      DV=(DSDT*(P-PX)-DPDT*(S-SX))/DET
      GO TO 400
  290 DHDT=(H1-HX)/DT
      DHDV=(H2-HX)/DV
      DPDT=(P1-PX)/DT
      DPDV=(P2-PX)/DV
      DET=DHDT*DPDV-DPDT*DHDV
      DT=((H-HX)*DPDV-(P-PX)*DHDV)/DET
      DV=(DHDT*(P-PX)-DPDT*(H-HX))/DET
      GO TO 400
  296 DHDT=(H1-HX)/DT
      DHDV=(H2-HX)/DV
      DSDT=(S1-SX)/DT
      DSDV=(S2-SX)/DV
      DET=DHDT*DSDV-DSDT*DHDV
      DT=((H-HX)*DSDV-(S-SX)*DHDV)/DET
      DV=(DHDT*(S-SX)-DSDT*(H-HX))/DET
      GO TO 400
C           SPECIAL TREATMENT FOR NOP=2, DESIGNED TO AVOID BAD ROOTS
  300 IF (KBR.EQ.0)  GO TO 320
C           CALCULATE SLOPE FROM BRACKETING VALUES
      DPDV=(PMAX-PMIN)/(VMAX-VMIN)
      V=VMAX
      PX=PMAX
      DV=DVBF*(P-PX)/DPDV
      DT=0.D0
      DVBF=0.5D0*DVBF
      GO TO 400
C           NOT YET BRACKETED - ALTER V TO SEEK GOOD POINT
  320 IF (V.LE.VC)  DV=-0.05D0*V
      IF (V.GT.VC)  DV=0.2D0*V
      IF (VMIN.GT.0.D0)  DV=0.2D0*V
      IF (VMAX.LT.1.0D30)  DV=-0.05D0*V
      GO TO 400
```

```
C           REGULATE THE MAXIMUM CHANGE
  400 DVM=0.2D0*V
      IF (V.LT.DVS1)  DVM=0.5D0*DVM
      IF (V.LT.DVS2)  DVM=0.5D0*DVM
      DTM=0.1D0*T
      IF (NOP.NE.2)  GO TO 440
C           SPECIAL PRECAUTIONS FOR NOP=2
      IF (KBR.EQ.0)  GO TO 440
      VT=V+DV
      IF ((VT.GE.VMIN).AND.(VT.LE.VMAX))  GO TO 440
C           BRACKETING LIMITATION
      DV=VMIN+(P-PMIN)*(VMAX-VMIN)/(PMAX-PMIN) - V
  440 DVA=DABS(DV)
      DTA=DABS(DT)
      IF (DVA.GT.DVM)  DV=DV*DVM/DVA
      IF (DTA.GT.DTM)  DT=DT*DTM/DTA
      T=T+DT
      V=V+DV
      KTR=KTR+1
      GO TO 1
C           NORMAL RETURN
  700 GO TO (710,720,720,740,740,760,760,780,790,796),  NOP
  710 P=PX
      U=UX
      H=HX
      S=SX
      RETURN
  720 U=UX
      H=HX
      S=SX
      RETURN
  740 P=PX
      U=UX
      S=SX
      RETURN
  760 P=PX
      U=UX
      H=HX
      RETURN
  780 H=HX
      U=UX
      RETURN
  790 S=SX
      U=UX
      RETURN
  796 P=PX
      U=UX
      RETURN
C           ERROR WRITES
  840 WRITE (6,842)  T,P,V,VMIN,VMAX
  842 FORMAT ('0PROP ERROR - T,P,V,VMIN,VMAX= ',5D15.5)
      RETURN
  880 WRITE (6,882)
  882 FORMAT ('0PROGRAM ERROR IN PROP')
      RETURN
  850 WRITE (6,852)  NOP,T,P,V,H,S,PX,HX,SX
  852 FORMAT ('0PROP NOT CONVERGENT FOR NOP = ',I3/
     1  1H ,7X,'T',14X,'P',14X,'V',14X,'H',14X,'S',14X,'PX',13X,
     2  'HX',13X,'SX'/1H ,8E15.5)
      RETURN
      END
```

```
      SUBROUTINE SAT(T,P,DPDT,NOP,SXXX)
C
C          SATURATION PRESSURE-TEMPERATURE ROUTINE
C
C          FOR NOP=1, CALCULATES PSAT(T) AND DP/DT ON SAT. LINE.
C          FOR NOP=2, CALCULATES TSAT(P) AND DP/DT; A TRIAL T IS NEEDED.
C
C          THE INTERNAL PARAMETER ERR CONTROLS THE ITERATION ACCURACY.
C
C          THE USER MUST FILL COMMON BLOCK CRIT WITH THE GAS
C          CONSTANT R AND THE CRITICAL T,V,P.
C
C          SXXX(T,P,DPDT) IS THE USER'S SUBSTANCE-SPECIFIC ROUTINE
C          THAT CALCULATES P,DPDT FOR INPUT T.
C
C          ALL QUANTITIES ARE DOUBLE PRECISION.
C
C_____
      IMPLICIT REAL*8  (A-H,O-Z)
      COMMON /CRIT/  R,TC,VC,PC
      GO TO (1,2),  NOP
C          SPECIFIED T
    1 IF (T.GT.TC)  GO TO 70
      CALL SXXX(T,P,DPDT)
      RETURN
C          SPECIFIED P - START WITH THE TRIAL T
    2 IF (P.GT.PC)  GO TO 74
      KTR=0
      ERR=1.0D-6*P
   10 IF (T.GT.TC)  T=TC-0.001D0
      CALL SXXX(T,PX,DPDT)
      DP=P-PX
      IF (DABS(DP).LT.ERR)  GO TO 20
      IF (KTR.GT.20)  GO TO 80
      DT=DP/DPDT
      DTA=DABS(DT)
      DTM=0.1D0*T
      IF (DTA.GT.DTM)  DT=DT*DTM/DTA
      T=T+DT
      KTR=KTR+1
      GO TO 10
   20 RETURN
C          ERROR WRITES
   70 WRITE (6,92)  T
      RETURN
   74 WRITE (6,94)  P
      RETURN
   80 WRITE (6,90)  T,P,DPDT,PX
      RETURN
   90 FORMAT ('0SAT NOT CONVERGENT FOR T,P,DPDT,PX=',4D15.5)
   92 FORMAT ('0SAT CALLED FOR T=',F6.1,'  >TC; GARBAGE RETURN')
   94 FORMAT ('0SAT CALLED FOR P=',1PD12.4,'  >PC; GARBAGE RETURN')
      END
```